Outlines of **Enzyme Chemistry**

Outlines of

Second
Edition

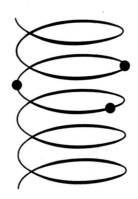

Revised &
Enlarged

New York · John Wiley & Sons, Inc.
London · Chapman & Hall, Limited

J. B. Neilands

Department of Biochemistry

Paul K. Stumpf

Department of Agricultural
Biochemistry

Enzyme Chemistry

With a chapter on the Synthesis of Enzymes

by

ROGER Y. STANIER

Department of Bacteriology

All of the University of California

Library of Congress Catalog Card Number: 58-10808

Printed in the United States of America

Preface to the Second Edition

The widespread acceptance of the proposition that enzyme chemistry can be presented as a general discipline, without reference to the detailed properties and characteristics of each individual enzyme, has been a source of some satisfaction to the authors of *Outlines of Enzyme Chemistry*. Thus the first edition of the book has found some value as a class text in this country and has been translated into the Italian and Japanese languages.

In spite of this measure of success, the authors have been keenly aware that the book suffered certain serious deficiencies with respect to both content and emphasis. Some of the deficiencies were perhaps unavoidable; who, for example, could have predicted in 1954 the vast strides about to be made in the mechanism of synthesis of the polynucleotides? And who could have predicted the hitherto unsuspected presence of metal ions in purified enzymes or the presence of a cofactor such as pyridoxal phosphate in crystalline phosphorylase?

In this second edition the authors have attempted to incorporate some such recent developments in enzymology. And in order to indicate the current trend in enzyme research, new chapters which deal with metal ion bonding, the mechanism of enzyme action, and the dynamics of nucleotide transformations, have been added.

To increase the usefulness of the book as a tool in the research laboratory we have appended a catalogue of over 500 enzymes. This list, though necessarily incomplete, provides some very general characteristics of each enzyme and gives a reference to the research literature.

The authors wish to take this opportunity to again express their appreciation to those individuals who helped with the preparation of the first edition. In connection with the second edition, special thanks must be tendered our colleagues in the Biochemistry and Virus Laboratory, particularly Dr. H. Fraenkel-Conrat.

J. B. NEILANDS
P. K. STUMPF

Berkeley, California
July, 1958

v

Preface to the First Edition

This book is designed to serve the following twofold purpose: (*a*) to introduce senior undergraduate and beginning graduate students to the general subject of enzyme chemistry, and (*b*) to provide background material for research workers in fields other than enzymology. Although many excellent advanced treatises on enzymes have already appeared, they are useful only to specialists, and, furthermore, their cost renders them prohibitive for class use.

The book is based on lecture material presented in a one-semester course given in the Department of Biochemistry of the University of California. This course is designed for students who have had a thorough grounding in chemistry and physiology as well as in biochemistry.

Over half of the book has been devoted to the general properties of enzymes. Brief sections have been included on specific coenzymes, enzymes, and enzyme systems. The study of metabolic problems at the enzyme level has also received attention. However, because there are too many individual enzymes to permit a discussion of each of them, we have studiously avoided writing a "catalogue of enzymes." We have, instead, attempted to treat the subject matter in outline form in order to bring into focus the entire field of enzyme chemistry.

Photographs of several eminent enzyme chemists appear in three chapters. It is obvious, however, that these few are by no means the only individuals who have made outstanding contributions to the field of enzymology. For practical reasons it has been possible to include photographs of only a small number of workers from representative fields of research.

We are deeply indebted to the many reviewers and others who helped in various ways to make this book a reality. We are particularly grateful to R. A. Alberty, P. D. Boyer, B. Chance, D. E. Green, A. C. Griffin, F. M. Huennekens, B. L. Horecker, M. J. Johnson, E. P. Kennedy, H. A. Lardy, H. Neurath, and E. R. Stadtman.

J. B. Neilands
P. K. Stumpf

Berkeley, California
January, 1955

Contents

ix

Photographs of Enzymologists

ENZYMOLOGIST	PAGE	ENZYMOLOGIST	PAGE
Barker, H. A.	67	Linderstrom Lang, K.	31
Boyer, P. D.	207	Lipmann, F.	296
Braunstein, A.	3	Lynen, F.	296
Calvin, M.	3	Meister, A.	206
Chance, B.	206	Myerhof, O.	97
Cori, C.	296	Michaelis, L.	97
Cori, G.	296	Northrop, J. H.	97
Doudoroff, M.	296	Ochoa, S.	31
Green, D. E.	206	Potter, Van R.	206
Greenberg, G. R.	207	Shemin, D.	67
Hopkins, F. G.	97	Stadtman, E. R.	206
Horecker, B. L.	206	Snell, E. E.	67
Kalckar, H.	67	Szent Györgyi, A.	296
Kennedy, E. P.	207	Theorell, H.	97
Kornberg, A.	206	Utter, M.	207
Krebs, H. A.	296	Vennesland, B.	67
Lardy, H. A.	206	Wood, H. G.	67
Lehninger, A. L.	206	Warburg, O.	97
Leloir, L. F.	296		

Nomenclature

Physical Constants

k	rate constant
k^0	zero-order rate constant
k^1	first-order rate constant
K_{eq}	equilibrium constant
K_{app}	apparent equilibrium constant
Ka	acidic dissociation constant
pKa	$\log 1/Ka$
pKa'	apparent pKa
A	ligand
pA	$\log 1/$A
K_s	stability constant
n	complexation number
C	total concentration
M	metal ion
v	velocity
V	maximum velocity
K_m	Michaelis constant
T.N.	turnover number
Ki	enzyme-inhibitor dissociation constant
ΔF°	standard free-energy change
$\Delta F'$	apparent free-energy change
E_0'	normal oxidation-reduction potential
F	faraday
$M.W.$	molecular weight
s	sedimentation coefficient
D	diffusion coefficient
$\overline{V}$	partial specific volume
M_{sD}	molecular weight by sedimentation and diffusion
u	electrophoretic mobility
pI	isoelectric point
O.D.	optical density
ϵ	molecular extinction coefficient

Coenzymes

DPN+   oxidized diphosphopyridine nucleotide
DPNH   reduced diphosphopyridine nucleotide
TPN+   oxidized triphosphopyridine nucleotide
TPNH   reduced triphosphopyridine nucleotide
NMN+   nicotinamide mononucleotide
PALPO   pyridoxal phosphate
PAMPO   pyridoxamine phosphate
TPP   thiamine pyrophosphate

AMP, ADP, ATP ⎤
CMP, CDP, CTP ⎥ mono-, di-, and triphosphates of adenosine, cyti-
GMP, GDP, GTP ⎰ dine, guanosine, and uridine
UMP, UDP, UTP ⎦

FMN   flavin mononucleotide
FAD   flavin adenine dinucleotide
CoA   coenzyme A (acetylation)

Enzymes

En   enzyme
EnS   enzyme-substrate compound
EnI   enzyme-inhibitor compound
ADH   alcohol dehydrogenase
LDH   lactic dehydrogenase

Metabolites

GSH   glutathione, reduced
GSSG   glutathione, oxidized
PEP   phosphoenolpyruvate
PGA   phosphoglyceric acid
GAP   glyceraldehyde phosphate
DAP   dihydroxyacetone phosphate
OAA   oxaloacetic acid

Miscellaneous

Pi   inorganic phosphate
PP   pyrophosphate
DNA   deoxyribonucleic acid
RNA   ribonucleic acid

Part 1
GENERAL PRINCIPLES

1

Introduction and History

1. Fermentation

The world's first biochemists were those primitive peoples who concerned themselves with the seemingly miraculous transformation of juices into alcoholic beverages. Such "biochemists" were at once the first enzymologists, since the chemical transformations wrought by them were catalyzed by enzymes contained within the living yeast cell.

During the 17th century several attempts were made to solve the over-all chemical nature of the fermentation process. These efforts culminated some one hundred years later in the experiments of Lavoisier (1) who showed by means of balance sheets that the sugar was converted to carbon dioxide and alcohol.

The 19th century witnessed both the identification of fermentation as a physiological act of the yeast cell and the introduction of the somewhat dogmatic view of Pasteur (2) that life and fermentation were inseparable. Many attempts were made in this period to extract the fermentation enzyme from yeast, but for one reason or another all of these yielded negative results. As is so often the case in science, the great discovery was made purely by accident. In 1897 E. Buchner (3) required a quantity of purified protein for therapeutic purposes. He ground yeast with sand, filtered off the broken cells, and added a large amount of sugar to the filtrate as a preservative. He was astonished to find that the sugar was rapidly fermented by the cell-free extract.

Harden and Young (4) made an important contribution in 1905 when they showed that Buchner's dialyzed zymase required the addition of a heat-stable cofactor or coenzyme. Thus within a single decade two fundamental discoveries—solubilization of zymase activity and introduction of the coenzyme concept—opened the route to the

3

eventual isolation and identification of all of the large number of individual enzymes and cofactors making up the zymase system.

2. Chemical Nature of Enzymes

Unfortunately mere solubilization of the fermentation enzymes provided little information about their chemical nature. In 1926 James B. Sumner (5) obtained a crystalline protein from the jack bean and showed that urease activity was intimately associated with the crystals. J. H. Northrop soon achieved the crystallization of a large number of proteolytic enzymes and prepared a monograph on this subject (6). Thus the protein nature of enzymes became firmly established. So far as is now known, all enzymes are proteins, and, indeed, most of the protein of metabolically active tissue is enzyme protein.

In the 1930 to 1940 era Warburg (7) and his school were able to crystallize or purify a large number of respiratory enzymes. Theorell (8), working in Warburg's institute, reversibly dissociated the "old yellow enzyme" into a protein part (apoenzyme) and a cofactor (prosthetic group). The separated components were inactive. This experiment opened up the possibility of studying the mode of binding of the cofactor to the protein.

3. Energetics and Metabolic Cycles

Harden and Young (4) had found in 1905 that inorganic phosphate as well as co-zymase caused a stimulation of carbohydrate oxidation in yeast juice. Many of the intermediates in carbohydrate oxidation were soon found to be sugar phosphates, and it became for a time the practice to assign such compounds the name of its discoverer, e.g., fructose-1,6-diphosphate = Harden and Young ester. However, the fundamental role of phosphate in these processes came from studies of muscle biochemistry. Lundsgaard (9) noted that a phosphagen, phosphocreatine, vanished from a contracting muscle in which the carbohydrate metabolism had been blocked by iodoacetate. Lohman (10), Meyerhof (11), Lipmann (12), and others brought cellular energetics to the enzyme level when they showed that the phosphate of certain of the esters produced as a result of carbohydrate oxidation existed in equilibrium with the phosphate of adenosine triphosphate and the phosphagens. These compounds were said to contain the "high-energy phosphate bond" ($\sim$P) and were characterized by a very large $-\Delta F°$ of hydrolysis. In a brilliant review article Lipmann (12) suggested that such phosphorylated intermediates represent the means whereby the cell is able to trap the chemical energy of carbohydrate, energy that is ultimately to be used in payment for the expensive synthetic reactions of life.

The studies on carbohydrate metabolism described above were carried out mainly with yeast and muscle. They did much to strengthen the concept of the unanimity of biological processes. As early as 1932 Harden (13) was able to write: "This mechanism for the decomposition of the sugar molecule is not confined to the yeast cell, for it has been found that the same processes are involved in the conversion of carbohydrate into lactic acid in muscle and in the decomposition of carbohydrates by bacteria, moulds, and the higher plants."

After a sufficient number of the individual steps in carbohydrate metabolism had been studied it became clear that certain reactions could be grouped into a metabolic cycle. Thus Szent-Györgyi 14) found evidence for the interconversion of the four-carbon dicarboxylic acids; Krebs (15) showed this to be part of a cyclic scheme now variously known as the citric acid, tricarboxylic, or Krebs cycle.

The existence of metabolic schemes and cycles naturally introduced the question of the subcellular organization of enzymes. For example, the entire fatty-acid oxidation scheme as well as various other systems was found to be associated with the particulate components of the cell (16).

4. Future of Enzymology

Consideration of the above brief discussion of the historical aspects of enzymology renders it apparent that this discipline has developed mainly along two routes.

There are those who have regarded the enzyme molecule simply as a catalytic protein. Such studies were preceded by the development of elaborate apparatus and techniques for obtaining the enzyme in a pure state. Research in this field has provided molecular and kinetic data for a number of crystallized enzymes and has led to general acceptance of the enzyme-substrate compound theory first advanced by Michaelis and Menten in 1913 (17).

On the other side of the ledger are those who have worked with the enzyme simply as a cog in the complicated metabolic machinery of the cell. Such investigators have cared little for the purity of their preparations; by the judicious use of inhibitors and by other devices they have "isolated" the activity of the individual enzymes. Their research has been rewarded by the establishment of a multitude of metabolic cycles and has given a more fundamental understanding of cellular energetics.

There is every reason to suppose that future research in enzymology will be vigorously pursued along the two main lines already pioneered. The organic and physical structure of the enzyme active site will be subjected to detailed investigation. Alternate pathways of metabolism will be uncovered as the tissues of a wider variety of species are scrutinized with analytical methods of increasing sensitivity. Research into the metabolism and synthesis of protein and nucleic acids will balance the already impressive fund of knowledge existing in the area of carbohydrate and fat metabolism.

It is to be hoped that these basic and fundamental studies in enzymology will one day find important application in the diverse fields of industry, agriculture, and medicine.

References

1. A. Lavoisier, *Traité Elementaire de Chymil* (1789).
2. L. Pasteur, *Compt. rend. acad. sci.,* *80,* 452 (1875).
3. E. Buchner, *Ber., 30,* 117 (1897).
4. A. Harden and J. W. Young, *J. Physiol., 32,* Proc. of Nov. 12 (1904, 1905); Proc. Chem. Soc., *21,* 189 (1905).
5. J. B. Sumner, *J. Biol. Chem., 69,* 435 (1926).
6. J. H. Northrop, *Crystalline Enzymes,* Columbia University Press, N. Y., 1939.
7. O. Warburg, *Wasserstoffubertragende Fermente,* Werner Saenger Press, Berlin, 1948.
8. H. Theorell, *Biochem. Z., 278,* 263 (1935).
9. E. Lundsgaard, *Biochem. Z., 217,* 162 (1930).
10. K. Lohmann, *Naturwiss., 17,* 624 (1929).
11. O. Meyerhof, *Ann. N. Y. Acad. Sci., 45,* 357 (1944).
12. F. Lipmann, *Advances in Enzymology, 1,* 99 (1941).
13. A. Harden, *Alcoholic Fermentation,* 4th ed. Longmans, Green and Co., London, 1932.
14. A. von Szent-Györgyi, in *Perspectives in Biochemistry,* Cambridge University Press, Cambridge, 1937.
15. H. A. Krebs, *Advances in Enzymology, 3,* 191 (1943).
16. E. P. Kennedy and A. L. Lehninger, *J. Biol. Chem., 180,* 1085 (1949).
17. L. Michaelis and M. L. Menten, *Biochem. Z., 49,* 333 (1913).

2

Chemical and Hydrogen
Ion Equilibria

1. Introduction (References 1–4)

Most textbooks of physical chemistry give a thorough development of equilibria and ionization. However, in biochemistry, certain equilibria are more important than others and should therefore be stressed. In textbooks of physical chemistry these are lost in a maze of detail. For these reasons it has seemed profitable to review these subjects briefly here.

Ionization is a phenomenon of the utmost importance to biochemistry in general and to enzymology in particular. The theory of ionization finds application in the preparation of buffers, isolation work, identification and analytical procedures, characterization of coenzymes, enzymes and the reactions catalyzed by them, etc. Specific examples of the close relationship between enzymology and ionization will be cited later.

2. Mass Action Law

One of the first men to enunciate the concept of mass action was C. Berthollet (1). In 1799 he theorized that certain deposits of Na_2CO_3 in Egypt had their origin in the reaction

$$CaCl_2 + Na_2CO_3 \rightleftharpoons CaCO_3 + 2NaCl$$

The equilibrium of this reaction lies so far to the right that the reverse reaction is normally never encountered. However, according to Berthollet, a high concentration of sodium chloride could act to push the reaction from right to left. This concept provided the notion both of reversibility and of the effect of concentration on extent of reaction.

3. Equilibrium Constant

In the usual enzymatic reaction where there are two substrates and two products we may write the following equilibrium constant, K_{eq}, for their reaction:

$$A + B \rightleftharpoons C + D$$

$$K_{eq} = \frac{[C][D]}{[A][B]}$$

A change in the concentration of any one of the four molecular species demands an adjustment in the ratio of the other three species present. When the equilibrium point is reached, the forward and back reactions have the same speed. All chemical reactions are striving to reach the equilibrium point, but the rate is often infinitely slow. *This is where enzymes play their key role.* By virtue of their catalytic powers, they speed up the reaction so that equilibrium is established much sooner than would otherwise be the case.

It should be clearly understood that all enzymatic reactions are reversible. "Irreversibility" is used in the same loose sense as "insoluble." It has qualitative meaning only.

To take just one example of the profound significance of ionization in enzymology the following reaction may be considered.

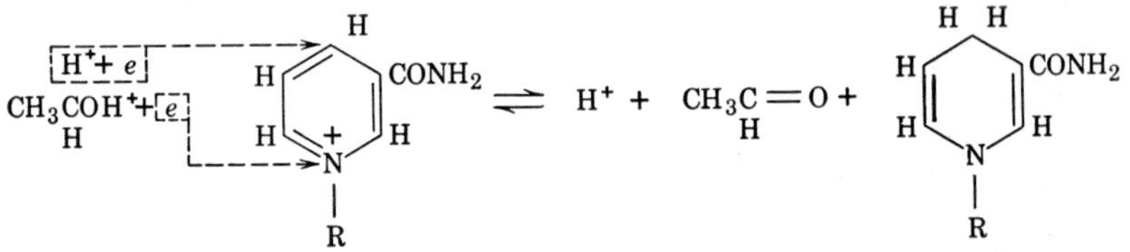

Diphosphopyridine nucleotide, DPN $^+$ Reduced diphosphopyridine nucleotide, DPNH

The enzyme alcohol dehydrogenase transfers a hydrogen atom from alcohol to the coenzyme. The other hydrogen atom may be thought to "separate" into a proton and an electron; the electron neutralizes the positive charge on the nitrogen atom in the pyridine ring. Therefore, the reduction of the ring at physiological pH leads to the generation of 1 equivalent of acid by virtue of the fact that a strongly basic quaternary nitrogen atom is converted to a weakly basic tertiary nitrogen atom.

One may write a partial or *apparent*[1] equilibrium constant for this

[1] The term "apparent" rather than "thermodynamic" will be used throughout this book where proper attention has not been paid to such factors as pH, ionic strength, effective concentrations (activities), and relative concentration of free and bound reactants.

reaction, K_{app}, which at pH 7.0 and room temperature happens to be (5, 6) as follows:

$$K_{app} = \frac{[CH_3CHO][DPNH]}{[C_2H_5OH][DPN^+]} = 1 \times 10^{-4} M$$

The *thermodynamic* equilibrium constant, K_{eq}, at any pH value between, for example, 7 and 11, would be:

$$K_{eq} = \frac{[CH_3CHO][DPNH][H^+]}{[C_2H_5OH][DPN^+]} = 1 \times 10^{-11} M$$

The relationship between K_{eq} and K_{app} from pH 7 to 11 is summarized in the tabulation. Thus the K_{app}, which contains the reactants and

pH	$[H^+]$		K_{app} (M)		K_{eq} (M)
7	10^{-7}	$\times$	1×10^{-4}	$=$	1×10^{-11}
8	10^{-8}	$\times$	1×10^{-3}	$=$	1×10^{-11}
9	10^{-9}	$\times$	1×10^{-2}	$=$	1×10^{-11}
10	10^{-10}	$\times$	1×10^{-1}	$=$	1×10^{-11}
11	10^{-11}	$\times$	1	$=$	1×10^{-11}

products of practical interest, is strictly dependent on pH. The reaction is shifted to the right in basic solution. In the absence of a buffer a reaction mixture containing DPN^+, substrate, and the appropriate dehydrogenase would become strongly acidic as the reduction proceeded.

4. Equilibria and Enzyme Concentration

Many textbooks carry the statement that enzymes do not affect the equilibrium point. This assertion may not be strictly true where reactants, products, and enzyme are all present in approximately equimolar ratios. In a brilliant investigation, Theorell and Bonnichsen (5) showed that molar proportions of crystalline alcohol dehydrogenase could in fact shift the apparent equilibrium point of its reaction by combining with the product DPNH. These observations may be of physiological significance where the enzyme is present in large amounts and is concentrated in intracellular bodies such as mitochondria. In addition, they show on which side of the equation we may expect to find a stable enzyme-substrate compound (see Chapter 14).

5. Ionization of Weak Acids

Accepting Brönsted's representation (7), an acid, HA, dissociates into protons and an anion.

$$HA \rightleftharpoons H^+ + A^-$$

Here, the K_{eq} may be referred to as the dissociation or ionization constant of the acid, Ka.

$$Ka = \frac{[H^+][A^-]}{[HA]} = \frac{[H^+][Salt]}{[Acid]}$$

Ka may be defined as being equal to the $[H^+]$ at half neutralization. At this point, $\frac{[A^-]}{[HA]} = 1$ and Ka is equal to the $[H^+]$.

Fundamentally these reactions are probably best described in terms of a proton transfer in which the solvent water acts as the acceptor.

$$HA + H_2O \rightleftharpoons H_3O^+ + A^-$$

It is unlikely that naked protons exist as such; they are probably combined with at least one molecule of water to give a species known as the *hydronium* or *oxonium* ion (H_3O^+). For purposes of simplification, however, the concentration of hydrogen ion in aqueous solution is usually written as a free proton, $[H^+]$.

Thus a comparison of the $[H^+]$ at half neutralization gives a convenient manner of comparing, for different acids, the magnitude of Ka. The *strength* of acids is directly proportional to the value of Ka. Some of the mineral acids are dissociated so completely that a Ka cannot be written for them.

The physiological $[H^+]$ of fluids and tissues is close to 10^{-7} mole per liter. The desirability that the $[H^+]$ be expressed as a small number was one of the principal reasons why Sørensen proposed the use of $-\log [H^+]$ or $\log 1/[H^+]$ or pH. We may therefore rearrange the above equation as follows:

$$[H^+] = Ka \frac{[HA]}{[A^-]}$$

$$\log [H^+] = \log Ka + \log \frac{[HA]}{[A^-]}$$

$$-\log [H^+] = -\log Ka - \log \frac{[HA]}{[A^-]}$$

$$p\text{H} = -\log Ka + \log \frac{[A^-]}{[HA]}$$

The abbreviation for $-\log Ka$ is pKa, and is the form of the ionization constant which appears in the Henderson-Hasselbalch equation,

$$p\text{H} = pKa + \log \frac{[A^-]}{[HA]}$$

A pKa value as measured with the glass electrode, without proper regard for *activities* (effective concentrations) of the reactants, ionic strength, etc., is designated as an "apparent pKa" or pKa'. Very exact methods for the determination of the pKa are given elsewhere (8, 14).

Although Sørensen originally believed that the activity of H^+ in solution could be expressed by concentration, latter developments rendered this view untenable. In fact pH is now recognized as a highly complicated quantity not related in a straight-forward manner to either $[H^+]$ or emf measurements. In contrast to this substantial confusion about the theoretical meaning of pH, great strides have been made in the technological and practical applications of this principle. In enzymology much quantitative work can still be done with pH as long as one bears in mind the fact that the omnipresent pH meter "sees" activity rather than concentration.

6. Example for the Ionization of a Weak Acid

Acetic acid

$$CH_3COOH \rightleftharpoons H^+ + CH_3COO^-$$

$$Ka = \frac{[H^+][CH_3COO^-]}{[CH_3COOH]} = 1.75 \times 10^{-5}$$

Since $\log 1.75 = 0.24$, $pKa = 5 - 0.24 = 4.76$. The complete titration curve for acetic acid is shown in Fig. 2.1.[2]

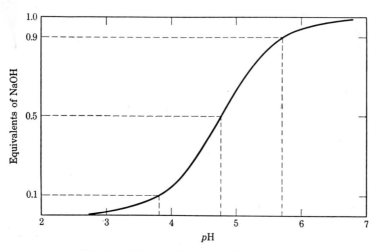

Fig. 2.1. The titration curve of acetic acid.

[2] A small amount of strong acid (or base, if acid is used as the titrating fluid) may be added at the start of the titration in order that the entire curve may be obtained.

7. The Dissociation of Water

Water is both an acid and a base. It dissociates according to the equation[3]

$$H_2O \rightleftharpoons H^+ + OH^-$$

$$K_{eq} = \frac{[H^+][OH^-]}{[H_2O]}$$

Water, however, is so slightly dissociated that the $[H_2O]$ is very large and may itself be regarded as a constant. Hence, at 25°,

$$K_w = [H^+][OH^-] = 10^{-14}$$

The ion product of 10^{-14} is evaluated by various methods, including the conductivity of water and hydrolysis of an ester. Changing these terms to their negative logarithms,

$$pK_w = 14 = pH + pOH$$

8. Ionization of Weak Bases

The ionization of a base capable of yielding a hydroxyl ion may be represented according to the reaction

$$BOH \rightleftharpoons B^+ + OH^-$$

$$Kb = \frac{[B^+][OH^-]}{[BOH]}$$

$$-\log [OH^-] = -\log Kb + \log \frac{[B^+]}{[BOH]}$$

In this instance $-\log Kb$ is abbreviated as pKb. It is the $-\log$ [OH] at half neutralization of the base. The term pKb clings to textbooks and handbooks; its great disadvantage is that it describes the strength of the base in an unfamiliar scale, namely, the hydroxyl-ion concentration scale. We may, of course, convert pKb to pKa by subtracting pKb from 14. Since

$$pK_w = pKa + pKb = 14$$

$$pKa = 14 - pKb$$

A simpler solution is to follow Brönsted's concept of bases. That is, the dissociation of bases is written from the acidic form. The OH^- does not enter the equation, and the pK is then pKa. *The ionization constant should always be reported as a pKa and never as a pKb.*[4]

[3] Or, more exactly (see above), $H_2O + H_2O \rightleftharpoons H_3O^+ + OH^-$.

[4] The only reason this abominable scale is quoted here is the fact that handbooks contain lists of ionization constants of bases quoted as the pKb.

9. Example for the Ionization of a Weak Base

Ammonia

$$NH_4^+ \rightleftharpoons H^+ + NH_3$$

$$Ka = \frac{[NH_3][H^+]}{[NH_4^+]} = 5.50 \times 10^{-10}$$

Since $\log 5.50 = 0.74$, $pKa = 10 - 0.74 = 9.26$. Figure 2.2 shows the titration curve for the ammonium ion.

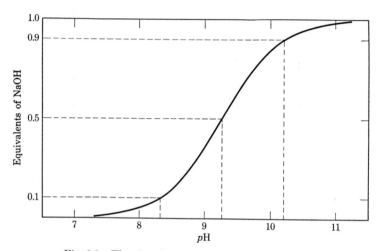

Fig. 2.2. The titration curve of the ammonium ion.

10. Determination of the *pKa*

The advantage in titrating from acidic to basic solution is that carbon dioxide is removed initially and it may subsequently be kept out of the sample by performing the titration in an atmosphere of N_2. Consequently, a small amount of a strong acid is often added at the start of the titration. Suitable methods for determination of the *pKa* are given in the literature (15).

Titration curves require correction for free acid or base at high and low *p*H values. Here, instead of all reacting with the sample, some of the added acid or base goes to change the *p*H of the solution. Figure 2.3 illustrates a method of solvent correction in the titration of a moderately strong (*pKa* = 3.8) organic acid. Curve *A* is the titration of the solvent and curve *B* that of the same volume of solvent plus solute. Corrections were made at *p*H values of 3.0, 2.6 and 2.3 by subtracting from the sample curve the number of equivalents of strong acid consumed in lowering the solvent blank to these same *p*H levels. A similar correction can be made for an ionization which occurs in the alkaline reaches of the *p*H scale. If the volume of the sample is kept low and the normality of the standard sodium hydroxide or hydrochloric acid is kept high (~1.0 *N*), this correction will

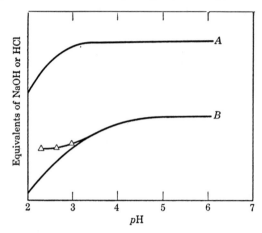

Fig. 2.3. Correction of the titration curve of an organic acid with *pKa* of 3.8 (curve *B*) by subtraction of the titration curve of an equivalent volume of solvent (curve *A*).

be small. Various methods for calculating the *pKa* have been described by different workers (8, 14, 15).

11. Evidence for Dipolar-Ion Formation in Amino Acids

The titration curve of glycine is shown in Fig. 2.4. The *pKa* values at 2.3 and 9.8 are known to represent the carboxyl and amino groups, respectively. We often accept this, as we accept that the world is round, without considering how much effort had to be expended in order to bring forth the proof.

Since the chemical analyses for the amino acids provide the general

$$\text{NH}_2$$
$$|$$
structure RCHCOOH, it was at first believed that the neutral form of the molecule exists in this non-ionized state. On addition of acid or base the following reactions, now known to be erroneous, were assumed to take place:

$$\text{NH}_2 \qquad\qquad \text{NH}_3^+$$
$$| \qquad\qquad\qquad |$$
$$\text{RCHCOOH} + \text{H}^+ \rightleftharpoons \text{RCHCOOH}$$
$$\text{NH}_2 \qquad\qquad \text{NH}_2$$
$$| \qquad\qquad\qquad |$$
$$\text{RCHCOOH} + \text{OH}^- \rightleftharpoons \text{RCHCOO}^- + \text{H}_2\text{O}$$

This accounted for the fact that the amino acids could be shown to migrate in an electric field to the cathode in acid solution and to the anode in alkaline solution. This view of the physical state of the neutral amino acids was discredited in 1923 by Bjerrum (9), when he

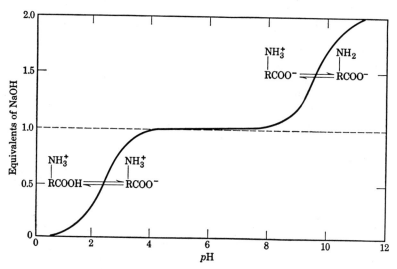

Fig. 2.4. The titration curve of glycine.

brought forth evidence that the neutral amino acid is a dipole (*Zwitterion,* inner salt, etc.) of the general structure $\overset{\overset{\text{NH}_3{}^+}{|}}{\text{R}}\text{CHCOO}^-$. The addition of acid or base to this compound gives

$$\overset{\overset{\text{NH}_3{}^+}{|}}{\text{R}}\text{CHCOO}^- + \text{H}^+ \rightleftharpoons \overset{\overset{\text{NH}_3{}^+}{|}}{\text{R}}\text{CHCOOH}$$

$$\overset{\overset{\text{NH}_3{}^+}{|}}{\text{R}}\text{CHCOO}^- + \text{OH}^- \rightleftharpoons \overset{\overset{\text{NH}_2}{|}}{\text{R}}\text{CHCOO}^- + \text{H}_2\text{O}$$

Thus the products on the addition of acid or alkali to the neutral molecule are identical; only the physical state of the neutral molecule is written in a different form.

Evidence for the dipolar ion state is summarized below (2, 3):

A. *Spectroscopy.* A covalent bond in the undissociated $-\text{COOH}$ gives a Raman line at 1730 cm^{-1}. This line is absent in neutral amino acids. Primary and secondary amines give a strong band in the region of 3300 cm^{-1}. In the charged amines and in neutralized amino acids this band is not present. Both carboxyl and amino groups absorb light in the wavelength region 200 to 180 mμ, and ionization causes a recognizable change in this absorption.

B. *Heats of Ionization.* The heats of ionization for aliphatic carboxylic acids and amines are known to be approximately +2000 and +12,000 calories per mole, respectively. These values are in the range found for the ionizations of the amino acids in acidic and basic solution, respectively.

C. *Electrostriction.* This is defined as an excessive contraction of the amino acid in water. As an example, 75 grams (1 mole) of glycolamide, $CH_2OHCONH_2$, added to a large amount of water causes a volume increase of 56.2 ml. However, 1 mole of the isomeric glycine causes an increase in volume of only 43.5 ml.

D. *High Densities and Melting Points.* Glycolamide melts at 117°; glycine at 232°. The densities of amino acids are also abnormally high. These facts point to an extremely compact molecule such as would be formed by intramolecular ionic forces of attraction in a dipole.

E. *Dielectric Constant.* The very high dielectric constant of water is related to its polar nature. However, amino acid solutions give even higher values than water, and the effect is maximum at the isoelectric point.

F. *Titrations in Formaldehyde.* The pKa of glycine at 9.8 is lowered when the titration is performed in formaldehyde. Formaldehyde is known to form a Schiff base with amino groups.

G. *Titrations in Organic Solvents.* The pKa of a carboxyl group increases whereas that of an amino group either decreases or does not change when the titration is performed in a solvent such as 50% ethanol or dimethylformamide (16). Thus the two pKa values of glycine would be moved closer together when the amino acid is titrated in a solvent-water system. The explanation for this phenomenon is not a simple one. It is probably related to both the participation of water in the reaction and to the fact that the release of a proton from an acidic group generates two charged species while, in contrast, the net charge during the ionization of a basic group remains constant.

H. *Titration of Model Compounds.* Provided a suitable substance can be obtained, the titration of a model compound with only one ionizable group should yield information referrable to the polyfunctional compound under investigation.

12. Ionizable Groups in Amino Acids

As may be seen in Fig. 2.4, the pKa values for glycine are at 2.3 and 9.8, corresponding to the $-COOH$ and $-NH_3^+$ groups, respectively. In accordance with Van Slyke and Kirk (10), these are numbered pKa_1 and pKa_2, respectively.

Table 2.1. Ionization of Groups in Amino Acids and Proteins

Group	Occurrence	Ionization Equilibria
α-Carboxyl	α-amino acids	$\overset{\overset{\displaystyle NH_3^+}{\mid}}{R}CHCOOH \rightleftharpoons H^+ + \overset{\overset{\displaystyle NH_3^+}{\mid}}{R}CHCOO^-$
Distal carboxyl	Aspartic; glutamic acids	$RCOOH \rightleftharpoons H^+ + RCOO^-$
Imidazole	Histidine	$\rightleftharpoons H^+ +$
α-Amino	α-amino acids	$\overset{\overset{\displaystyle NH_3^+}{\mid}}{R}CHCOO^- \rightleftharpoons H^+ + \overset{\overset{\displaystyle NH_2}{\mid}}{R}CHCOO^-$
Distal amino	Lysine	$RNH_3^+ \rightleftharpoons H^+ + RNH_2$
Phenolic hydroxyl	Tyrosine	$\rightleftharpoons H^+ +$
Sulfhydryl	Cysteine	$RSH \rightleftharpoons H^+ + RS^-$
Guanidino	Arginine	$NH_2\overset{\overset{\displaystyle NH_2^+}{\|\|}}{C}NHR \rightleftharpoons H^+ + NH_2\overset{\overset{\displaystyle NH}{\|\|}}{C}NHR$

Figure 2.5 shows the titration curve of aspartic acid. Here the α-COOH and distal COOH have sufficiently similar pKa values that their titration curves are not well resolved. The distal COOH is slightly less acidic than the α-COOH, and so its pKa lies at a slightly higher pH.

Figure 2.6 gives the curve for lysine. Here, as a consequence of the acid-strengthening effect of the carbonyl oxygen of the carboxyl group, the distal amino group is a slightly stronger base than the α-amino group.

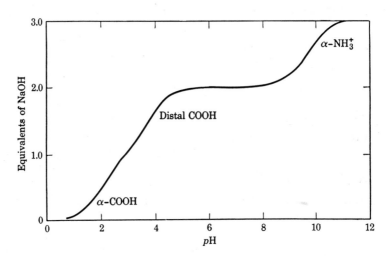

Fig. 2.5. The titration curve of aspartic acid.

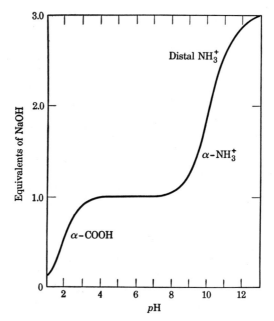

Fig. 2.6. The titration curve of lysine.

In addition to distal carboxyl and amino groups, the ionization of sulfhydryl, phenolic hydroxyl, imidazole, and guanidino groups should be considered. The first two behave as acids, i.e., they donate protons; the second two take up protons and are therefore bases. The ionization of the various groups found in amino acids and proteins is summarized in Table 2.1.

13. Factors Influencing the Magnitude of the *pKa*

The carboxyl group in glycine is a stronger acid group than that in acetic acid because, in the amino acid, the adjacent positive charge on the amino group tends to push the proton off the carboxyl group. This phenomenon is referred to as the "acid strengthening" effect of a positively charged group. The distal carboxyl groups of aspartic and glutamic acids are intermediate in strength between the α-carboxyl of glycine and the carboxyl of acetic acid. The pKa_2 of glycine, 9.8, may be compared with that of glycine ethyl ester, 7.7. In neutral glycine the pKa_2 is the resultant of a combination of the acid-strengthening effect of the carbonyl oxygen atom in the carboxyl group and the acid-weakening effect of the negative charge. The inductive effect of a carbonyl oxygen can be illustrated by the pKa values of pyruvic and lactic acids, 2.7 and 3.9, respectively. The distal amino groups of lysine and β-alanine are stronger bases than the α-amino groups, whereas the amino group of aniline has a pKa of 4.6. The three ionizable acid groups in phosphoric acid may be thought of as identical in strength. However, once the molecule bears one negative charge, the second proton is held on to give a pKa_2 of ~ 7 and the third to give $pKa_3 > 12$.

In general, the strength of an ionizing group depends on (*a*) the inherent structure of the group, and (*b*) the nature of the neighboring groups. Additional effects are produced by temperature, concentration, the type of solvent, etc.

14. Composite Ionization Constants

The correct interpretation of titration curves for substances that contain *more than one* ionizable group is by no means an easy task.[5] In pyridoxine, for example, pKa' values are found at pH 5.00 and 8.96. By reference to pyridine and phenol, these might be assumed to

---

[5] If the ionization constant is "spectrophotometrically operable" the simplest procedure is probably to compare the spectra of the unknown substance with that of a simple model compound containing only one ionizable group. If the ionization constant is not spectrophotometrically operable then one of the criteria listed on p. 15 may be invoked.

be the pyridinium and phenolate ionizations, respectively. However, the N-methyl pyridoxine derivative has only the pKa' at 5; the other lies in very basic solution and must be the quaternary N. Hence, pyridoxine ionizes as shown. This interpretation of the ionization

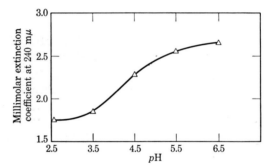

sequence is substantiated by the spectral changes found in pyridoxine, pyridine, and phenol over similar pH ranges (11). In fact, careful spectrophotometric analysis of this system has given pKa' values in excellent agreement with those found by titration (17, 18).

Similarly, in the case of the interesting antibiotic cycloserine, spectrophotometric measurements were employed in order to show that in

Fig. 2.7.   Spectrophotometric determination of pKa'_1 of cycloserine (19).

aqueous solution the ionization sequence proceeds mainly through the *Zwitterion* (19). The pKa'_1 of 4.5 found by both titration and spectrophotometry (Fig. 2.7) can only be interpreted in terms of a *Zwitterion* intermediate.

In the amino acid cysteine a further complication is introduced in the form of a third ionizable proton. The first proton to be discharged is no doubt that of the carboxyl group. On the other hand,

$$
\begin{array}{ccc}
 & \underset{\substack{| \\ H-C-CH_2-S^- \\ | \\ NH_3^+}}{COO^-} & \\
\underset{\substack{| \\ H-C-CH_2-SH \\ | \\ NH_3^+}}{COO^-} & \xrightarrow{Ka'_A} \quad \underset{\substack{Ka'_2 \rightleftharpoons \; \rightleftharpoons Ka'_3}}{} \quad \xleftarrow{Ka'_C} & \underset{\substack{| \\ H-C-CH_2-S^- \\ | \\ NH_2}}{COO^-} \\
 & \underset{Ka'_B} {} \quad \underset{Ka'_D}{} & \\
 & \underset{\substack{| \\ H-C-CH_2-SH \\ | \\ NH_2}}{COO^-} & \\
\end{array}
$$

considerable controversy has arisen concerning the sequence of ionization of the amino and thiol groups. Edsall (20) proposed to regard the secondary and tertiary dissociations of cysteine as *composite* ionizations. Since the product of the "microscopic" ionizations on either the *Zwitterion* or neutral uncharged pathway (assuming a fully ionized carboxyl group) must equal the product of the measured values, then

$$ Ka'_2 Ka'_3 = Ka'_A Ka'_C = Ka'_B Ka'_D $$

From this unique relationship only one microscopic constant needs to be determined in order to evaluate the remaining three.

Titration of two model compounds, cysteine betaine and S-methylcysteine, has given independent values for both Ka'_A and Ka'_B, respectively (21). Both of these cysteine analogues exhibit only a single ionization in the neutral region. In cysteine betaine the quaternary nitrogen atom serves as a permanent positive pole and the assumption is made that its effect on the dissociation of a neighboring thiol group should be comparable to that of the substituted ammonium ion in cysteine. Similarly the blocked thiol group of S-methylcysteine should have about the same effect on the ionization of a neighboring ammonium ion as does the undissociated SH group of cysteine. In any event in S-methylcysteine the strongly inductive effect of the sulfur atom has been retained. The results, recorded in Table 2.2, yield values for pKa'_A, pKa'_B, pKa'_C and pKa'_D of cysteine of 8.65, 8.75, 10.05, and 9.95, respectively. Use of the absorption spectrum of S^- (22, 23) gives 8.53, 8.86, 10.36, and 10.03, respectively (24) for this same set of constants.

Table 2.2. Apparent Ionization Constants of Cysteine, Cysteine Betaine and S-methylcysteine in 0.15 N NaCl at 25° (21).

	pKa'_2	pKa'_3
Cysteine	8.30	10.40
Cysteine betaine	8.65	—
S-methyl cysteine	8.75	—

Thus there is little doubt that here we are dealing with a thiol group which is only a slightly stronger acid than the substituted ammonium ion as it occurs in this amino acid. The latter grouping is abnormally acidic because of the presence of the sulfur atom; the thiol group in turn is greatly acidified by the positive charge of the nitrogen atom. The above discussion applies only to cysteine, since it has been found that every aminothiol should be considered on its own merits (24). The composite-type ionization exhibited by cysteine obviously has many important biological implications. For instance, the thiol group of a protein N-terminal cysteinyl residue would be vastly more acidic than a thiol group in a C-terminal cysteinyl structure.

Tyrosine, which from the standpoint of ionization can be regarded as an analogue of cysteine, apparently does not undergo composite ionization (25).

In the elucidation of an ionization sequence the use of spectrophotometry, organic solvents, and model compounds all play a useful role and all have their particular advantages and disadvantages.

Spectrophotometry, although sensitive and informative in terms of structure, can be tedious and inaccurate in the absence of automatic recording apparatus. Buffer effects and the presence of trace contaminants such as metal ions may introduce serious errors. Most important of all is the fact that many ionizations are "spectrophotometrically inoperable."

15. The Isoelectric State

The stepwise ionization of glycine from acid to base solution is given by the following structures. The intermediate dipole, which

$$
\begin{array}{ccc}
NH_3^+ & NH_3^+ & NH_2 \\
| & | & | \\
H_2CCOOH \rightleftharpoons & H_2CCOO^- \rightleftharpoons & H_2CCOO^- \\
+1 \text{ net} \quad pKa_1=2.3 & 0 \text{ net} \quad pKa_2=9.8 & -1 \text{ net}
\end{array}
$$

bears a *net charge* of zero, is the *isoelectric* species. The symmetrical shape of the curve in Fig. 2.4 shows that this form will be most abundant halfway between the carboxyl and amino group ionizations.

The isoelectric point, pI, for monoaminomonocarboxylic acids is

$$pI = (pKa_1 + pKa_2)/2$$

The titration of aspartic acid results in the following transformations:

$$\overset{\displaystyle NH_3^+}{\underset{+1 \text{ net}}{HOOCCH_2\overset{|}{C}HCOOH}} \underset{pKa_1=2.1}{\rightleftharpoons} \overset{\displaystyle NH_3^+}{\underset{0 \text{ net}}{HOOCCH_2\overset{|}{C}HCOO^-}} \underset{pKa_2=3.9}{\rightleftharpoons}$$

$$\overset{\displaystyle NH_3^+}{\underset{-1 \text{ net}}{{}^-OOCCH_2\overset{|}{C}HCOO^-}} \underset{pKa_3=9.8}{\rightleftharpoons} \overset{\displaystyle NH_2}{\underset{-2 \text{ net}}{{}^-OOCCH_2\overset{|}{C}HCOO^-}}$$

Thus, for the same reason given above for glycine, the maximum amount of the isoelectric species is found midway between pKa_1 and pKa_2. Again,

$$pI = (pKa_1 + pKa_2)/2$$

For lysine, a diaminomoncarboxylic acid, the ionic species are

$$\overset{\displaystyle NH_3^+}{\underset{+2 \text{ net}}{NH_3^+CH_2CH_2CH_2CH_2\overset{|}{C}HCOOH}} \underset{pKa_1=2.2}{\rightleftharpoons}$$

$$\overset{\displaystyle NH_3^+}{\underset{+1 \text{ net}}{NH_3^+CH_2CH_2CH_2CH_2\overset{|}{C}HCOO^-}} \underset{pKa_2=9.0}{\rightleftharpoons}$$

$$\overset{\displaystyle NH_2}{\underset{0 \text{ net}}{NH_3^+CH_2CH_2CH_2CH_2\overset{|}{C}HCOO^-}} \underset{pKa_3=10.5}{\rightleftharpoons}$$

$$\overset{\displaystyle NH_2}{\underset{-1 \text{ net}}{NH_2CH_2CH_2CH_2CH_2\overset{|}{C}HCOO^-}}$$

Here

$$pI = (pKa_2 + pKa_3)/2$$

The term "isoionic point" is defined as the pH at which the number of protons attached to basic groups is equal to the number of protons dissociated from acidic groups in a protein molecule. The article by Alberty (4) gives a more detailed definition of both the isoelectric and isoionic points.

16. Summary of pKa and pI Values

Some of the commonly accepted pKa and pI values for amino acids are listed in Table 2.3. The figures quoted will fluctuate somewhat with such factors as temperature and ionic strength.

Table 2.3. Summary of pKa and pI Values

Amino Acid	pKa_1	Group	pKa_2	Group	pKa_3	Group	pI
Aspartic	2.1	α-COOH	3.9	COOH	9.8	α-NH$_2$	3.0
Glutamic	2.2	α-COOH	4.3	COOH	9.7	α-NH$_2$	3.2
Tyrosine	2.2	α-COOH	9.1	α-NH$_2$	10.1	OH	5.7
Cysteine	2.0	α-COOH	8.3	α-NH$_2$, + SH	10.4	SH, + α-NH$_2$	5.1
Arginine	2.0	α-COOH	9.0	α-NH$_2$	12.5	Guanidino	10.8
Lysine	2.2	α-COOH	9.0	α-NH$_2$	10.5	NH$_2$	9.7
Histidine	1.8	α-COOH	6.1	Imidazole	9.2	α-NH$_2$	7.6

17. Practical Application of Ionization Constants

Buffers. The Henderson-Hesselbalch equation shows that at 1 pH unit above and below the pKa the ratio of salt to acid is 10 and 0.1, respectively. For this reason, substances are generally not used as buffers more than 1 pH unit away from the pKa. Lists of pKa values are given in chemical handbooks.

Isolation Work. The solubility of compounds is often dependent on pH. A knowledge of ionization is essential for the intelligent use of the electrophoresis apparatus and ion-exchange columns.

Analytical Work. The use of indicators, the identification of compounds through their pKa values or isoelectric points, and the use of formaldehyde and solvents in amino acid titrations demand an understanding of ionization.

Structural Work. Very often the fluorescence, spectral properties, and magnetic characteristics of compounds are pH-dependent.

Kinetics. The role of pH in reactions involving pyridine nucleotides has already been emphasized. Chapter 11 will be devoted exclusively to a discussion of the effect of pH on enzymes.

A paper by Dixon (12) shows the direct application of ionization to enzymology. Alberty (13) has derived equations for the initial reaction rates for enzyme mechanisms involving interaction between the enzyme, hydrogen ions, and buffer ions.

18. Apparatus

The utility of the pH meter can be greatly increased if the instrument is attached to a strip-chart recorder. An automatic buret with a drive synchronized with the chart movement will then provide automatic tracings of the entire titration curve. Recording titrators capable of producing such *variable* pH curves have been commercially available for some time.

An alternate type of apparatus that maintains a *constant* pH and plots a trace of volume of titration fluid added as a function of time was constructed in Linderström-Lang's laboratory by Jacobsen and Léonis (26). This apparatus, termed a "*p*H stat," is extremely useful for obtaining kinetic data on many types of chemical and enzymatic reactions.

In 1955 the construction and utility of an apparatus capable of *either* variable or constant *p*H titrations was described by Neilands

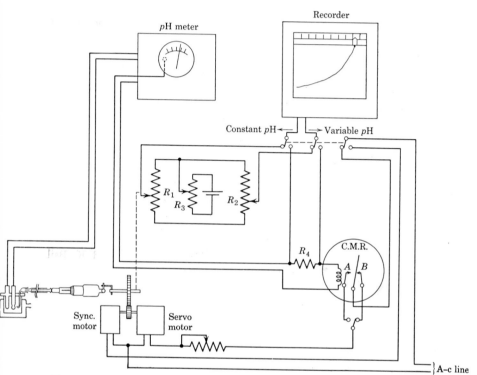

Fig. 2.8. Simplified diagram of the difunctional recording titrator (27).

R_1 Volume-to-voltage potentiometer.
R_2 Zero-adjustment potentiometer.
R_3 Adjustment circuit for recorder scale.

(For a further description see the text or the original article.)

and Cannon (27). This instrument is perhaps best termed a "difunctional recording titrator" (see Figure 2.8). A *p*H meter amplifies the potential obtained from the electrodes and converts it to a proportional current which is passed through a resistance R_4 and the contactmeter relay. The latter is used in *constant* *p*H titrations and is provided with adjustable contacts A and B which set the *p*H. A change in pH drives the pointer against A (or B) and corrective reagent is then added to the reaction vessel by the servo motor. In *variable* pH titrations the signal to the recorder is obtained from the voltage drop across R_4. The value of this resistor determines the number of pH units equivalent to full-scale deflection of the recorder pen.

References[6]

General

1. W. M. Clark, *Topics in Physical Chemistry*, Williams and Wilkins Co., Baltimore, 1948.
2. E. J. Cohn and J. T. Edsall, *Proteins, Amino Acids, and Peptides*, Reinhold Publishing Corp., N. Y., 1943.
3. F. Haurowitz, *The Chemistry and Biology of Proteins*, Academic Press, N. Y., 1950.
4. R. A. Alberty, in *The Proteins*, edited by H. Neurath and K. Bailey, Academic Press, N. Y., 1953. Chapter 6.

Bibliography

5. H. Theorell and R. Bonnichsen, *Acta Chem. Scand.*, *5*, 1105 (1951).
6. E. J. Racker, *J. Biol. Chem.*, *184*, 313 (1950).
7. J. N. Brönsted, *Chem. Revs.*, *5*, 231 (1928).
8. H. S. Simms, *J. Am. Chem. Soc.*, *48*, 1239 (1926).
9. N. Bjerrum, *Z. physik. Chem.*, *104*, 147 (1923).
10. D. D. Van Slyke and E. Kirk, *J. Biol. Chem.*, *102*, 651 (1933).
11. V. R. Williams and J. B. Neilands, *Arch. Biochem. and Biophys.*, *53*, 56 (1954).
12. M. Dixon, *Biochem. J.*, *55*, 161 (1953).
13. R. A. Alberty, *J. Am. Chem. Soc.*, *76*, 2494 (1954).
14. F. Daniels and R. A. Alberty, *Physical Chemistry*, John Wiley & Sons, N. Y., 1955.
15. T. V. Parke and W. W. Davis, *Anal. Chem.*, *26*, 642 (1954).
16. J. M. Vandenbelt, C. H. Spurlock, M. Giffels, and M. W. Eash, *Science*, *121*, 646 (1955).
17. A. K. Lunn and R. A. Morton, *The Analyst*, *77*, 718 (1952).
18. D. E. Metzler and E. E. Snell, *J. Am. Chem. Soc.*, *77*, 2431 (1955).
19. J. B. Neilands, *Arch. Biochem. and Biophys.*, *62*, 151 (1956).
20. J. T. Edsall, quoted by L. R. Ryklan and C. L. A. Schmidt, *Arch. Biochem.*, *5*, 89 (1944).
21. M. A. Grafius and J. B. Neilands, *J. Am. Chem. Soc.*, *77*, 3389 (1955).
22. L. H. Noda, S. A. Kuby, and H. A. Lardy, *J. Am. Chem. Soc.*, *75*, 913 (1953).
23. G. Gorin, *J. Am. Chem. Soc*, *38*, 767 (1956).
24. R. E. Benesch and R. Benesch, *J. Am. Chem. Soc.*, *77*, 5877 (1955).

[6] For a modern and comprehensive treatment of the practical and theoretical aspects of pH determination the reader is referred to: R. G. Bates, *Electrometric pH Determinations*, John Wiley and Sons, N. Y., 1954.

25. C. L. Gemmill, *Arch. Biochem. and Biophys.*, *55*, 359 (1955).
26. C. F. Jacobsen and J. Léonis, *Compt. rend. trav. lab. Carlsberg, Ser. chim.*, *27*, 333 (1951).
27. J. B. Neilands and M. D. Cannon, *Anal. Chem.*, *27*, 29 (1955).

3

Metal-Ion Equilibria

1. Introduction (Reference 2)

Our current knowledge of the true equilibria involved in metal-ion binding is derived mainly from a doctoral dissertation published by Jannik Bjerrum in Denmark in 1941 (1). His work established a close association between the twin processes of metal and hydrogen-ion binding and thus the two phenomena have been treated in succeeding chapters in this volume. An extensive account of nearly all aspects of metal-ion coordination chemistry can be found in the book by Martel and Calvin (2). A recent publication edited by Bailar (3) and papers by Williams (4) and Irving (5) are also recommended for reading.

Some of the definitions and terms used are somewhat unusual and hence deserve explanation. A metal ion may combine with a complexing agent or *ligand* to give a structure that either may or may not contain at least one ring. In the first of these two possibilities the central metal ion is held in a compound known as a *chelate* (Gr. *chelos* = claw); in the latter case the substance is called a *complex* compound. The chelate compounds are of somewhat greater biological interest, since these substances generally hold the metal ion with greater tenacity than does the complex.

Applying the mass law to the association between a metal ion, M, and a ligand, A, and using [ ] to signify concentration, we obtain

$$M + A = MA$$
$$K_s = [MA]/[M][A]$$

The equilibrium constant for this reaction, K_s, is variously termed the *stability, binding, association,* or *formation* constant and is by far the most significant property of the metal-ion coordination compounds. An orderly arrangement of the stability constants of a single ligand for a series of different metal ions at once reveals the metal-binding specificity of the ligand. The stability constant may be evaluated through the use of a variety of physical methods of which the most reliable is probably that of electrometric titration.

2. Theoretical Relation to H^+ Binding

It will be recalled that in Chap. 2 we quoted ionization constants as dissociation constants, Ka. Such reactions may be equally well described as association phenomena, in which case the equilibrium constant becomes a stability constant, Ka_s.

$$H^+ + A \rightleftharpoons HA$$

$$Ka_s = \frac{[HA]}{[H^+][A]}$$

Thus when $[HA] = [H^+]$, Ka_s is found as $1/[A]$. Placing the equation in logarithmic form yields

$$\log Ka_s = \log 1/[A] + \log [HA]/[H^+],$$

from which it is apparent that $\log Ka_s = \log 1/[A]$ when $[HA]$ and $[H^+]$ are equal.

If we consider a proton-binding species, A, as a ligand (complexing agent) and the hydrogen ion as a central (metal) ion, then the number of moles of ligand bound per mole of central ion, $\bar{n}$, is given by

$$\bar{n} = \frac{[HA]}{[H^+] + [HA]}$$

Thus the value $\bar{n}$, which has been termed the *complexation number*, is the average concentration of bound ligand divided by the total concentration of central ion (all forms). As a first approximation,

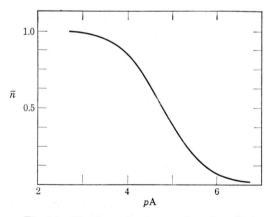

Fig. 3.1. The formation curve of acetic acid.

at values of $\bar{n}$ of 0.1 and 0.9, the ratio $[\mathrm{HA}]/[\mathrm{H^+}]$ is 0.1 and 10, and hence $\log 1/[\mathrm{A}]$ is equal to $\log Ka_s + 1$ and to $\log Ka_s - 1$, respectively. At $\bar{n}$ 0.5, $[\mathrm{HA}]/[\mathrm{H^+}]$ is exactly equal to 1.0 and $\log 1/[\mathrm{A}] = \log Ka_s$. Hence a plot of $\bar{n}$ versus $-\log$ [ligand] or $p\mathrm{A}$ will yield what Bjerrum has designated a *formation curve*. Figure 3.1 shows the appropriate data for acetic acid ($Ka_s = 5.72 \times 10^4$; $\log Ka_s = 4.76$).

3. The Stability Constant for a 1:1 Complex, MA

In the simplest case of complex formation a single ligand, A, is bound to a central metal ion, M. The stability constant is given by

$$K_s = [\mathrm{MA}]/[\mathrm{M}][\mathrm{A}]$$

The average number of moles of bound A per mole of metal ion, $\bar{n}$, is again

$$\bar{n} = [\mathrm{MA}]/([\mathrm{MA}] + [\mathrm{M}]) = [\mathrm{MA}]/\mathrm{C_M}$$

where $\mathrm{C_M}$ is the total metal concentration. When $\bar{n} = 0.5$, then $[\mathrm{MA}] = [\mathrm{M}]$, and $K_s = \dfrac{1}{[\mathrm{A}]}$ or $\log K_s = p\mathrm{A}$. Thus it is only necessary to determine the two variables, $\bar{n}$ and $[\mathrm{A}]$.

Titration of a weak acid in the presence of a metal ion that is bound will displace the titration curve to a lower, i.e., more acidic region of the $p\mathrm{H}$ axis. Correspondingly, formation of the hydroxide of the metal ion will be delayed. The apparent increase in the acidity of HA can be attributed to the superposition on the hydrogen ion equilibrium of a new equilibrium involving the metal ion. In other words, the metal ion promotes the dissociation of HA through combining with A, which happens to be the common ligand for $\mathrm{H^+}$ and M.

The concentration of A can be calculated at any $p\mathrm{H}$ from the known acidic dissociation constant, Ka.

$$[\mathrm{HA}] = \mathrm{C_A} - [\text{strong base, e.g., NaOH}]$$

where $\mathrm{C_A}$ is the total initial concentration of weak acid. Since $[\mathrm{HA}] = [\mathrm{H^+}][\mathrm{A}]/Ka$, then $[\mathrm{H^+}][\mathrm{A}]/Ka = \mathrm{C_A} - [\mathrm{NaOH}]$,

or
$$[\mathrm{A}] = \mathrm{C_A} - [\mathrm{NaOH}]/([\mathrm{H^+}]/Ka)$$

Since $\bar{n}$ has been defined as $[\mathrm{MA}]/\mathrm{C_M}$ (see above), then

$$\bar{n}\mathrm{C_M} = [\mathrm{MA}] = \mathrm{C_A} - [\mathrm{A}] - [\mathrm{HA}]$$
$$= [\mathrm{NaOH}] - [\mathrm{A}]$$

and
$$\bar{n} = \frac{[\mathrm{NaOH}] - [\mathrm{A}]}{\mathrm{C_M}} = \frac{\mathrm{C_A} - [\mathrm{A}](1 + [\mathrm{H^+}]/Ka)}{\mathrm{C_M}}$$

K. Linderstrom-Lang

M. Calvin

S. Ochoa

A. Braunstein

Thus A and $\bar{n}$ may be calculated for a series of pH levels along the titration curve. The formation curve will be as shown in Fig. 3.1 with $\log K_s = p\mathrm{A}$ at $\bar{n} = 0.5$.

4. The Stability Constant for a 2:1 Complex, MA₂ (General Case)

The equations for the stepwise binding of a ligand to a metal ion are

$$\mathrm{M} + \mathrm{A} \rightleftharpoons \mathrm{MA}$$

$$k_1 = [\mathrm{MA}]/[\mathrm{M}][\mathrm{A}]$$

$$[\mathrm{MA}] + [\mathrm{A}] \rightleftharpoons [\mathrm{MA_2}]$$

$$k_2 = [\mathrm{MA_2}]/[\mathrm{MA}][\mathrm{A}]$$

and so forth, where k_1, k_2 . . . are the successive constants for the part reactions. For the sake of simplicity, we shall consider only two such successive equilibria. The stability constant for the over-all process is then given by the following equation:

$$K_s = k_1 k_2 = [\mathrm{MA_2}]/[\mathrm{M}][\mathrm{A}]^2$$

The average number of A bound per metal ion, $\bar{n}$, is again

$$\bar{n} = ([\mathrm{MA}] + 2[\mathrm{MA_2}])/([\mathrm{M}] + [\mathrm{MA}] + [\mathrm{MA_2}])$$

$$= ([\mathrm{MA}] + 2[\mathrm{MA_2}])/\mathrm{C_M}$$

Dividing both sides of the last equation by $1 - \bar{n}$ gives

$$\bar{n}/(1 - \bar{n}) = [([\mathrm{MA}] + 2[\mathrm{MA_2}])/([\mathrm{M}] + [\mathrm{MA}] + [\mathrm{MA_2}])] \div (1 - \bar{n})$$

which, after substitution of $([\mathrm{MA}] + 2[\mathrm{MA_2}])/\mathrm{C_M}$ for $\bar{n}$ on the right side yields

$$\bar{n}/(1 - \bar{n}) = ([\mathrm{MA}] + 2[\mathrm{MA_2}])/([\mathrm{M}] - [\mathrm{MA_2}])$$

$$= [\mathrm{MA}]/[\mathrm{M}] \text{ at low values of } [\mathrm{MA_2}]$$

When this value of $[\mathrm{MA}]/[\mathrm{M}]$ is substituted into the equilibrium expression for the first step we have

$$k_1 = \bar{n}/[(1 - \bar{n})[\mathrm{A}]]$$

From this it is apparent that at $\bar{n} = 0.5$, $\log k_1 = p\mathrm{A}$. Similarly, if 1 is substracted from, and $2 - \bar{n}$ is divided into, both sides of the equation for $\bar{n}$ we get

$$(\bar{n} - 1)/(2 - \bar{n}) = ([\mathrm{MA_2}] - [\mathrm{M}])/(2[\mathrm{M}] + [\mathrm{MA}])$$

$$= [\mathrm{MA_2}]/[\mathrm{MA}] \text{ at low values of } [\mathrm{M}]$$

Hence an approximation of k_2 is given by

$$k_2 = (\bar{n} - 1)/[(2 - \bar{n})[A]]$$

and $$k_2 = 1/[A] \quad \text{at} \quad \bar{n} = 1.5$$

However, just as with the binding of H^+ to a divalent anion, such as that of glutamate or aspartate, the individual steps may not be well separated. Thus the equations developed above for k_1 and k_2 will generally, without further refinement, be only approximate. On the other hand, the overall stability constant, K_s, may be described exactly. It will be recalled that

$$\bar{n} = ([MA] + 2[MA_2])/([M] + [MA] + [MA_2])$$

and hence at a value of $\bar{n} = 1$

$$[MA] + 2[MA_2] = [M] + [MA] + [MA_2]$$

and

$$[MA_2] = [M]$$

Since

$$K_s = [MA_2]/[M][A]^2 \quad \text{then at } \bar{n} = 1.0$$

$$K_s = 1/[A]^2 \quad \text{or} \quad \log K_s = 2\,pA$$

Figure 3.2 shows the formation curves for a series of ligands for which the individual steps in the formation of MA_2 are separated by

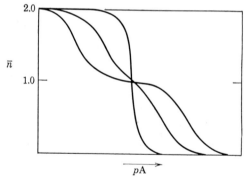

Fig. 3.2. Formation curves for 2:1 complexes in which the individual steps are separated by varying degrees.

varying degrees. Correction factors (1) may be applied in order to evaluate k_1 and k_2 from such curves or, alternately, method H of Irving and Rossotti (5) will give exact values of k_1 and k_2, even when these constants are of the same order of magnitude.

5. The Stability Constant for a 2:1 Complex, MA_2 (Specific Case)

The binding of an amino acid to a divalent metal ion may be taken as an example of the formation of a 2:1 chelate compound. This reaction has been investigated in some detail by Albert (6), and the appropriate equations have been derived by Philips (7). We shall consider as a specific example the binding of glycine to nickel chloride.

The exclusive binding species, the anion or A^-, is in equilibrium with the *Zwitterion*, HA, and the cation, H_2A^+. The anion associates with the nickel ion according to the following successive steps:

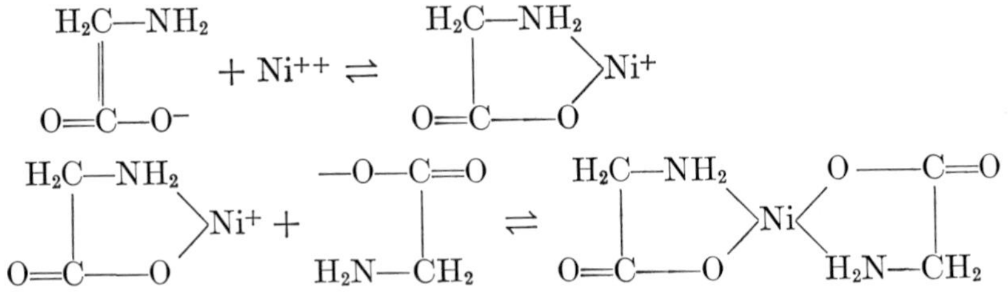

$$
\begin{array}{ccc}
H_2C\!-\!NH_2 & & H_2C\!-\!NH_2 \\
\| & +\,Ni^{++} \rightleftharpoons & | \quad\quad\ \rangle Ni^+ \\
O\!=\!C\!-\!O^- & & O\!=\!C\!-\!-\!O
\end{array}
$$

$$
\begin{array}{cccc}
H_2C\!-\!NH_2 & -O\!-\!C\!=\!O & H_2C\!-\!NH_2 & O\!-\!-\!C\!=\!O \\
| \quad\quad \rangle Ni^+\ + & | & \rightleftharpoons & | \quad\quad\ \rangle Ni\langle \quad\quad | \\
O\!=\!C\!-\!-\!O & H_2N\!-\!CH_2 & O\!=\!C\!-\!-\!O & H_2N\!-\!CH_2
\end{array}
$$

From the titration data on free glycine we obtain the two ionization constants, Ka_1 and Ka_2.

It will be recalled that $Ka_1 = [H^+]\,[HA]/[H_2A^+]$ and by rearrangement we have $[H_2A^+] = [H^+]\,[HA]/Ka_1$. From this expression we remove [HA] by its equivalent $[H^+]\,[A^-]/Ka_2$ and so obtain $[H_2A^+] = [H^+]^2\,[A^-]/Ka_1\,Ka_2$.

The total concentration of free and bound protons is given by

$$C_{H^+} = [HA] + 2[H_2A^+] + [H^+] - [OH^-]$$

or

$$C_{H^+} = C_A + [HCl] - [NaOH]$$

By equating the right sides of these equations we have

$$2[H_2A^+] + [HA] = C_A + [HCl] - [NaOH] - [H^+] + [OH^-]$$

The terms [HCl] and [NaOH] alternate, depending on which was used in the titration, and represent the concentration that would have resulted from adding these reagents to an equivalent volume of pure water. By replacing $[H_2A^+]$ and [HA] by their algebraic equivalents (derived above), we get

$$2[H^+]^2[A^-]/Ka_1\,Ka_2 + [H^+][A^-]/Ka_2$$
$$= C_A + [HCl] - [NaOH] - [H^+] + [OH^-]$$

or

$[A^-] = (C_A + [HCl] - [NaOH] - [H^+] + [OH^-])/$

$$(2[H^+]^2/Ka_1\,Ka_2 + [H^+]/Ka_2)$$

At all pH values between 4 and 10 both $[H^+]$ and $[OH^-]$ become $< 10^{-4}$ and hence may be neglected. The equation for the definition of $\bar{n}$ is

$$\bar{n}\,C_{Ni^{++}} = [Ni^+A] + 2[NiA_2]$$

Now $C_A = [A^-] + [HA] + [H_2A^+] + [NiA^+] + 2[NiA_2]$ from which $[NiA^+] + 2[NiA_2]$ may be eliminated by $\bar{n}\,C_{Ni^{++}}$ to give

$$C_A = [A^-] + [HA] + [H_2A^+] + \bar{n}\,C_{Ni^{++}}$$

Eliminating $[HA]$ and $[H_2A^+]$ by their equivalent quantities (see above) yields

$$C_A = [A^-] + ([H^+][A^-]/Ka_2) + ([H^+]^2[A^-]/Ka_1\,Ka_2) + \bar{n}\,C_{Ni^{++}}$$

and by rearrangement we get the desired equation for $\bar{n}$,

$$\bar{n} = \{C_A - [A^-](1 + [H^+]/Ka_2 + [H^+]^2/Ka_1\,Ka_2)\}\,1/C_{Ni^{++}}$$

Figure 3.3 shows an actual titration of 5 ml of 0.01 M glycine, i.e., 50 micromoles, both alone and in the presence of 25 μ moles of nickel

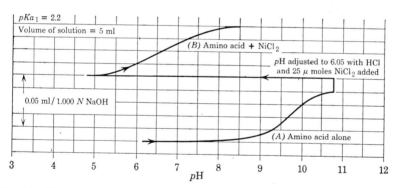

Fig. 3.3. Titration curves of glycine alone (A) and in the presence of 0.5 molar equivalent of nickel chloride (B).

chloride. The experiment was carried out in the difunctional pH recorder (8). Some of the data derived from these titrations have been recorded in Table 3.1. When a formation curve is constructed, the value of $2pA^-$ at $\bar{n} = 1.0$ or log K_s is 10.8 (Fig. 3.4).

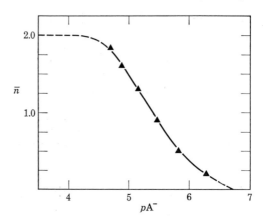

Fig. 3.4. Formation curve for a system containing glycine and 0.5 molar equivalent of nickel chloride (see Table 3.1).

Table 3.1. Electrometric Titration Data for $50\,\mu$ Moles of Glycine with $25\,\mu$ Moles of Nickel Chloride in 5 ml of Solution at $25°$ ($pKa_1 = 2.2$, $pKa_2 = 9.7$)

pH	$[A^-]$	$-\log [A^-]$	$\bar{n}$
5.5	5.6×10^{-7}	6.29	0.20
6.0	1.5×10^{-6}	5.82	0.50
6.5	3.4×10^{-6}	5.47	0.90
7.0	7.0×10^{-6}	5.15	1.30
7.5	1.2×10^{-5}	4.90	1.60
8.0	2.0×10^{-5}	4.70	1.84

6. Factors Affecting the Structure and Stability of Chelate Compounds

In the amino acid chelate compounds described above, a single bond was drawn between the nitrogen atom and metal ion. This was done in order to emphasize that the bond type in chelate compounds is still under investigation. However, a recent infrared analysis of bis-(glycino)-copper[II] has indicated that the bonding from the central metal is essentially ionic for the carboxyl and covalent for the amino groupings (9).

Evidently the structure and stability (specificity) of chelate compounds is a consequence of the summation of a multitude of effects. The latter can be divided into those derived from either the chelating ligand or the metal ion. A number of the more important of each of these effects will now be listed.

(I) Ligand effects

(a) *Nature of the ligand atoms.* In biochemicals the principal donor elements will be O, N, and S. These in turn will be provided by carboxyl, hydroxyl, carbonyl, amino, and thiol groupings (10).

(b) *Ligand basicity.* The binding of a proton and metal ion appear to have much in common. Thus in a strictly homologous series a linear relationship is often found between the pKa and log K_s (11).

(c) *Ring size.* Five-membered rings are generally favored although robust six-membered rings may be formed when double bonds are present (12).

(d) *Steriochemistry of the ligand.* The decreased stability of chelates of cycloserine, as contrasted to those for serine, is probably a consequence of the distortion of the chelate ring in the cyclic amino acid (13).

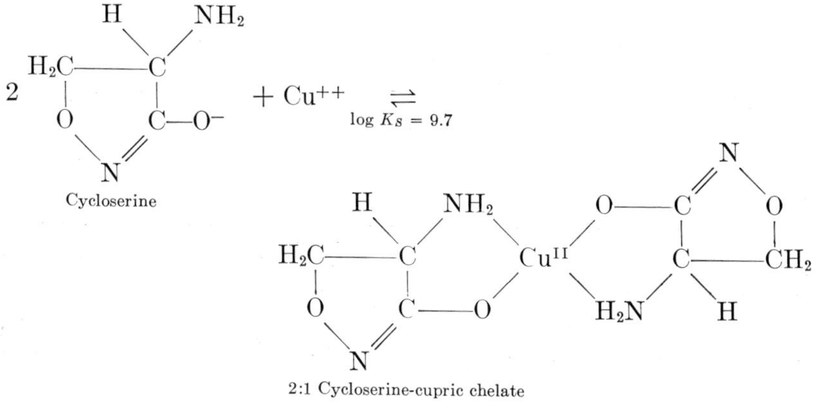

Cycloserine

2:1 Cycloserine-cupric chelate

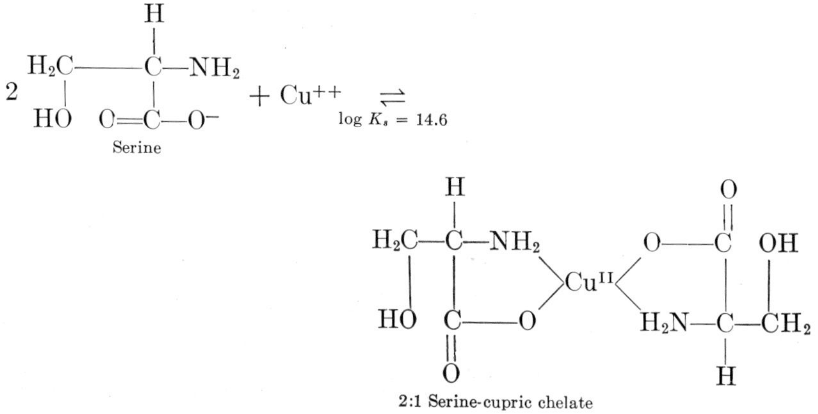

Serine

2:1 Serine-cupric chelate

(II) Metal-ion effects

(a) *Nature of the metal ion.* Mellor and Maley (14) found that with a large number of different ligands the stability constants with divalent metal ions follows the series

$$Cu > Co > Zn > Fe > Mn > Mg$$

(b) *Charge and radius.* In the absence of over-riding complica-tions, the stability constants of ionic-type chelates should increase with either decreasing ionic radius or increasing ionic charge (2).

(c) *Coordination number.* This is defined as the number of ligand atoms that can be covalently bonded to a given metal ion. Table 3.2

Table 3.2. The Coordination Numbers of Physiologically Important Metal Ions

Coordination Numbers

	2	4	4, 6	6	8
Metal ions	Cu^I	Cu^{II}, Zn	Co^{II}	Mg, Ca, Co^{III} Fe^{II}, Fe^{III}, Mn^{II}, Mn^{III}	Mo

lists the coordination numbers for the physiologically important metal ions (2).

(d) *Steriochemistry of the metal ion.* The individual metal ions exhibit a definite preference for the manner in which the attached ligand atoms are arranged in space. The most common steric arrangements are tetrahedral, planar (square), and octahedral. Thus the favored bond orientation is octahedral for iron and cobalt, tetrahedral for zinc, and square planar for copper (12).

In summary it might be said that a generally favorable structure for chelation can be represented as,

where the atoms X and Y are either O, N, or S. When $X = Y = N$, a strong preference will be shown for divalent metal ions around the copper end of the first transition series. But when $X = Y = 0$, somewhat more effective binding can be expected at the magnesium end of the series (see Fig. 3.5).

Some of the well-known synthetic metal-binding agents and the naturally occurring substances to which they are related are listed in Table 3.3.

Table 3.3. Some Related Synthetic and Naturally Occurring Chelate Compounds

Synthetic Chelates Natural Chelates

Ethylenediaminetetraacetic acid (EDTA) (2).

Ketose-amino acid. R = amino acid side chain (15).

8-Hydroxyquinoline (oxine) (16).

Isoalloxazine nucleus. R = ribitol side chain (17).

1,10 Phenanthroline (ortho) (3).

Metallo-porphyrin (partial structure) (18).

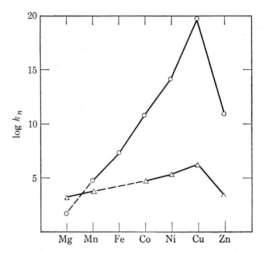

Fig. 3.5. The stability constants of complexes of the divalent ions of the first transition series with ethylenediamine (k_2, ○) and oxalate (k_1, △). (4)

7. Application to Enzymology

According to the enzyme-trace substance hypothesis of Green (19) any material which occurs in minute concentration in tissues must, *a priori*, be associated with enzymatic activity. Metal ions which are found in living tissues and which are known to participate in enzymatic reactions include Fe, Cu, Co, Zn, Mn, Mg, Ca, K, and Mo. The latter element is a relatively recent addition to the list. The searching inquiry that is now being made into the nature of the enzyme active site has revealed the presence of hitherto unsuspected metal ions, c.f. zinc as a component of some of the DPN-linked dehydrogenases (20).

In vitro studies with a host of purified enzymes has shown that traces of metal ions may activate, inhibit, or be without influence on the catalyzed reaction. In those instances in which an effect is found the metal ion may act through combination with substrate (or product), cofactor, protein, or any combination of these three entities. It should be noted that in detecting a metallo-enzyme, failure to inactivate the protein by dialysis against powerful synthetic chelating agents cannot be accepted as proper evidence for the absence of a metal ion. Ultimate analyses are best made in such cases by emission spectroscopy.

Binding of the metal ion to small molecules such as that of the substrate or cofactor can generally be studied by the procedures outlined in this chapter. Such studies may elucidate the mechanism of action of the trace metal and may even lead to the establishment of model enzyme systems without protein. For example, Snell (21) has applied this technique to several of the vitamin B_6 catalyzed transformations of the amino acids. Binding of the metal ion to the protein is more difficult to study, i.e., the site of interaction is often unknown, the molecular weight ratio (metal ion)/(enzyme protein) is generally very small, and so forth. Nevertheless Klotz (22) has clearly established that metals ions may serve as a bridge to bind small molecules to proteins.

References

A collection of stability constants has been compiled by J. Bjerrum, G. Schwarzenbach, and L. G. Sillén. (*Stability Constants;* Part I, *Organic Ligands;* Part II *Inorganic Ligands and Solubility Products.* The Chemical Society, London, 1957).

1. J. Bjerrum, *Metal Ammine Formation in Aqueous Solution,* P. Hasse and Son, Copenhagen, 1941.
2. A. E. Martel and M. Calvin, *Chemistry of the Metal Chelate Compounds,* Prentice-Hall, N. Y., 1952.
3. J. C. Bailar, editor, *The Chemistry of the Coordination Compounds,* Reinhold Pub. Co., N. Y., 1956.
4. R. J. P. Williams, *Biological Reviews, 28,* 381 (1953).
5. H. Irving and H. S. Rossotti, *J. Chem. Soc., 3397* (1953).

Bibliography

6. A. Albert, *Biochem. J., 47,* 531 (1950).
7. J. N. Philips, *Biochem. J., 50,* 697 (1952).
8. J. B. Neilands and M. D. Cannon, *Anal. Chem., 27,* 29 (1955).
9. D. N. Sen, S. Mizushima, C. Curran and J. V. Quagliano, *J. Am. Chem. Soc., 77,* 211 (1955).
10. R. J. P. Williams, *Special Lectures in Biochemistry,* 1954–55, H. K. Lewis Co., London.
11. M. Calvin and K. W. Wilson, *J. Am. Chem. Soc., 67,* 2003 (1945).
12. J. Bjerrum, *Chemical Reviews, 46,* 381 (1950).
13. J. B. Neilands, *Arch. Biochem. Biophys., 62,* 151 (1956).
14. D. P. Mellor and L. E. Maley, *Nature, 161,* 436 (1948).
15. J. B. Neilands and P. M. Townsley, *Federation Proc., 15,* 320 (1956).
16. A. Albert, *Special Lectures in Biochemistry,* 1954–55, H. K. Lewis Co., London.
17. A. Albert, *Biochem. J., 54,* 646 (1953).
18. R. Lemberg and J. W. Legge, *Hematin Compounds and Bile Pigments,* Interscience Pub. Co., New York, 1949.
19. D. E. Green, *Advances in Enzymology, I,* 177 (1941).
20. B. Vallee, *Advances in Protein Chemistry, 10,* 317 (1955).
21. E. E. Snell, *Special Lectures in Biochemistry,* 1954–55, H. K. Lewis Co., London.
22. I. M. Klotz, in *The Proteins,* edited by H. Neurath and K. Bailey, Academic Press, N. Y., 1953.

4

Isolation Methods

1. General Considerations (References 1–3)

Much confusion exists in the literature concerning the words "purified" and "isolated." Enzymologists often claim to have achieved an "isolation" when in reality they have isolated only the special catalytic activity of an enzyme. "Isolation" should be reserved for those rare instances where an investigator has tried and failed to demonstrate the chemical contamination of his preparation.

The problem of enzyme isolation is exceedingly important. Very often it represents the ultimate proof of the mechanism of a certain postulated reaction. It cannot be denied that the use of extracts, breis, and homogenaes in conjunction with specific inhibitors has yielded much valuable information on the chemical mechanisms of life. However, in the absence of the pure enzymes, the individual steps often remain obscure. It is a self-evident fact that many of the physical and chemical properties of the enzymes can be properly measured only on the pure materials. Many other types of experiments are facilitated by the use of pure enzymes, among which might be mentioned the investigation of enzyme-substrate compounds and the study of the effect of enzyme concentration on the apparent equilibrium constant of the catalyzed reaction.

The very high *turnover numbers* (T.N.) for some crystalline enzymes, for example lactic dehydrogenase, are evidence that they may have suffered very little decomposition during the isolation process. Relatively high yields of the activity may also be taken as presumptive evidence that little denaturation has occurred. For certain systems the spectroscopic, titration and kinetic data on the enzyme-substrate compounds formed within living cells agree closely with data obtained on the purified enzymes *in vitro*. Chance (4) has been able to show that the catalase inside the cells of anaerobic cultures of *Micrococcus lysodeikticus* has the same affinity for methyl hydrogen peroxide and hydrogen cyanide as the crystalline bacterial enzyme. A comprehensive treatment of the principles and procedures in enzyme isolation is found in the article by Schwimmer and Pardee (1).

2. Activity Measurements

Much of the labor and a good deal of the success in the isolation procedure hinge on the assay method. The fundamental principles of enzyme assay will be covered in the section on kinetics.

The concentration of an enzyme in a crude brei usually cannot be measured by a direct method such as a color test. Instead, one must resort to a determination of its activity. Occasionally a direct spectrophotometric measurement of the light absorption by a prosthetic group is possible, e.g., with the hemoproteins catalase, peroxidase, and cytochrome.

Because of its great speed, simplicity, specificity, and sensitivity, almost any type of optical test is the method of choice. Other methods include titration assays and measurement of gas exchange.

Figure 4.1 shows a spectrophotometric recording of the reduction of diphosphopyridine nucleotide by malic dehydrogenase of heart; Fig. 4.2 gives a record of the hydrolysis of triacetin by orange peel acetyl

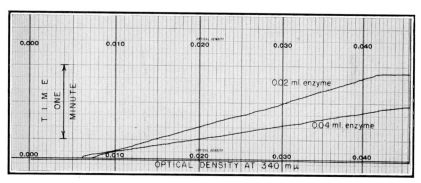

Fig. 4.1. Spectrophotometric recording of the activity of malic dehydrogenase (46).

esterase. In the latter instance the volume of 0.02 N NaOH added at a maintained pH level is recorded as a function of time. Enzyme concentrations are readily calculated from these types of data (44).

The simplest kinetic system for assay purposes is one in which the reaction is zero order. However, certain enzymes require toxic, insoluble or expensive substrates, and then it may be necessary to use lower substrate concentrations and express activity in terms of a first-order reaction rate constant. (See Chapter 7.)

The number of factors that affect enzyme activity is very great indeed (5). Some of them will be discussed in detail later. (See Part 2.)

At the initial stages of isolation it is necessary to select an arbitrary unit. For example, under carefully specified conditions 1 "unit" of enzyme gives "B μM of product in C time." This may later be re-

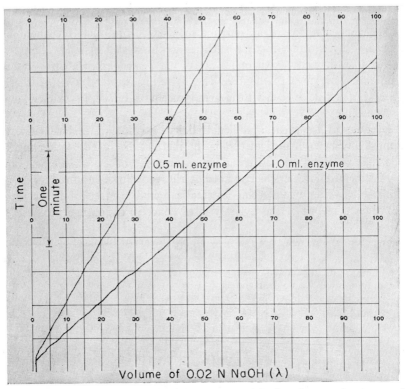

Fig. 4.2. A recording of the hydrolysis of triacetin by the acetyl esterase of orange peel as a function of time at constant [H+], i.e. pH **7.00**. Reproduced from *Analytical Chemistry*, American Chemical Society, Washington (44).

fined, when one has the pure enzyme, to: "A microgram of enzyme gives B μM of product in C time." After the molecular weight has been measured, the activity can be expressed as "A μM of enzyme gives B μM of product in C time." This is the absolute method of expressing enzyme activity, and it is often referred to as the *turnover number* (T.N.). Warburg (6) introduced the term "moles substrate/mole enzyme/minute" as the T.N. unit.

3. Purity Measurements

The degree of enrichment may be expressed as units/dry weight. Determination of dry weight is tedious and often includes salts which are of no consequence from the purity standpoint since they can be dialyzed out of the preparation at will. Methods that are often used are total nitrogen by Kjeldahl, trichloroacetic acid precipitation, tyrosine determination, and biuret color. An ingenious method is that of M. J. Johnson (7), in which the total organic solids is measured by oxidation of the sample with "cleaning solution." The reaction is

$$Cr_2O_7^= + 6e + 14H^+ \rightleftharpoons 2Cr^{+++} + 7H_2O$$

The electrons are supplied by the sample, and the disappearance of the yellow color of the dichromate is followed colorimetrically. Warburg (6) introduced the use of an optical density (O.D.) measurement at 280 mμ.[1] This test measures the absorption caused by aromatic amino

Table 4.1. The Extinction Coefficients at 280 mμ for Some Isolated Enzymes

Enzyme	Extinction Coefficient at 280 mμ (1 mg/ml in a 1.00-cm cell)	Reference
Rabbit muscle triose phosphate dehydrogenase	1.0	9
Beef heart cytochrome *c*	1.9*	10
Horse liver alcohol dehydrogenase	0.5	11
Beef liver glutamic dehydrogenase	1.0	12
Beef heart lactic dehydrogenase	1.5	13
Rhodanese	1.8	14
Enolase	0.9	6

* The high value here may be attributed in part to the porphyrin component.

acids in the protein molecule. As a general rule, an optical density at 280 mμ of 1.0 for a 1.00-cm cell corresponds to about 1 mg of protein per milliliter. The figure is relatively constant since most proteins contain roughly the same percentage of aromatic amino acids. Table 4.1 gives the extinction coefficients at 280 mμ for some isolated enzymes.

[1] When, in Beer's law, $\log I_0/I = kcl$, the concentration and cell length are both given in unity (i.e., 1 mole per liter per cm), then the log ratio of incident to emergent light intensity equals the constant k. This constant is the *extinction coefficient*. Some workers use the natural logarithm in Beer's law, and the constant so obtained is known as the *absorption coefficient*. The *absorption coefficient* is larger than the *extinction coefficient* by a factor of 2.3.

Kalckar (8) has given a formula:

$$1.45 \text{ O.D.}_{280 \text{ m}\mu} - 0.74 \text{ O.D.}_{260 \text{ m}\mu} = \text{mg protein/ml}$$

calculated from the data of Warburg (6), which permit a rough estimation of protein in the presence of nucleic acid. The method is based on the fact that protein absorbs more strongly at 280 than at 260 mμ, whereas with nucleic acid the reverse is true.

In any isolation procedure the yield as well as purity is important, and these should be all presented in tabular form when the preparation of an enzyme is described. This permits following the progress of the procedure over each step. Straub's (15) paper on the isolation of lactic dehydrogenase contains a good illustration of this principle (Table 4.2).

Table 4.2. The Yield and Purity of Heart Lactic Dehydrogenase at Each Purification Step. Straub (15)

	Total Protein, grams	Lactic Dehydrogenase, grams
Water extract of 5.5 kg heart muscle	177	3.5
Calcium phosphate gel eluate	26	2.1
First ammonium sulfate precipitate	5.2	1.3
First acetone precipitate	2.5	0.9
Second ammonium sulfate precipitate	1.1	0.65
Second acetone precipitate	...	0.46
Crystals	0.36	0.36

4. Starting Material

The availability and cost of the starting material will always be of prime importance. Since the concentration of a single enzyme may vary enormously in different tissues, it is important to select a tissue in which the enzyme is present in high concentration. For this reason, yeast, bacteria, and fungi have certain advantages as source materials. They have a further advantage in that the cells may be cultivated under conditions favorable for the production of the enzyme in question. One disadvantage, however, is the difficulty in obtaining large quantities of microbial cells other than yeast.

An early experiment should be designed to check the stability of the enzyme with respect to temperature and pH. Stability against salts, solvents, adsorbents, etc., will be apparent when the yield in units is compared after each step. The possible presence of activators or inhibitors in the crude extracts should not be overlooked.

The preparation of "acetone powders" (16) removes water, fat, and pigments. The enzyme can often be rather selectively removed from this powder by extraction with buffer. The temperature of the acetone used in making the powder can be varied so as to denature more or less protein. If the desired enzyme is sufficiently stable, a very great amount of cellular protein may be denatured and rendered insoluble by acetone at room temperature. Many acetone powders have been ruined on the Büchner funnel by washing with peroxide-containing ether. A rough index of the history of an animal acetone powder can be derived from the color of the buffer extract. Gentle treatment preserves the hemoglobin in an intact form so that the extract is reddish rather than brownish. Since acetone powders may be stored in a desiccator in the cold, they are very convenient as a source of a small amount of an enzyme used intermittently over the course of weeks or months.

5. Fractionation Procedures

Once the starting material has been selected, a series of steps can be applied to effect the extraction and eventual isolation of the enzyme. The reader should see the book by Cowgill and Pardee (2) for details of how these methods are carried out. A few specific examples of the successful use of certain methods will be cited.

A. *Sedimentation.* If liver tissue is homogenized gently, as in the Potter-Elvehjem (17) apparatus (Fig. 4.3) rather than in the common blending devices, many of the mitochondrial and other particulate cell bodies will remain intact. These may be rather easily sedimented out of solution, and with them goes a repertoire of enzymes. (See Chapter 21.) Physical separation by sedimentation is, however, practical only in the initial phases of preparation.

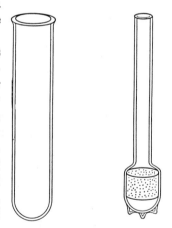

Fig. 4.3. The Potter-Elvehjem homogenizer (17).

B. *Extraction.* An early classification relegated enzymes to one of two classes, the soluble or *lyoenzymes* and the bound or *desmoenzymes*. This is a poor classification, since the desmoenzymes are probably those enzymes for which the proper methods of solution have not yet been found.

The acetone-powder is, by virtue of its fat-free nature, often the easiest material from which to effect solution. In any event, a fine grinding will almost certainly represent the first step. Methods for removing enzymes from microorganisms include autolysis, lysozyme digestion, grinding, freezing-and-thawing, sonic disintegration, shaking with solvents,[2] shaking with fine glass beads, and, finally, explosion by sudden release of pressure (45).

C. *Salt Fractionation.* Ammonium sulfate has proved to be the single most useful salt in enzyme fractionation. Its advantages are high solubility in water (760 g/l) and a roughly neutral reaction (pH 5 to 6) in concentrated solution. Dixon (18) has published a nomogram for the preparation of ammonium sulfate solutions, and Kunitz (19) has developed an equation for calculating the amount of ammonium sulfate to be added to a solution to give a desired final concentration. One disadvantage in the use of ammonium sulfate in slightly alkaline solutions is that, even at pH 9.3, 50% of the ammonium ion has already been converted to ammonia. The pH of ammonium sulfate solutions should be controlled by means of a buffer.

Sodium sulfate was used extensively in the crystallization of beef liver glutamic dehydrogenase by Olson and Anfinsen (12). Care must be exercised to carry out operations above 32° in order to avoid crystallization of the decahydrate, $Na_2SO_4 \cdot 10H_2O$. Sodium chloride, magnesium sulfate, potassium phosphates, and sodium acetate are all used to a lesser extent.

D. *Solvent Fractionation.* The water-miscible solvents that find favor in enzyme isolation are acetone, ethanol, methanol, and dioxane.

Acetone has enjoyed favor as the historically important solvent in this work. One general procedure is to start with a temperature below zero and work to higher temperatures. Fractionation is then continued up to the highest temperature that will not cause serious loss in yield.

Acetone absorbs strongly in the ultraviolet, and it must be thoroughly dialyzed away or removed from the preparation by distillation under reduced pressure before the product is subjected to spectral analyses.

Ethanol has found increasing application in the isolation of enzymes. It has been used to obtain crystalline lactic dehydrogenase from rat liver (20). The initial extracts of this enzyme were contaminated by many components whose solubilities in ammonium sulfate were very similar.

E. *Solvent-Metal Ion Fractionation.* An ingenious method of separating blood proteins has been introduced by Cohn (21) and his

---

[2] Morton (41) has had great success in solubilizing enzymes with butanol-water mixtures. Such solutions now bear in some quarters the popular name of "mortonol."

associates. These investigators have used a combination of metal ions and solvents, particularly Zn^{++} and ethanol. The Zn^{++} salts of proteins are often much less soluble than the sodium or potassium salts and are more easily thrown out of solution by the solvents. The metal ion may subsequently be removed by treatment of the complex with citrate, ethylenediamine tetraacetate, or ion-exchange resin.

F. *Adsorption.* A variety of substances have been used as protein adsorbents. One of the earliest preparations was Willstätter's (22) hydrated aluminum oxide (C γ). Calcium phosphate gel has also proved very useful (23), and bentonite has been employed in the isolation of lysozyme (3).

G. *Adsorption Chromatography.* Column chromatography on adsorbents has not been very effective for protein separation. However, Agner (24) was able to prepare catalase with calcium phosphate gel. This same adsorbent has been critically examined by Swingle and Tiselius (25) for general protein chromatography. Zechmeister (26) has published a review on the general subject of enzyme chromatography, and Zittle (47) reviewed current work in this interesting field.

A novel approach is the biochemically specific adsorbent of Lerman (27). In this method the isolation of the enzyme depends on its catalytic specificity rather than on its general properties as a protein. Thus, in the isolation of mushroom tyrosinase, various adsorbents containing *p*-azophenol and related groups were prepared from aromatic ethers of cellulose. Definite purification of the enzyme was achieved.

H. *Ion-Exchange Chromatography.* The brilliant success of this technique in the isolation of low-molecular-weight compounds such as amino acids and nucleotides has not yet been duplicated in the protein field. In 1950, cytochrome *c* was purified by passage through a column of amberlite IRC-50 (10), and this same method was useful in isolating cytochrome with a neutral *pI* from *Ustilago* (28). Ribonuclease (29) and lysozyme (30) have also been purified in a similar manner. The same procedure has been tried without success for certain higher-molecular-weight enzymes (31). Ion-exchange chromatography is essentially an electrophoretic separation in which the resin serves as one electrode and gravity as the other. It may yet develop into a valuable tool as the chemical industry places more new resins in the hands of enzymologists.[3]

[3] Cellulose powder may be treated with chloroacetic acid to form a cation exchanger or with 2-chloro-N, N-diethylethylamine to form an anion exchanger. Such exchangers have proven quite useful for chromatographic purification of enzymes (42).

Sulfonic acid cation exchanger

Carboxylic acid cation exchanger

I. *Partition Chromatography.* R. R. Porter (**32, 33**) has extended the process of partition chromatography to the protein field. This method appears applicable for proteins over a wide molecular-weight range. The limiting factors are apparently the solubilities of the proteins in the various possible solvent systems and their resistance to denaturation either by surface adsorption or by the organic solvent itself. Carpenter (**51**) has made a detailed study of the behavior of insulin on partition columns.

J. *Isoelectric Precipitation.* Since proteins show minimum solubility at the *pI*, it is of considerable value to ascertain in the early stages of a preparation how much purification can be achieved by the simple expedient of *p*H adjustment. A very large number of successful isolations have followed this method, although certain enzymes, e.g., lactic dehydrogenase of heart, are irreversibly denatured at the isoelectric point.

K. *Complex Formation.* Warburg (**6**) and his school have made use of precipitations with nucleic acid. Protamine has been used to a lesser extent as a complexing agent. Some enzymes, e.g., muscle lactic dehydrogenase (**34**), were isolated as the inactive mercury salts. Reactivation was achieved by dialysis against cysteine or potassium

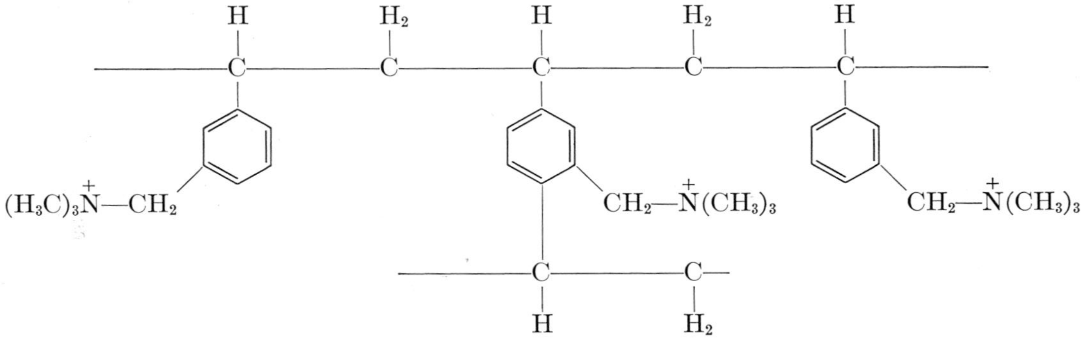

Quaternary amine anion exchanger

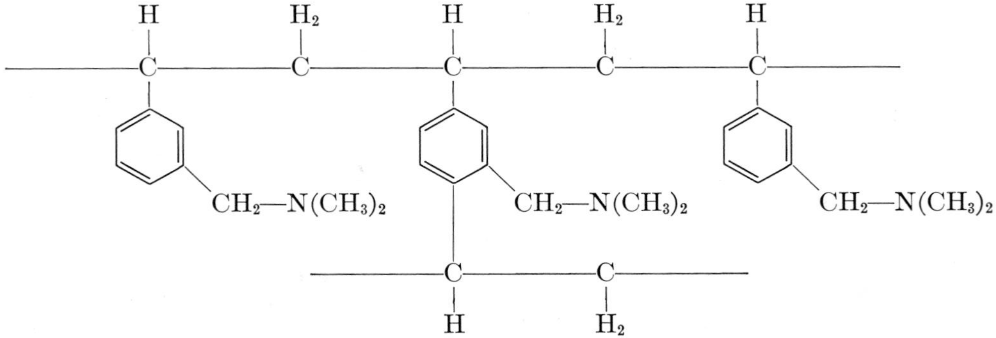

Tertiary amine anion exchanger

cyanide. Basic lead acetate is employed to throw down undesired proteins.

L. *Denaturation Reactions.* Brief periods of heating, from 50° to 70°, are often used as one of the early steps. The method is successful in the crystallization of alcohol dehydrogenase from yeast (35). Denaturation with trichloracetic acid is used in the isolation of cytochrome *c* (36). Denaturation in alkaline solution and foam denaturation are employed occasionally (37). Shaking with chloroform is a very effective way to remove contaminating proteins (see ref. 1).

M. *Dialysis.* Theorell and Åkeson (38) have designed an electrodialysis cell for separating proteins from salt.

A current of air blown over a dialysis bag containing a protein solution is an exceedingly gentle method to effect concentration. As long

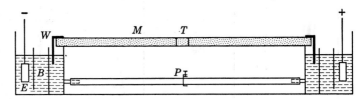

Fig. 4.4. Schematic diagram of a preparative zone electrophoresis cell (48).

B   Buffer compartment with baffles   P   Pressure-equalizing tube
E   Platinum electrodes   M   Medium, such as starch, sponge
W   Filter paper wick   rubber
                                          T   Trench for sample

as evaporation continues, the solution will remain at a low temperature.

N. *Preparative Electrophoresis.* Large cells, containing up to 100 ml, may be used with special electrodes in the electrophoresis apparatus. Svensson and Brattsten (39) have built an apparatus which combines electrophoresis with continuous gravitational flow. The method is very good if the protein happens to be colored. Kunkel and Tiselius (40) have written a comprehensive article on the subject of paper electrophoresis. Methods such as these, in which the components are completely separated, have been designated as "zone electrophoresis."

Zone electrophoresis on a starch bed or on blocks of sponge rubber has become a very popular tool for protein isolation. The review by Stern (48) contains rather complete details of the construction and use of this apparatus. In Fig. 4.4 a schematic diagram is shown for a

preparative zone electrophoresis cell. A popular type of column electrophoresis equipment is illustrated in Fig. 4.5.

Attention should also be directed to the novel technique of Kolin
(49). Here buffer solutions of unequal density are layered over each
other to give a pH gradient in a vertical tube. The sample is intro-

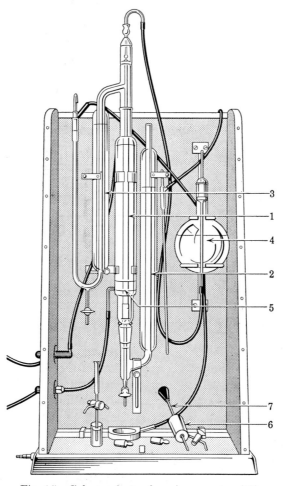

Fig. 4.5. Column electrophoresis apparatus (50)

1. Water-cooled column	5. Glass filter disk
2. Anode vessel	6. Glass adapter
3. Cathode vessel	7. Capillary tube
4. Mariotte flask	

Courtesy of *Ivan Sorvall, Inc.*, Norwalk.

duced and when the current is turned on the various proteins migrate
to their isoelectric point and stop. The method is capable of very
rapid resolution, since the further the proteins are from their pI the
more rapidly they will migrate to their isoelectric zone.

The "electrophoresis-convection" apparatus of Kirkwood (see ref.
43) may be applicable for separating less complex mixtures. Electrophoresis-convection may be regarded as a refinement of the process
of electrodecantation, as illustrated in Fig. 4.6. The pH throughout the
apparatus is alkaline to the isoelectric point of the protein, and the
protein has migrated to the anode. This will cause a higher density
next to the right side of the membrane, and the protein will settle

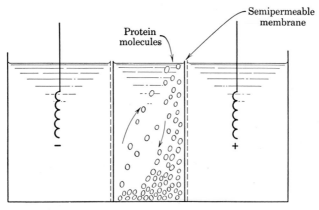

Fig. 4.6. A schematic illustration of the electrophoresis convection principle.

down on that side, thus giving rise to convection and eventually to a
collection of the component in the bottom of the cell.

O. *Crystallization.* The final step in enzyme isolation should be
carried out with the same care as is exercised in parallel experiments
in organic chemistry. Since there is often little difference in the refractive index of ammonium sulfate solutions and protein crystals drifting
in suspension, it is helpful to swirl the solution and look for silkiness.
Silkiness is indicative of the presence of rods or plates.

However, the presence of crystals is in itself a very poor index of
homogeneity. Therefore, it is necessary to carry out elaborate "criteria of purity" experiments even after the crystalline enzyme has
been obtained. This subject will be treated at length in the following
chapter.

References

General

1. S. Schwimmer and A. Pardee, *Advances in Enzymology, 14,* 375 (1953).
2. R. W. Cowgill and A. B. Pardee, *Biochemical Research Techniques,* John Wiley and Sons, New York, 1957.
3. S. P. Colowick and N. O. Kaplan, editors, *Methods in Enzymology, I,* pp. 25–138, Academic Press, N. Y., 1955.

Bibliography

4. B. Chance, *Abstracts,* 124th Am. Chem. Soc. Meeting, Chicago, September, 1953.
5. Van R. Potter, in *Respiratory Enzymes,* edited by H. A. Lardy, Burgess Publishing Co., Minneapolis, Minn., 1949, p. 264.
6. O. Warburg, *Wasserstoffübertragendefermente,* Werner Saenger Press, Berlin, 1948.
7. M. J. Johnson, *J. Biol. Chem., 181,* 707 (1949).
8. H. Kalckar, *J. Biol. Chem., 167,* 461 (1947).
9. J. F. Taylor, S. F. Velick, G. T. Cori, C. F. Cori, and M. W. Slein, *J. Biol. Chem., 173,* 619 (1948).
10. S. Paléus and J. B. Neilands, *Acta Chem. Scand., 4,* 1024 (1950).
11. H. Theorell and R. Bonnichsen, *Acta Chem. Scand., 5,* 1105 (1951).
12. J. A. Olson and C. B. Anfinsen, *J. Biol. Chem., 197,* 67 (1952).
13. J. B. Neilands, *J. Biol. Chem., 199,* 373 (1952).
14. B. Sörbo, *Acta Chem. Scand., 7,* 1129 (1953).
15. F. B. Straub, *Biochem. J., 34,* 483 (1940).
16. Van R. Potter, in *Manometric Techniques,* Umbreit, Burris, and Stauffer, Burgess Publishing Co., Minneapolis, 1951, p. 218.
17. Van R. Potter and C. A. Elvehjem, *J. Biol. Chem., 114,* 495 (1936).
18. M. Dixon, *Biochem. J., 54,* 457 (1953).
19. M. Kunitz, *J. Gen. Physiol., 35,* 423 (1952).
20. D. M. Gibson, E. O. Davisson, B. K. Bachhawat, B. R. Ray, and C. S. Vestling, *J. Biol. Chem., 203,* 397 (1953).
21. E. J. Cohn et al., *J. Am. Chem. Soc., 72,* 465 (1950).
22. R. Willstätter, H. Kraut, and O. Erbacher, *Ber., 58,* 2448 (1925).
23. D. Keilin and E. F. Hartree, *Proc. Roy. Soc. (London), B124,* 397 (1937).
24. K. Agner, *Biochem. J., 32,* 1702 (1938).
25. S. M. Swingle and A. Tiselius, *Biochem. J., 48,* 171 (1951).
26. L. Zechmeister, *Forschritte der Chemie organischer Naturstoffe, 8,* 341 (1951).
27. L. S. Lerman, *Proc. Natl. Acad. Sci., 39,* 232 (1953).
28. J. B. Neilands, *J. Biol. Chem., 197,* 701 (1952).
29. C. H. W. Hirs, W. H. Stein, and S. Moore, *J. Am. Chem. Soc., 73,* 1893 (1951).
30. H. H. Tallan and W. H. Stein, *J. Am. Chem. Soc., 73,* 2976 (1951).
31. J. B. Neilands, unpublished observations.
32. A. J. P. Martin and R. R. Porter, *Biochem. J., 49,* 215 (1951).
33. R. R. Porter, *Biochem. J., 53,* 320 (1953); Brit. Med. Bull. *10,* No. 3 (1954).
34. F. Kubowitz and P. Ott, *Biochem. Z., 314,* 84 (1943).

35. E. Negelein and H. J. Wulff, *Biochem. Z., 293*, 351 (1937).

36. D. Keilin and E. F. Hartree, *Biochem. J., 39*, 289 (1945).

37. A. Abrams and H. Klenow, *Arch. Biochem. Biophys., 34*, 285 (1951).

38. H. Theorell and Å. Åkeson, *Arkiv Kemi, Mineral. Geol., 16A*, No. 8 (1942).

39. H. Svensson and I. Brattsten, *Arkiv Kemi, 1*, 401 (1949).

40. H. G. Kunkel and A. Tiselius, *J. Gen. Physiol., 35*, 89 (1951).

41. R. K. Morton, *Nature, 166*, 1092 (1950).

42. H. A. Sober and E. A. Peterson, *J. Am. Chem. Soc., 76*, 1711 (1954); *78*, 756 (1956).

43. R. A. Alberty, in *The Proteins,* edited by H. Neurath and K. Bailey, Academic Press, 1953, Chapter 6.

44. J. B. Neilands and M. D. Cannon, *Anal. Chem., 27*, 29 (1955).

45. W. B. Hugo, *Bact. Revs., 18*, 87 (1954).

46. R. G. Wolfe and J. B. Neilands, *J. Biol. Chem., 221*, 61 (1956).

47. C. A. Zittle, *Advances in Enzymology, 14*, 319 (1953).

48. K. G. Stern, in Physical Techniques in Biological Research, edited by G. Oster and A. W. Pollister, Academic Press, N. Y., 1956.

49. A. Kolin, *Proc. National Acad. Sc., 41*, 101 (1955).

50. P. Flodin and J. Porath, *Biochem. Biophys. Acta, 13*, 175 (1954).

51. F. H. Carpenter, *17th Biology Colloquium,* Oregon State College, Corvallis, p. 18 (1956).

5

Criteria of Purity

1. Chemical Nature of Enzymes

The physical and chemical properties of enzymes were early recognized to parallel those of the proteins. However, even after the activity of Sumner's (3) urease had been found to be closely associated with a crystalline protein, there was always the question whether the protein was identical with the enzyme or whether it was in some way only adventitiously associated with the active principle. After the development of a direct method for measuring the molecular weight (*M.W.*) of proteins, namely, via a determination of both its sedimentation velocity in a gravitational field and its velocity of diffusion, there could be no longer any doubt that the isolated protein was identical with the enzyme.[1] Once *M.W.* was known, the activity of the enzyme could be determined after the addition of various fractional equivalents of a potent inhibitor. Complete inhibition should result after the ratio of moles inhibitor/moles enzyme has reached a small whole number.

Criteria of purity for an enzyme are therefore the same as those used in protein chemistry. This is a very important topic in enzymology since most quantitative work on the isolated enzyme demands that it be rigorously pure. Li (1) has prepared a comprehensive review on this subject. Also, the article by Pirie (2), although written in 1940, is still regarded as a classic.

Examples of the occurrence of more than one active form are numerous enough to suspect the natural existence of enzymes in a "microheterogeneous" state (29).

---

[1] According to a report by Binkley (27), hydrolytic enzyme activity can be found in certain polynucleotide fractions. Also, self-digestion of pepsin apparently forms a polypeptide with enzymatic activity (28). Similar experiments have been carried out with ribonuclease (31, 32, 33), papain (34) and trypsin (35).

2. Crystallinity

Crystallinity is in itself an extremely unreliable index of purity. Some examples of crystalline enzymes which are heterogeneous mixtures are heart lactic dehydrogenase (4, 5), ribonuclease (6), and even, when not protected from CO_2, lysozyme (7). Sumner's crystalline urease turned out to contain several components. Since denatured enzymes cannot be crystallized, a beautifully crystalline preparation usually represents a material containing only a small number of components.

3. Maximum Activity

An easy but rather poor method for testing the likelihood of contamination is to examine the specific activity after repeated fractionation. If the enzyme is pure, its specific activity will remain constant. The "unit" may be divided by any of the quantities chosen in Chapter 4 to represent the amount of enzyme taken, e.g., dry weight, total nitrogen, protein nitrogen, biuret color, optical density at 280 $m\mu$, or total organic matter.

A constant specific activity cannot be accepted as proof of purity since the fractionation procedure employed may have simply achieved zero separation.

4. Maximum Per Cent of a Characteristic Constituent

For the same reasons as given above for the specific activity test, the content of some highly characteristic chemical group in the enzyme should reach a maximum which is a constant for the pure enzyme. Thus the cytochrome c of 0.34% Fe (8) had to be regarded as impure when Theorell and Åkeson (9) later isolated the same compound with 0.43% Fe. The same technique was applied in isolating the old yellow enzyme, in which the flavin content was measured.

No definite assurance can be given that the experimentally determined maximum per cent of the characteristic group is equal to the true figure for the pure enzyme, for the group under investigation may be characteristic of both the enzyme and impurities. In discussing the early work on peroxidase, Warburg (10) has pointed out the fallacy of assuming that the ratio iron content/activity could be used as and index of purification.

5. Salt Fractionation

The theory of this test is based on the phase rule, and it is applicable except where solid solutions are formed. In general, two experimental approaches are possible: the enzyme may be added in increments to a salt solution, or conversely, the pure salt may be added to a solution of the enzyme. The two techniques are referred to as the "constant" and the "variable" solvent solubility tests, respectively (30).

The first method has been pioneered by Northrop (11) and works very well except when solid solutions are formed. The original references (12, 13) should be consulted for the full explanation. The type of diagram obtained is illustrated in Fig. 5.1. The number of breaks, found by analyzing the protein content of the filtrate after various

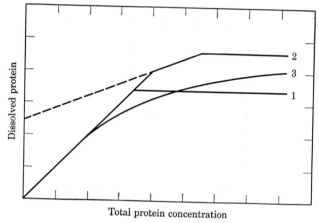

Fig. 5.1. Constant solvent solubility curves for a pure protein, 1, a mixture of two proteins, 2, and a solid solution, 3.

additions of solid protein, is equal to the number of components. Thus a pure substance would show only a single break.

In the second method, increments of salt are added to a fixed volume of dilute protein solution, and, after temperature equilibration, the protein content of the filtrate is measured. This is the technique that has been used by Derrien (14), Roche, Derrien, and Mautte (15), and expanded by Falconer and Taylor (16). It is convenient to measure the protein content of the filtrate by direct spectrophotometric observation. Some enzymes, such as hemoproteins, absorb at higher wavelengths, and with these it is possible to make measurements at two or more wavelengths. Thus we need a series of tubes containing 3 to 4 ml of a buffered solution of the enzyme; the concentration of the enzyme may be of the order of 0.1%. Crystallization during the test invalidates the results. Dixon's nomogram (17) gives the proper amount of salt to be added. The pure salt is added and dissolved, and the solutions are allowed to stand at constant temperature (e.g., 5°) for 24 hours. They are then centrifuged or filtered through acid-washed papers (filter paper usually contains soluble ultraviolet-absorbing materials), and the optical density is measured at 280 mμ. The optical density must be corrected for the volume of salt added.

When the curve obtained above is compared with the activity curve, the solubility characteristic of the active principle is apparent at once.

An excellent example of the Falconer-Taylor technique is given in the data of Brown (18). Figure 5.2 is a reproduction of his work on

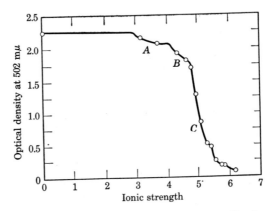

Fig. 5.2. Variable solvent solubility curve for twice crystallized ox liver catalase (18). Reproduced from *Biochemical Journal,* Cambridge University Press, London and New York.

the salting-out of twice-crystallized ox-liver catalase. It is obvious that three main components, *A, B,* and *C,* with appreciable absorption at 502 mμ, are present. The same method has been used for crystalline heart lactic dehydrogenase (5). Two components appeared on the salting-out diagram, in agreement with the electrophoresis experiments on this enzyme.

6. Electrophoresis

The wide choice of *p*H and its consequent profound effect on the mobility of the proteins lend great versatility to the electrophoresis method.

Most types of apparatus have cells resembling those shown in Fig. 5.3. Theorell (19, 20) built the original instruments and employed them extensively for isolating new enzymes (9). Tiselius (21) de-

signed the modern cell and refrigerated the apparatus at a temperature close to the temperature of maximum density of the buffer. The
shape of this cell is such that the heat from the electric field is dissipated as rapidly as possible.

Figure 5.3 shows the method of filling the cell. It is usually necessary to have a 1% solution of the enzyme; standard cell volumes
range from about 3 to 10 ml. In position 1 of Fig. 5.3 the cell is shown
with enough protein solution to completely fill the bottom compartment. In position 2 the central and top sections have been pushed
to the right, the left limb has been cleaned out and filled with buffer,
and the right limb has been filled with protein solution. In 3 the

Compensation

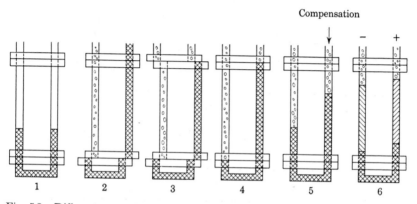

Fig. 5.3. Different stages in the loading and operating of the electrophoresis apparatus.

top section has been returned to its original position, and the two
channels have been filled with buffer. In 4 the central section has
been pushed into place, and in 5 the level has been compensated
downwards (arrow) by adding pure buffer to the right limb. This
brings both boundaries into the optical path. In position 6 the current has separated the two proteins, represented by cross hatching,
into a negatively charged species migrating relatively slowly to the
anode while a more rapid component migrates to the cathode.

The concentration gradients through the boundaries are analyzed
by the change in refractive index. The lens system employed is known
as the *schlieren* method. Figure 5.4 shows diagrammatically the
nature of the schlieren image. Each component will provide such a
peak, and the area under the peak is proportional to the concentration. This follows from the fact that the refractive indices for dif-

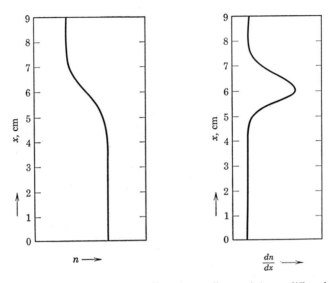

Fig. 5.4. Plot of refractive index gradient in a cell containing a diffuse boundary at a height of 6 cm.

ferent proteins are essentially the same. The electrophoretic pattern of crystalline heart lactic dehydrogenase is shown in Fig. 5.5.

Alberty (22) has prepared an excellent review on the principles and use of the electrophoresis apparatus.

Paper electrophoresis is much simpler and should be very useful for purity analysis (23).

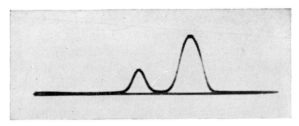

Fig. 5.5. The electrophoretic pattern of crystalline heart lactic dehydrogenase. Migration direction is to the right (4). Reproduced from *Science,* American Association for the Advancement of Science, Washington.

7. Sedimentation

Sedimentation in the ultracentrifuge offers a method of determining heterogeneity with respect to size. Figure 5.6 shows the sedimentation pattern of crystalline lactic dehydrogenase of heart (24). This is the same preparation that was found by other methods to consist of at least two components!

The method is rapid and economical of material. Only 1 ml of a 1% solution is needed. The schlieren lens system is used to follow the

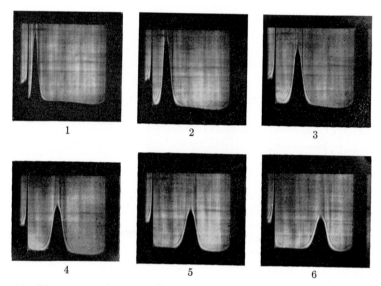

Fig. 5.6. The sedimentation pattern of crystalline lactic dehydrogenase of heart. The six pictures were taken at 15-minute intervals, starting with 1 (24).

concentration changes in the cell, and modern instruments feature refrigeration. The reader is referred to the monograph of Svedberg and Pedersen (25) and the review by Schachman (36).

8. Absorption Spectra

Most proteins may be expected to contain some aromatic amino acids and should therefore exhibit an absorption band with a peak somewhere around 275 to 280 mμ. Once a hemoprotein enzyme has been spectrally characterized, subsequent preparations can be easily checked for protein contamination by measuring the extinction first at some longer wavelength where the iron porphyrin absorbs and then at 280 mμ. A decrease in the ratio visible absorption/ultraviolet absorption signifies contamination. A ratio O.D.$_{280\ m\mu}$/O.D.$_{260\ m\mu}$ of 1.6 or larger indicates the absence of appreciable amounts of nucleic acid.

9. Immunological Method

When the protein nature of the contaminants is suspected, anaphylactic or precipitin reactions are useful. A method has been devised in which the antigen-antibody reaction is carried out in a gel such as agar. The components are visible as precipitated zones in the gel. Becker (26) has reviewed the general subject of immunological reactions in gels.

References

General

1. C. H. Li, in *Amino Acids and Proteins*, by D. M. Greenberg, Charles C. Thomas Publishing Co., Springfield, Ill., 1951.
2. N. W. Pirie, *Biol. Revs., 15*, 377 (1940).

Bibliography

3. J. B. Sumner, *J. Biol. Chem., 69*, 435 (1926).
4. J. B. Neilands, *Science, 115*, 143 (1952).
5. J. B. Neilands, *J. Biol. Chem., 199*, 373 (1952).
6. C. H. W. Hirs, W. H. Stein, and S. Moore, *J. Am. Chem. Soc., 73*, 1896 (1951).
7. H. H. Tallan and W. H. Stein, *J. Am. Chem. Soc., 73*, 2976 (1951).
8. H. Theorell, *Biochem. Z., 279*, 463 (1935).
9. H. Theorell and Å. Åkeson, *J. Am. Chem. Soc., 63*, 1804 (1941).
10. O. Warburg, *Heavy Metal Prosthetic Groups*, Oxford Press, London, 1949.
11. J. H. Northrop, *Crystalline Enzymes*, Columbia University Press, N. Y., 1939.
12. J. H. Northrop and M. Kunitz, *J. Gen. Physiol., 13*, 781 (1930).
13. M. Kunitz and J. H. Northrop, *Cold Spring Harbor Symposium*, 1938.
14. Y. Derrien, *Bull. soc. chim. biol., 26*, 1091 (1944).
15. J. Roche, Y. Derrien, and M. Mautte, *Bull. soc. chim. biol., 23*, 1114 (1941).
16. J. S. Falconer and D. B. Taylor, *Nature, 155*, 303 (1945).
17. M. Dixon, *Biochem. J., 54*, 457 (1953).
18. G. L. Brown, *Biochem. J., 51*, 569 (1952).
19. H. Theorell, *Biochem. Z., 275*, 1 (1934); *278*, 291 (1935).
20. H. Theorell, in *Handbook of Biological Experimentation, 10*, 1097 (1938).
21. A. Tiselius, *The Harvey Lectures, 35*, 37 (1939–1940).
22. R. A. Alberty, *J. Chem. Education, 25*, 426, 619 (1948).
23. H. G. Kunkel and A. Tiselius, *J. Gen. Physiol., 35*, 89 (1951).
24. J. B. Neilands, *J. Biol. Chem., 199*, 373 (1952).
25. T. Svedberg and K. O. Pedersen, *The Ultracentrifuge*, Clarendon Press, Oxford, 1940.
26. E. Becker, *Symposium Federation Meeting*, Chicago, Spring, 1953.
27. F. Binkley, *Proc. Roy. Soc., B142*, 170 (1954).
28. G. E. Perlman, *Nature, 173*, 406 (1954).
29. J. R. Colvin, D. B. Smith, and W. H. Cook, *Chem. Revs., 54*, 687 (1954).
30. O. Smithies, *Biochem. J., 58*, 31 (1954).
31. M. Uziel, W. H. Stein and S. Moore, *Federation Proc., 16*, 263 (1957).

32. C. B. Anfinsen, *J. Biol. Chem., 221,* 405 (1956).

33. F. Richards, *Compt.-rend. trav. Lab. Carlsberg, Serie chim., 29,* 329 (1955).

34. R. L. Hill and E. L. Smith, *Biochem. Biophys. Acta, 19,* 376 (1956).

35. G. P. Hess and E. Wainfan, *J. Am. Chem. Soc., 80,* 501 (1958).

36. H. K. Schachman, in *Methods in Enzymology,* IV, Academic Press, New York, 1957.

6

Characterization

1. Introduction (References 1, 2)

Enzymes, by virtue of their catalytic activity, can be characterized in a little more detail than simple proteins. But even after all the physical constants for the pure enzyme have been measured (2), the complete structure of the molecule, like that of any other protein, remains a mystery. The existing knowledge of the chemistry and biochemistry of the purified enzyme proteins is collected in the book edited by Neurath and Bailey (1).

Several elegant new methods have been advanced for the elucidation of amino acid sequence in proteins. Some of these methods have been applied to the simpler enzymes such as ribonuclease (58), and it is to be hoped that the method of sequence determination will eventually become only a routine problem in protein chemistry.

Considerable ingenuity is necessary in characterizing the mode of linkage of the prosthetic group to the protein. The challenge is formidable for those enzymes, especially certain dehydrogenases, which are almost always isolated with the coenzyme part completely dissociated.

2. Solubility

The procedure of Falconer and Taylor (3), discussed in Chapter 5, is most helpful because it shows at a glance the salting-out characteristics of the enzyme. The solubility studies of Northrop (4) must be carried out with proper attention to factors like temperature and ionic strength.

The accurate record of the solubility of an enzyme can be used in isolating the enzyme from different sources and predicting its occurrence in the preparation of other enzymes.

D. Shemin

H. A. Barker

E. E. Snell

H. G. Wood

B. Vennesland

H. Kalckar

3. Electrometric Titration

The acid-base titration curves for proteins will be roughly similar in shape to those for the monoaminomonocarboxylic acids. The shape of the titration curve should be identical with the pH-mobility curve in electrophoresis.

The titration curve of cytochrome c, taken from a paper by Theorell and Åkeson (5), is shown in Fig. 6.1. From this figure Theorell and Åkeson were able to decide that between pH 5.5 and 8.5 there were two equivalents of some group titrated. The heat of ionization

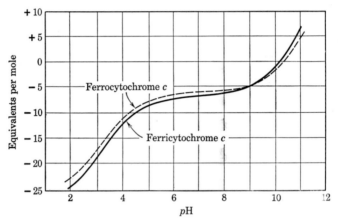

Fig. 6.1. The acid-base titration curve of cytochrome c (5). Reproduced from *Journal of the American Chemical Society,* American Chemical Society, Washington.

was calculated, and, from the known heat of ionization of the imidazole group, it was concluded that only one of these groups could be histidine. Since the chemical analysis showed three moles of histidine per mole of enzyme, 2 of the imidazole groups obviously lay outside their normal range. Theorell concluded that these 2 groups are concerned in the binding of the iron porphyrin prosthetic group to the protein. The detailed structure of cytochrome c is shown in Fig. 6.6.

Steinhardt and Zaiser (6) have found that preliminary exposure of horse carbonyl hemoglobin to dilute acid results in the liberation of several additional carboxyl groups. Thus the possibility of unfolding or even denaturation of the protein during titration must be considered.

Difference titration curves for the apo and holoenzymes should give information on the nature of the prosthetic group linkages. However, the great difference in molecular weights between the protein and coenzyme parts makes such experiments difficult. The problem is discussed at length by Cohn and Edsall (7) and by Tanford (68, 69).

4. Electrophoretic Mobility and *pI*

An excellent review by Alberty (8) has appeared on this aspect of enzyme characterization.

The electrophoretic mobility u is defined as $u = v/E$, where v is the velocity of migration of the boundary in cm sec^{-1} and E is the electrical field strength. This last quantity is provided by the relation $E = i/q\kappa$, where i is the current flowing through the cell, q is the cross-

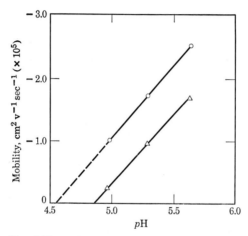

Fig. 6.2. The *p*H-mobility relationship for the two components of crystalline lactic dehydrogenase of heart (9). Reproduced from *Journal of Biological Chemistry*, American Society of Biological Chemists, New Haven.

sectional area of the cell, and κ is the specific conductance of the solution. Combining the two expressions gives $u = vq\kappa/i$. Actual values of u are of the order of 10^{-5} cm^2 volt^{-1} sec^{-1}. The mobility is dependent on several factors in addition to *p*H, chief among which might be mentioned the ionic strength of the buffer.

Figure 6.2 gives the electrophoretic mobility versus *p*H for the two components of crystalline lactic dehydrogenase of heart (9). It was not possible, because of irreversible precipitation, to carry out mobility experiments at a *p*H lower than 5. Under such conditions the mobility can be *extrapolated* only to the zero value, a somewhat uncertain procedure.[1]

[1] For a graph showing mobility over a wider *p*H range see the paper on aldolase by Velick (53).

The same enzyme obtained from rat liver has different mobility characteristics (10). Rat liver lactic dehydrogenase shows only one component, and the mobility could be measured on either side of the pI. The enzyme was isoelectric at pH 6.3.

The actual position of the pI on the pH scale has little relation to the total number of acidic and basic functional groups in the molecule. It may be possible to have an equal number of amino and carboxyl groups but to have the majority of the carboxyl groups covered up in the amide form. The pI would be high. If, for instance, the protein contained only one or two basic functional groups per mole, then the presence of only a very few acidic groups would impart a low pI to the molecule. The possibility of buffer ion binding by the protein should not be overlooked in all electrophoresis experiments.

5. Diffusion Coefficient

The diffusion coefficient, D, is a required quantity in the calculation of the molecular weight by sedimentation, $M.W._{sD}$.

The diffusion rate as given by Fick's equation is

$$\frac{ds}{dt} = -Dq \frac{dc}{dx}$$

Here ds/dt is the amount of substance diffusing per second, q is the cross-sectional area of the cell, and dc/dx is the concentration gradient. Several methods are available for measuring the rate of free diffusion; a popular method is the height-area technique of Longsworth (11).

Free diffusion measurements may be carried out in the standard Tiselius electrophoresis cell, and good results are obtained if the boundaries are properly sharpened and the rate extrapolated to zero time. Several types of cells have been designed strictly for diffusion work (12). The magnitude of D may be obtained by the rate of spreading during sedimentation in the ultracentrifuge, although this method is less accurate.

Instead of the classical free diffusion method, the protein may be allowed to diffuse through a sintered glass disk (13). This method has not been widely used for enzyme work although it is applicable to impure preparations since the enzyme can be detected by its activity.

The diffusion coefficient is a reflection of the size and shape of the protein molecule. There is not enough accumulated information to say that D for enzymes differs in any real sense from that for non-catalytic proteins. The D_{20} for the pure major fraction of crystalline heart lactic dehydrogenase (9) is about 5.3×10^{-7} cm^2 sec^{-1}, while that for liver glutamic dehydrogenase (14) is 2.54×10^{-7} cm^2 sec^{-1}. The molecular weights of the two enzymes are 135,000 and 1,000,000, respectively.

6. Sedimentation Coefficient and M.W.$_{sD}$.

The sedimentation coefficient s is given by the expression

$$s = \frac{dx/dt}{\omega^2 x}$$

where dx represents the change in distance of the refractive index gradient from the axis of rotation over the seconds dt and ω^2 is the radians per second.

Sedimentation coefficients, s, are of the order of 10^{-13} second; S means[2] that s has been multiplied by 10^{13}. Again, there is nothing characteristic in the sedimentation constants for enzymes since they may range from values of 1 to 2×10^{-13} second for cytochrome c, ribonuclease, and lysozyme (15) to 26.6×10^{-13} second for crystalline glutamic dehydrogenase of liver (14). An accurate determination of s entails a study of the sedimentation velocity as a function of the protein concentration. The protein concentration may then be extrapolated to zero in order to obtain the value to be used in calculating $M.W.$

The molecular weight is obtained directly from the equation

$$M.W. = \frac{RTs}{D(1 - \bar{V}\rho)}$$

where R is the gas constant, T the absolute temperature, s the sedimentation constant, D the diffusion constant, $\bar{V}$ the partial specific volume, and ρ the density of the solution (16).

The value of $\bar{V}$ lies close to 0.74 to 0.75 ml g^{-1} for a great many proteins and is used in calculating an approximate molecular weight.

From the data given for crystalline horse-liver alcohol dehydrogenase (17), the calculation of its molecular weight may be reconstructed.

$$R = 8.314 \times 10^7 \text{ ergs per mole per degree}$$
$$T = 293°\text{K}$$
$$s_{20} = 4.9 \times 10^{-13} \text{ second}$$
$$D_{20} = 6.5 \times 10^{-7} \text{ cm}^2 \text{ sec}^{-1}$$
$$\bar{V} = 0.751 \text{ ml g}^{-1}$$
$$\rho = 0.998 \text{ g ml}^{-1}$$

$$M.W. = \frac{8.314 \times 10^7 \times 293 \times 4.9 \times 10^{-13}}{6.5 \times 10^{-7}(1 - 0.751 \times 0.998)} = 73,000$$

[2] S represents the Svedberg unit, 10^{-13} sec.

The development of a synthetic boundary cell should expand the scope of the sedimentation method to include molecules of coenzyme size (18).[3]

7. Spectral Properties

Unless it happens to contain a prosthetic group absorbing in the near ultraviolet or visible, little information can be obtained about the structure of a pure enzyme from its spectral properties. However, an estimate of the aromatic amino acid content of a protein is often possible by a close analysis of the ultraviolet band (19). Glyceral-

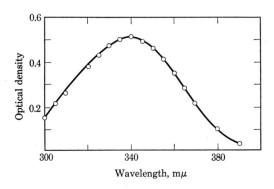

Fig. 6.3. Absorption spectrum of reduced muscle glyceraldehyde-3-phosphate dehydrogenase (20). Reproduced from *Journal of Biological Chemistry,* American Society of Biological Chemists, New Haven.

dehyde-3-phosphate dehydrogenase was suspected to contain diphosphopyridine nucleotide because there was an abnormal amount of absorption around 260 mμ (20). Also (Fig. 6.3), the reduced enzyme possessed the characteristic band of DPNH at 340 mμ.

If the isolated enzyme contains or can be made to react with a prosthetic group which absorbs light, real possibilities exist for the study of the nature of such combination. Thus the types of heme-linked groups in the hemoproteins have been thoroughly investigated by spectral methods (21). Theorell and Chance (22) and Chance and Neilands (23) have found that certain apodehydrogenases can be titrated with their coenzymes; from the extent of the resulting spectral shift, it is possible to calculate the apparent dissociation constants for the enzyme-coenzyme species. The nature of the bonding of its coenzyme by glyceraldehyde-3-phosphate dehydrogenase has been studied by spectrophotometric methods (24). In addition, this method is the

[3] See also the paper by Kegeles (54) on the synthetic boundary cell.

single best technique for detecting and studying the properties of enzyme-substrate compounds (25). (See Chapter 14.)

Warburg's work (26) on the action of light on the CO compound of cytochrome oxidase still stands as a classic example of the value of spectrophotometric research in enzymology. In studying a series of model compounds Warburg found that CO would complex with several metal porphyrins but that the CO-iron porphyrins were the only ones that could be photodissociated. By plotting activity of the enzyme in CO versus wavelength of illuminating light he was able to obtain the famous "photochemical absorption spectrum" for cytochrome

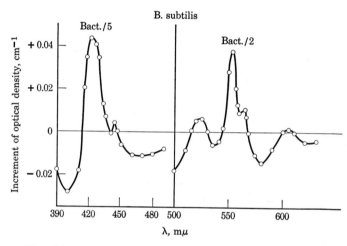

Fig. 6.4. The difference spectra of the steady-state oxidized and fully reduced cytochrome components of *Bacillus subtilis* (27). Reproduced from *Bacteriological Reviews*, Williams and Wilkins Company, Baltimore.

oxidase. The shape of the spectrum so obtained suggests that the enzyme is an iron porphyrin protein.

It is always a moot question whether the isolated enzyme is identical with that occurring inside the cell. The intense and highly characteristic spectra of the metalloporphyrin proteins permits a direct observation of the enzyme in both the oxidized and reduced state and in the form of its derivatives as these species exist within the cell. The reader is referred to the comprehensive review by Smith (27), in which spectra for the various cytochromes of microorganisms have been recorded. The method of difference spectra, as perfected by Chance (28), allows for a relatively great magnification of the bands. Figure 6.4 shows the difference spectra of the steady-state oxidized and completely reduced cytochromes of *Bacillus subtilis*. At very low temperatures the spectra of hemoproteins are intensified and sharpened (56).

8. Michaelis Constants and Turnover Numbers

The Michaelis constant will be derived in succeeding chapters. We shall use the symbol K_m, rather than K_s, in memory of a truly great contributor to enzyme kinetics. The K_m is probably the single most important constant for an enzyme, since this quality sets it apart from enzymatically inert proteins.

Warburg (29) introduced the turnover number, T.N., as an absolute expression of the velocity. The T.N. will be a constant for the enzyme and equal to V, the maximum velocity, when V is expressed in equivalent units. Unfortunately, Warburg's T.N. uses the minute rather than second unit; the second unit has not yet displaced the minute unit in enzyme literature. The T.N. and V will be discussed in Chapter 8, describing the effect of substrate concentration on the velocity.

9. Characterization of the Protein Part

The active site on an enzyme may represent a very small fraction of the whole molecule. Only special reagents are able to seek out and react with this site without causing general denaturation of the enzyme (30, 55).

One reagent which eminently fulfills these conditions is p-chloromercuribenzoate. This compound forms mercaptides with the SH group of both low-molecular-weight compounds and proteins.

Boyer (31) has found an elegant new way to measure this combination. At neutral pH the absorption spectrum of p-chloromercuribenzoate is increased about 150% when it attaches to the protein. Both the rate of combination and the stoichiometry can be determined rather easily in this technique. Inhibition by p-chloromercuribenzoate is usually reversible with excess cysteine or glutathione; this simply shows that the reagent has probably reacted with an SH group, has not caused general denaturation, and has not exerted its inhibition by other non-specific poisoning.

The SH group has become really very common as an active functional group in enzymes. Table 6.1 contains a list of some of the dehydrogenases that are inhibited by SH reagents.

Table 6.1. Inhibition of Dehydrogenases by SH Reagents

Dehydrogenase	Source	SH Reagent Tested	Reference
Glyceraldehyde-3-PO$_4$	Rabbit muscle	p-Chloromercuribenzoate	24
Glyceraldehyde-3-PO$_4$	Yeast	Iodoacetate	32
Alcohol	Yeast	p-Chloromercuribenzoate	33
Alcohol	Horse liver	p-Chloromercuribenzoate	17
Malic	Heart	Iodoacetate	34
Glutamic	Beef liver	p-Chloromercuribenzoate	14
Lactic	Heart	p-Chloromercuribenzoate	35

Another reagent that reacts dramatically with certain hydrolytic enzymes to effect a total suppression of activity is diisopropyl fluorophosphate (DFP). Aldridge and Davison (36) have performed a critical experiment to test the mechanism of action of the organophosphorus inhibitors. They examined the effect on cholinesterase of a series of compounds of the general structure

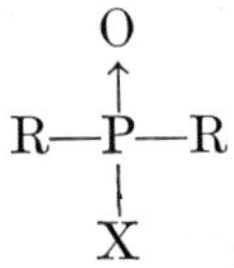

$$
\begin{array}{c}
O \\
\uparrow \\
R\text{—}P\text{—}R \\
\vert \\
X
\end{array}
$$

R represents a type of alkoxyl group whereas X may be a halogen atom or a group of different constitution (see following structures).

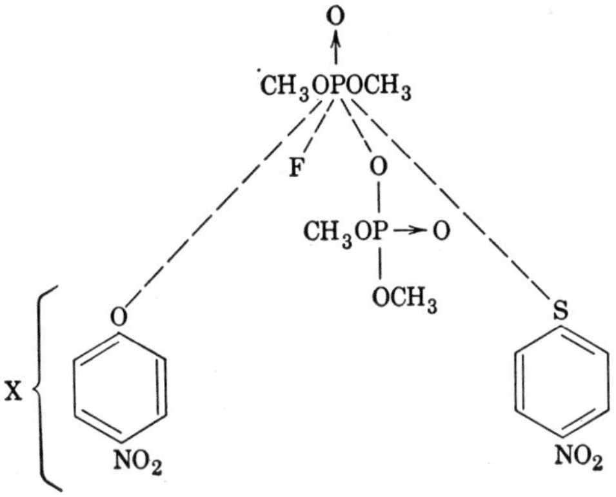

All four compounds were potent inhibitors of the enzyme. After removal of excess inhibitor, it was found that *all four derivatives of the enzyme recovered activity at the same rate.* Experiments with the four corresponding diethyl derivatives of the enzyme showed that all four of these also recovered at a single rate. These facts indicated that the inhibitors acted by a direct phosphorylation of the enzyme to give, in each case, *the identical derivative.* A similar mechanism and stoichiometry had been worked out earlier for chymotrypsin by Jansen and Balls (37).

Enzymes have thus far managed to keep secret their intimate mechanism of action. Similarly, we do not yet know the amino acid sequence of any enzyme. It is quite possible, therefore, that no general explanation for protein catalytic activity will be forthcoming until we have solved the problem of amino acid sequence.

The work of Sanger (40) on the complete sequence for insulin shows that progress is being made in this direction. In the synthetic field there has now been achieved the synthesis of the octapeptide hormone oxytocin (41).

In the past few years a rash of sequence methods has appeared (42). We shall discuss here one of the methods that seems to have great promise, namely, that of Edman (43) and the Frankel-Conrats (44).

In 1927 Bergmann prepared phenyl cabamyl peptides and noted that the phenyl carbamyl group labilized the peptide bond. Edman

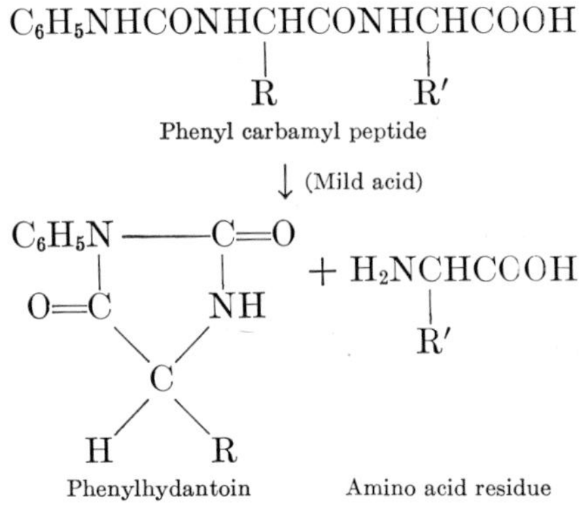

$$C_6H_5NHCONHCHCONHCHCOOH$$

$$R \qquad R'$$

Phenyl carbamyl peptide

↓ (Mild acid)

$$C_6H_5N \text{———} C{=}O$$
$$O{=}C \qquad NH \qquad + H_2NCHCCOH$$
$$\diagdown \diagup \qquad\qquad R'$$
$$C$$
$$\diagup \diagdown$$
$$H \qquad R$$

Phenylhydantoin   Amino acid residue

used the phenyl *thio* carbamyl derivatives of the peptide in order to obtain ring closure under the mildest conditions. Splitting of the peptide does not involve water, and the reaction may be performed in an inert solvent such as nitromethane saturated with HCl. This solvent will give instantaneous and quantitative cleavage of phenyl thiocarbamyl peptides. The following reactions illustrate the Edman procedure (57).

Later modifications in the method call for the use of aqueous solvents in place of nitromethane. Dahlerup-Petersen et al. (45) have recommended that the thiohydantoin, which is relatively unstable in aqueous solution, can be removed by continuous benzene extraction. Paper chromatographic methods may be applied in order to identify either the thiohydantoin derivative itself or the amino acid which can

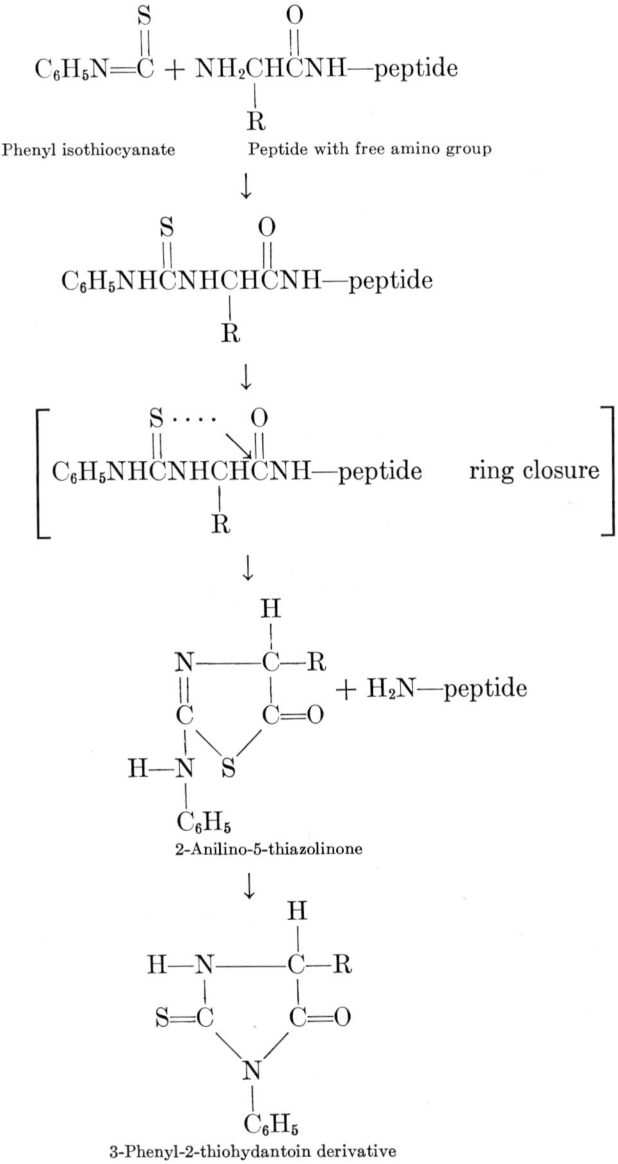

$$\underset{\text{Phenyl isothiocyanate}}{C_6H_5N{=}\overset{\overset{\text{S}}{\|}}{C}} + \underset{\text{Peptide with free amino group}}{NH_2CH\underset{\overset{|}{R}}{\overset{\overset{\text{O}}{\|}}{C}}NH{-}\text{peptide}}$$

↓

$$C_6H_5NH\overset{\overset{\text{S}}{\|}}{C}NHCH\underset{\overset{|}{R}}{\overset{\overset{\text{O}}{\|}}{C}}NH{-}\text{peptide}$$

↓

$$\left[\quad C_6H_5NH\overset{\overset{\text{S}\cdots}{\|}}{C}NHCH\underset{\overset{|}{R}}{\overset{\overset{\text{O}}{\|}}{C}}NH{-}\text{peptide}\qquad \text{ring closure}\quad\right]$$

↓

$$\begin{array}{c} \text{H} \\ | \\ N\text{———}C\text{—R} \\ \| \qquad\quad | \\ C \qquad\quad C{=}O \\ | \quad\diagdown\diagup \\ H\text{—N}\quad S \\ | \\ C_6H_5 \end{array} \quad + \; H_2N\text{—peptide}$$

2-Anilino-5-thiazolinone

↓

$$\begin{array}{c} \text{H} \\ | \\ H\text{—N}\text{———}C\text{—R} \\ | \qquad\qquad | \\ S{=}C \qquad\quad C{=}O \\ \diagdown\qquad\diagup \\ N \\ | \\ C_6H_5 \end{array}$$

3-Phenyl-2-thiohydantoin derivative

be obtained from it by hydrolysis. Since the peptide is continuously regenerated, it may be recovered and reacted with a further mole of phenyl isothiocyanate.

Ribonuclease is the enzyme which has been most thoroughly studied from the point of view of amino acid sequence. Anfinsen (58) at the National Heart Institute and Moore, Stein and Hirs at the Rockefeller Institute have elaborated the picture shown in Fig. 6.5 for ribonuclease.

The nuclear magnetic resonance spectrum of ribonuclease exhibits several peaks, each of which arises from a different type of proton source (67).

Since most substrates are of sufficient size to cover only a limited area of the protein molecule, enzyme chemists have in recent years began an intensified search for the enzyme active center. This can

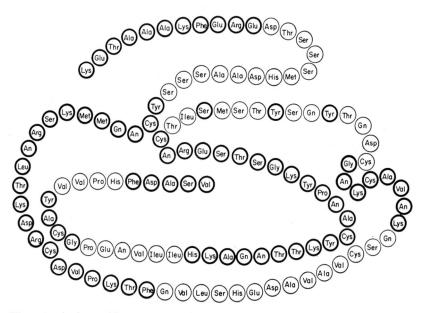

Fig. 6.5. Amino acid sequence and structure of ribonuclease. There is some uncertainty about the sequence in the neighbourhood of half-cystines No. 6 and No. 2. (Courtesy of C. B. Anfinsen, National Heart Institute). Note: the accepted amino acid abbreviations have been used (66).

perhaps be viewed as a return to the original "lock-and-key" idea proposed by Emil Fischer (59) at the turn of the 20th century. Thus the active center is defined as a particular constellation (not necessarily a linear sequence) of amino acid residues at the area which binds the substrate and/or cofactor.

In spite of the incisiveness of the methods mentioned above, it is still not practical to attempt a complete sequence determination on a monomeric protein where the molecular weight is in excess of about 20,000. Hence more rewarding results may in general be obtained through an attempt to characterize only the active center. The problem then arises as to how the latter can be labeled or otherwise distinguished.

Two particularly favorable cases will be recited here; that of (a) cytochrome *c*, where the active center is covalently bonded to a colored heme molecule, and (b), chymotrypsin, where the active site can be phosphorylated with a P^{32}-labeled inhibitor such as diisopropylfluorophosphate.

(*a*) *Cytochrome c*. Tuppy and Bodo (60) and Tuppy and Paléus (61) degraded cytochrome *c* with proteolytic enzymes. The heme-bearing peptides were separated by chromatography and the amino

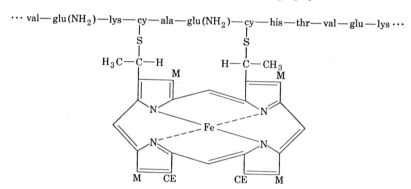

Fig. 6.6. Structure of a hemopeptide from cytochrome *c* (63). Standard abbreviations are used for the amino acids (66). M = methyl; CE = carboxymethyl.

acid sequence determined by the Sanger (40) techniques. Some physical measurements were added by Ehrenberg and Theorell (62) and the final structure proposed for a twelve-amino acid hemopeptide is as shown in Fig. 6.6.

(*b*) *Chymotrypsin*. Reaction of chymotrypsin with P^{32}-labeled organophosphorus inhibitor followed by partial hydrolysis of the phosphoryl enzyme has yielded the peptide

. . . . asp-ser (P^{32})-gly-glu-ala-val . . . .

as the active center (38, 39, 64). There is some evidence that another enzyme of quite different substrate specificity may contain an identical peptide at the active center. The second enzyme is phosphoglucomutase, a protein which is known to form a phosphoseryl intermediate (65).

10. Characterization of the Prosthetic Group

The usual methods of organic chemistry may in general be used to determine the structure of the isolated prosthetic group.

Figure 6.7 shows the electrometric titration curve of pyridoxamine phosphate (46). This curve was obtained with the glass electrode used in combination with the continuously recording pH meter. The primary phosphate ionization is too strong to be measured with the glass electrode. However, from the rest of the curve the phenolic hydroxyl, secondary phosphate, ring nitrogen, and amino group ionizations are all clearly visible. Such an experiment not only gives information on the structure but also shows the pKa values, the neutral equivalent, and the purity. From the titration curve shown, the pKa' values at

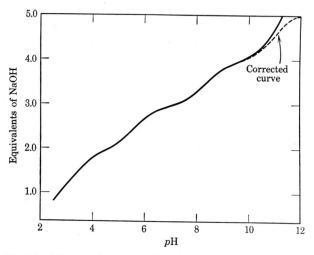

Fig. 6.7. The titration curve of pyridoxamine phosphate (46).

25° and in 0.15 M NaCl are 3.69, 5.76, 8.61, and 10.92 for the phenolic hydroxyl, secondary phosphate, ring nitrogen, and amino groups, respectively. The primary phosphoryl dissociation lies below pH 2.5. It is apparent that simple electrometric titration is a very powerful tool in characterizing a coenzyme such as pyridoxamine phosphate.

As more and more enzymes are isolated, they are found to contain metals, or a metal coenzyme complex, as the active center. Examples are the identification of xanthine oxidase as a molybdoflavoprotein and various dehydrogenases as zinc-proteins. Snell and co-workers (47) have shown that metals stimulate non-enzymatic transamination.

The structure of these compounds is of vast importance in deciding the nature of enzymatic catalysis. The work of Bjerrum (48) has placed the reaction of amino compounds with metals on a quantitative basis so that the avidity of a series of cations for a certain chelating agent can be described in terms of a stability constant (49). (See

Chapter 3.) Albert (50) has called attention to the metal binding properties and biological activity of certain antibiotics. According to him, it is the metal chelate and not the antibiotic as such that is poisonous.

The complex forming species of the amino acids is the anion, i.e., the form present in alkaline solution. If the pH is such that the amino acid is present largely as the *Zwitterion*, the chelating reaction still proceeds quantitatively by a displacement of protons. Hydroxyl ions compete with the chelating agent or "ligand" for the metal. At higher pH, depending on the stability of the complex, the metal may be lost as the hydroxide.

11. Linkage of Prosthetic Group to Protein[4]

The bonds attaching the coenzyme to the protein can be studied often by direct spectrophotometric methods. This has been done with the hemoproteins, flavoproteins, and certain dehydrogenases. In the alcohol dehydrogenase study (17), the spectrum of the dehydrogenase-reduced diphosphopyridine nucleotide compound could be broken up with p-chloromercuribenzoate. The implication is that an SH group of the proteins is in one way or another bound to the coenzyme. Such spectral methods will no doubt be used to study the bonding of pure transaminase to its coenzymes since the coenzymes have complex and characteristic spectra.

The iron porphyrin proteins can be studied by the methods of magnetochemistry. The partial electronic structure of the iron atom is shown in Fig. 6.8. Iron is capable of forming either ionic or covalent bonds with neighboring groups. In completely ionic bonding the atom has 5 and 4 unpaired electrons in the outer shells of the ferric and ferrous forms, respectively. The atoms with unpaired electrons are termed "paramagnetic." By means of properly sensitive instruments the degree of paramagnetism can be determined accurately even in proteins containing a fraction of a per cent of iron. In the micro apparatus devised by Theorell and Ehrenberg (51) a measurement is made of the force necessary to maintain the sample at a fixed position in the magnetic field. The number of unpaired electrons is given by the total paramagnetism divided by the number of Bohr magnetrons corresponding to one unpaired electron. Atoms containing no unpaired electrons are designated "diamagnetic."

Figure 6.8 also illustrates the state of the iron atom in cytochrome

---

[4] A general method of splitting a holoenzyme into the coenzyme and apoenzyme portions is to dissolve the protein in fairly concentrated ammonium sulfate solution and then lower the pH to 2 or 3.

c (52). The oxidized compound is largely diamagnetic; in fact, its paramagnetism corresponds to only one unpaired electron. Reduced cytochrome c is completely diamagnetic, and hence it is obvious that the atom is covalently bonded to the enzyme.

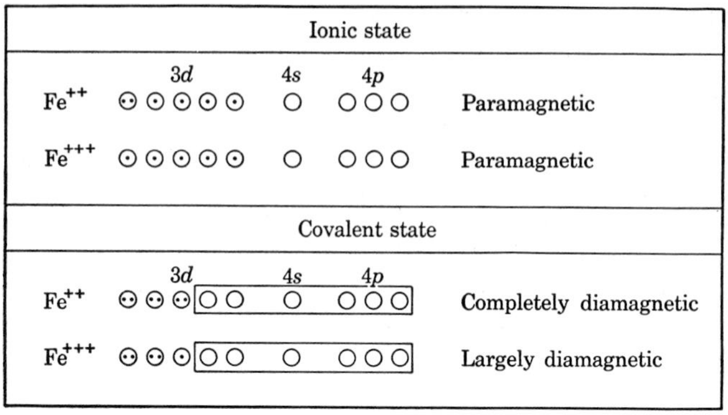

Fig. 6.8. Magnetic state of the iron atom in ionic and covalent bonding.

Ionic bonding would allow the electrons in the outer shells to "spread" out so that a large paramagnetism would be measured. The covalent bonding in cytochrome c involves two d energy levels, the s level, and three p levels. This particular type of bonding is therefore noted as d_2sp_3.

References

General

1. H. Neurath and K. Bailey, *The Proteins,* Academic Press, N. Y., 1953.
2. H. K. Schachman, in *Methods in Enzymology, IV,* Academic Press, N. Y., 1957.

Bibliography

3. J. S. Falconer and D. B. Taylor, *Nature, 155,* 303 (1945).
4. J. H. Northrop, *Crystalline Enzymes,* Columbia University Press, N. Y., 1939.
5. H. Theorell and Å. Åkeson, *J. Am. Chem. Soc., 63,* 1818 (1941).
6. J. Steinhardt and E. M. Zaiser, *J. Biol. Chem., 190,* 197 (1951).
7. E. J. Cohn and J. T. Edsall, *Proteins, Amino Acids, and Peptides,* Reinhold Publishing Corp., N. Y., 1943.
8. R. A. Alberty, in *The Proteins,* edited by H. Neurath and K. Bailey, Academic Press, N. Y., 1953.
9. J. B. Neilands, *J. Biol. Chem., 199,* 373 (1952).
10. D. M. Gibson, E. O. Davisson, B. K. Bachhawat, B. R. Ray, and C. S. Vestling, *J. Biol. Chem., 203,* 397 (1953).
11. L. G. Longsworth, *Ann. New York Acad. Sci., 41,* 267 (1941).

12. H. Neurath, *Chem. Revs., 30,* 357 (1952).

13. J. H. Northrop and M. L. Anson, *J. Gen. Physiol., 12,* 543 (1929).

14. J. A. Olson and C. B. Anfinsen, *J. Biol. Chem., 197,* 67 (1952).

15. H. P. Lundgren and W. H. Ward in Greenberg's *Amino Acids and Proteins,* Charles C. Thomas Publishing Co., Springfield, Ill., 1951.

16. T. Svedberg and K. O. Pedersen, *The Ultracentrifuge,* Clarendon Press, Oxford, 1940.

17. H. Theorell and R. K. Bonnichsen, *Acta Chem. Scand., 5,* 1105 (1951).

18. E. G. Pickels, W. F. Harrington, and H. K. Schachman, *Proc. Natl. Acad. Sci., 38,* 943 (1952).

19. E. R. Holiday and A. G. Ogston, *Biochem. J., 32,* 1166 (1938).

20. J. F. Taylor, S. F. Velick, G. T. Cori, C. F. Cori, and M. W. Slein, *J. Biol. Chem., 173,* 169 (1948).

21. H. Theorell, *Advances in Enzymology, 7,* 265 (1947).

22. H. Theorell and B. Chance, *Acta Chem. Scand., 5,* 1127 (1951).

23. B. Chance and J. B. Neilands, *J. Biol. Chem., 199,* 383 (1952).

24. S. F. Velick, J. E. Hayes, and J. Harting, *J. Biol. Chem., 203,* 527 (1953).

25. B. Chance, *Advances in Enzymology, 12,* 153 (1951).

26. O. Warburg, *Heavy Metal Prosthetic Groups,* Oxford Press, England, 1949.

27. Lucille Smith, *Bact. Revs., 18,* 106 (1954).

28. B. Chance, *Nature, 169,* 215 (1952).

29. O. Warburg, *Wasserstoffübertragendefermente,* Werner Saenger Press, Berlin, 1948.

30. H. Olcott and H. Fraenkel-Conrat, *Chem. Revs., 41,* 151 (1947).

31. P. D. Boyer, *J. Am. Chem. Soc., 76,* 4331 (1954).

32. H. L. Segal and P. D. Boyer, *J. Biol. Chem., 204,* 265 (1953).

33. E. S. G. Barron and S. Levine, *Arch. Biochem. Biophys., 41,* 175 (1952).

34. D. E. Green, *Biochem. J., 30,* 2095 (1936).

35. J. B. Neilands, *J. Biol. Chem., 208,* 225 (1954).

36. W. N. Aldridge and A. N. Davison, *Biochem. J., 55,* 763 (1953).

37. E. F. Jansen, M. D. F. Nutting, R. Jang, and A. K. Balls, *J. Biol. Chem., 185,* 209 (1950).

38. J. A. Cohen, R. A. Osterbann, M. G. Warringa and H. S. Jansz, *Discussions Faraday Soc., 20,* 114 (1955).

39. N. K. Schaffer, S. Harshman, R. R. Engle and R. W. Drisko, *Federation Proceedings, 14,* 275 (1955).

40. F. Sanger, *Advances in Protein Chemistry,* 7, Academic Press, N. Y., 1952.

41. V. du Vigneaud et al., *J. Am. Chem. Soc., 75,* 4879 (1953).

42. H. Khorana, *Quarterly Reviews,* VI, 1952.

43. P. Edman, *Acta Chem. Scand., 4,* 283 (1950).

44. H. Fraenkel-Conrat and J. Fraenkel-Conrat, *Acta Chem. Scand., 5,* 1409 (1951).

45. B. Dahlerup-Petersen, K. Linderström-Lang, and M. Ottesen, *Acta Chem. Scand., 6,* 1013 (1953).

46. V. R. Williams and J. B. Neilands, *Arch. Biochem. and Biophys., 53,* 56 (1954).

47. D. E. Metzler and E. E. Snell, *J. Am. Chem. Soc., 74,* 979 (1952).

48. N. Bjerrum, *Metal Ammine Formation in Aqueous Solution,* P. Haase and Son, Copenhagen, Denmark, 1941.

49. A. Albert, *Biochem. J.*, *47*, 531 (1950).

50. A. Albert, *Nature, 172*, 201 (1953).

51. H. Theorell and A. Ehrenberg, *Arkiv Fysik, 3*, 299 (1951).

52. H. Theorell, *J. Am. Chem. Soc., 63*, 1820 (1941).

53. S. Velick, *J. Phys. Colloid Chem., 53*, 135 (1949).

54. G. Kegeles, *J. Am. Chem. Soc., 74*, 5532 (1952).

55. H. Fraenkel-Conrat, *Methods in Enzymology*, Vol. IV, Academic Press, N. Y., 1957.

56. R. W. Estabrook and B. Mackler, *J. Biol. Chem., 224*, 637 (1957).

57. P. Edman, *Nature, 177*, 667 (1956).

58. C. B. Anfinsen, *Federation Proceedings, 16*, 783 (1957).

59. E. Fischer, *Ber., 27*, 2985 (1894).

60. H. Tuppy and G. Bodo, *Monatsh. Chem., 85*, 1024 (1954).

61. H. Tuppy and S. Paléus, *Acta Chem. Scand., 9*, 353 (1955).

62. A. Ehrenberg and H. Theorell, *Nature, 176*, 158 (1955).

63. H. Theorell, in *Currents in biochemical research,* Interscience Pub. Co., N. Y. (1956).

64. F. Turba and G. Gundlach, *Biol. Z., 327*, 186 (1955).

65. D. E. Koshland and M. J. Erwin, *J. Am. Chem. Soc., 79*, 2657 (1957).

66. E. Brand and J. T. Edsall, *Ann. Rev. Biochem., 16*, 224 (1947).

67. M. Saunders, A. Wishnia and J. G. Kirkwood, *J. Am. Chem. Soc., 79*, 3289 (1957).

68. C. Tanford, in *Electrochemistry in Biology and Medicine,* John Wiley & Sons, N. Y., 1955.

69. C. Tanford *et al., J. Am. Chem. Soc., 77*, 6409, 6414 (1955).

Part 2

PHYSICAL CHEMISTRY

7

Reaction Rates

1. Introduction

A basic knowledge of the theory and techniques used in analyzing reaction rates is of the utmost value in enzymology. Activity measurements are a prerequisite for an expression of the purity of a crude enzyme. For example, the term "specific activity" is defined as the units of enzymatic activity/unit of sample. The sample unit may be given as milligrams of dry weight, total protein, optical density at 280 mμ, etc.

We have already seen (Chapter 2) that a measurement of the effect of pH on the apparent equilibrium constant allows for a convenient test of the stoichiometry of a postulated reaction since a definite number of moles of H^+ should be exchanged per mole of reactants.

Following the rate of an enzyme's activity is a very convenient way to measure its concentration.[1] This is important in all enzyme isolation work, in studying enzyme levels of tissue in health and disease, in industry, etc.

We may also mention that a study of the effect of the substrate concentration on reaction rates gave the first clue that enzymes act by forming an intermediate enzyme-substrate compound.

No attempt will be made to develop the proof of the equations used in this chapter. These may be found in physical chemistry textbooks or in advanced treatises (1, 2).[2] Our discussion will involve only the order and not the type of reaction. For example, the decomposition of molecular bromine at high temperature is a true monomolecular reaction, and its kinetics is that of the first order.

$$Br_2 \rightleftharpoons 2Br$$

[1] Either disappearance of substrate or appearance of product may be followed.
[2] Every attempt will be made in Part 2 of this book to include all the elementary algebraic manipulations used in deriving the equations of special interest.

In the hydrolysis of sucrose,

$$\text{Sucrose} + H_2O \rightleftharpoons \text{Glucose} + \text{Fructose}$$

the mechanism is probably bimolecular, although the order is again first. Here, the water concentration is great enough to be essentially constant; lower reaction orders are, therefore, common in systems where water takes part. Thus, if we speak only of the order rather than the molecular type of reaction involved, we shall not have committed ourselves to any specific reaction mechanism.

2. Equilibrium Constant

We have already mentioned the equilibrium constant, K_{eq}, in the section on ionization in Chapter 2.

$$A + B \rightleftharpoons C + D$$

$$K_{eq} = \frac{[C][D]}{[A][B]}$$

K_{eq} has a very direct bearing on the rate of reactions since it is derived from the mass law, which states: *The rate of a chemical reaction is proportional to the active masses (concentrations) of the reactants.* Hence, for the above reaction we may record

$$v_1 = k_1[A][B] \quad \text{and} \quad v_2 = k_2[C][D]$$

where k_1, k_2 are the velocity constants for the forward and back reactions, respectively, and v_1 and v_2 are the corresponding velocities. At equilibrium, by definition, the rate of the forward and back reactions is equal, so that $v_1 = v_2$, or

$$k_1[A][B] = k_2[C][D]$$

$$\frac{k_1}{k_2} = \frac{[C][D]}{[A][B]} = K_{eq}$$

Thus, ideally, $k_1/k_2 = K_{eq}$. If K_{eq} is large, k_1 will be large in relation to k_2. Experimentally, therefore, one would allow this reaction to run from left to right rather than the converse. It is important to note that K_{eq} gives information only on the *ratio* of the velocity constants and tells nothing about their absolute magnitude. Occasionally it may be possible to shift the equilibrium and thus move the reaction in any desired direction by removing one of the products. For example, Straub (3) used HCN in the lactic dehydrogenase system in order to trap the pyruvate formed.

$$CH_3COCOOH + HCN \rightleftharpoons CH_3\overset{\overset{\displaystyle CN}{|}}{C}OHCOOH$$

Pyruvic acid
cyanohydrin

Semicarbazide is widely used in carbonyl systems, e.g., in trapping acetaldehyde, and it usually seems quite innocuous to the enzyme (4). Once K_{eq} is known, it is possible to predict the ratio of products/ reactants after the reaction has come to rest. The sum of reactants and products must, of course, be 100%. These data are valuable when it is desired to use enzymes for analytical purposes (5), i.e., when the reaction should go to completion.

By studying the effect of enzyme concentration on K_{eq}, Theorell (6, 7) has found a brilliant new application of this constant in enzymology. Enzymatically determined equilibria are usually performed with very dilute solutions of the enzyme so that the enzyme never enters into the reaction on a molar basis. Thus, varying the enzyme concentration several hundred fold should be without effect on K_{eq}. If, on the other hand, large amounts of enzyme are used so that its molar concentration is comparable to that of products, reactants, and enzyme, the enzyme may shift the experimentally measured equilibrium constant, K_{app}, by an amount depending on the extent of combination of the enzyme with the reactants. This allows prediction on which side of the equation the "most stable" enzyme-substrate compounds will be found. Alberty (8) has given a thorough mathematical treatment for this phenomenon, the experimental details of which have been outlined in Chapter 14.

In succeeding chapters we will have an opportunity to see how K_{eq} is related to the oxidation-reduction potential and the free energy of a reaction. All these constants are interrelated, and K_{eq} is often the most direct laboratory route to the most fundamental property of a chemical reaction, namely, its free-energy change.

3. Zero-Order Reaction

In the *zero-order* reaction, the rate is constant and independent of the substrate concentration. If x is the product, t the time, and k^0 the order reaction rate constant, then $dx/dt = k^0$. In this equation x may be expressed in any convenient unit: micromoles, per cent, etc. If the unit happens to be micromoles and the time is in minutes, then the units of k^0 will be μM min^{-1}. The data in Fig. 7.1 indicate a k^0 of 2.

At high substrate concentrations, enzymatic reactions are frequently of zero order. Using a given amount of enzyme, either x or t may be found since k^0 is constant. If 1 unit of an impure enzyme is set equal to a certain k^0, then, for any quantity of enzyme taken,

$$\frac{k^0(\text{measured})}{k^0(1 \text{ unit})} = \text{units}$$

If the enzyme is pure, we may write

$$\frac{k^0(\mu M \text{ min}^{-1})}{\mu M \text{ enzyme}} = \text{Turnover number (T.N.)}$$

It is desirable, whenever possible, to use the initial-reaction portion of the curve in any quantitative treatment of the reaction kinetics

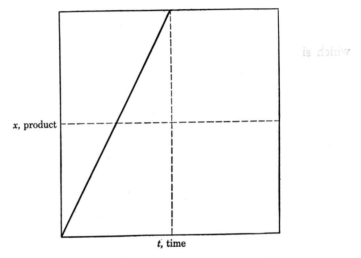

Fig. 7.1. Graphical illustration of a zero-order reaction.

since in this phase the concentration of the product will be too low to interfere with the activity. The rate observed is therefore more likely to be independent of the properties of the solvent, and it will represent a characteristic property of the enzyme.

In testing for zero-order kinetics the reaction is simply allowed to run on for a double length of time. The concentration of the product should double.

4. First-Order Reaction

Sometimes it is necessary to use conditions under which the reaction is of the *first* order. Then the rate at any time is proportional to the existing substrate concentration. First-order curves are often reported with insoluble or expensive substrates because under these conditions insufficient substrate is used to saturate the enzyme. If the substrate is toxic to the enzyme, for example hydrogen peroxide and catalase, a high substrate concentration is undesirable. The activity of the enzyme may be so weak that it is necessary to let the reaction proceed a very long time in order to get enough product for analysis. The terminal portion of any enzymatic reaction will generally be of first order.

The general form of the first-order equation is

$$dx/dt = k^1(a - x)$$

where a is the initial substrate concentration and x the concentration of substrate converted, and k^1 is the first-order reaction rate constant.

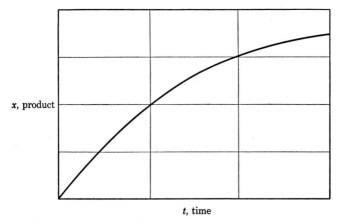

t, time

Fig. 7.2. Graphical illustration of a first-order reaction.

Hence $a - x$ is the prevailing substrate concentration, and the rate is proportional to this quantity. Figure 7.2 shows a graph of the first-order reaction. The rate is constantly decreasing, and, in theory, infinite time will be required to complete the reaction. Integration gives the useful form of this equation:

$$k^1t = 2.3 \log a/(a - x)$$

It must be noted that the term $a/(a - x)$ is a ratio meaning initial/prevailing substrate concentration and is therefore independent of the particular units of substrate concentration employed. Accordingly, k^1 will have only the dimensions of reciprocal time, i.e., k^1 min^{-1}.

The basic principle of the first-order plot is that, *for every equal interval of time, a certain constant fraction of the material undergoes reaction.* At 50% decomposition or time, $t_{\frac{1}{2}}$,

$$k^1 t_{\frac{1}{2}} = 2.3 \log 100/(100 - 50)$$

$$t_{\frac{1}{2}} = 0.69/k^1$$

This shows that the time to decompose half of the substrate is a constant. Suppose that 20% is decomposed in 1 minute. How much will be decomposed at 2 and 3 minutes, respectively? At 1 minute, k^1 may be calculated:

$$k^1 t = 2.3 \log \frac{100}{100 - 20}$$

$$k^1 = 0.22 \text{ min}^{-1}$$

At 2 minutes:

$$0.22 \times 2 = 2.3 \log \frac{100}{100 - x}$$

$$x = 36\%$$

And at 3 minutes:

$$0.22 \times 3 = 2.3 \log \frac{100}{100 - x}$$

$$x = 49\%$$

A shorter algebraic route to the same answer is to take 20% of the substrate remaining after 1 minute, i.e., 20% of 80 = 16%. Added to the 20% for the first minute this gives 36% at 2 minutes. In the 2- to 3-minute interval 20% of 64, or 13%, will decompose, so that the total after 3 minutes is 49%.

On transposing terms in the integrated equation we obtain

$$\frac{k^1}{2.3} = \frac{\log a/(a - x)}{t}$$

A plot of $\log a/(a - x)$ versus t should yield a straight line with slope equal to $k^1/2.3$. This is a method of testing for the first-order equation.

If a double quantity of enzyme results in the same amount of reaction in half the time, it is clear that k^1 is directly proportional to the enzyme concentration. That is, 50% decomposition in 1 minute means a k^1 of 0.69 min^{-1}, and 50% decomposition in 0.5 minute corresponds to a k^1 of 1.38 min^{-1}. Hence,

$$\frac{k^1(\text{measured})}{k^1(1 \text{ unit})} = \text{units}$$

5. Application to Enzymology

For almost any enzymatic reaction, if the substrate concentration is initially very high, the rate will at first describe a zero-order course and then later fall off into a more or less first-order reaction plot. The entire reaction is therefore a mixture which cannot be described by a single reaction order.

Irrespective of the reaction order, the rate of the reaction will always be proportional to the enzyme concentration. The rate is equal to [Product]/time and hence

$$[\text{Enzyme}] \text{ time} = [\text{Product}]$$

This property of enzymes has been known for many years and is termed the *enzyme-time-product* relationship. For example, a paper published in 1890 entitled *Invertase: a Contribution to the History of an Enzyme or Unorganized Ferment*, by O'Sullivan and Tompson, contains the following statement:

". . . granted that the acidity is in the most favorable proportion, we find a very simple rule holds good, namely: The time necessary to reach any given percentage of inversion is in inverse proportion to the amount of the invertase."

Some of their results bearing on this point have been tabulated in Table 7.1. A more recent illustration of this same principle can be seen in Fig. 4.2.

Table 7.1. Invertase-Time-Inversion Relationship (9)

Experiment, number	Invertase, grams	Time to Point of No Optical Activity, minutes
1	0.15	283.0
2	0.45	94.8
3	1.50	30.7

References

General

1. F. M. Huennekens, in *Technique of Organic Chemistry*, edited by S. L. Friess and A. Weissberger, Interscience Publishers, N. Y., Vol. VIII, 1953.
2. S. Glasstone, K. J. Laidler, and H. Eyring, *The Theory of Rate Processes*, McGraw-Hill Book Co., N. Y., 1941.

Bibliography

3. F. B. Straub, *Biochem. J., 34*, 483 (1940).
4. H. Theorell and R. Bonnichsen, *Acta Chem. Scand., 5*, 1105 (1951).
5. R. K. Bonnichsen and H. Theorell, *Scand. J. Clin. Lab. Inv., 3*, 58 (1951).
6. H. Theorell, *8ᵉ Conseil de Chimie de l'Institut International de Solvay, Bruxelles*, p. 395, 1950.
7. H. Theorell and B. Chance, *Acta Chem. Scand., 5*, 1127 (1951).
8. R. A. Alberty, *J. Am. Chem. Soc., 75*, 1925 (1953).
9. C. O'Sullivan and F. W. Tompson, *J. Chem. Soc., 57*, 834 (1890).

8

Effect of Substrate Concentration
on Velocity

1. General Considerations (References 1–4)

The concept that enzymes act by forming an intermediate enzyme-substrate complex is now more than a half century old. In 1902 Henri (5) and Brown (6) carried out experiments on the effect of the sucrose concentration on the activity of sucrase. The general type of curve obtained is that shown in Fig. 8.3; i.e., at low concentrations the substrate has a marked effect, but at higher concentrations practically no effect, on the velocity.

Henri interpreted the diphasic nature of such a curve to mean that the enzyme formed an intermediate complex with its substrate and that reaction could not take place without the formation of this intermediate complex. All subsequent work has proved the correctness of this view. The conditions prevailing at low and high substrate concentration, [S], are crudely illustrated in Fig. 8.1. At low substrate concentrations two factors control the rate of the reaction: (a) the "intrinsic" rate of the enzyme-catalyzed reaction, and (b) the frequency of collision of the enzyme with its substrate. The second factor will be directly proportional to the concentration of substrate molecules (see Fig. 8.1). As the [S] is increased, the collision frequency no longer becomes a factor in the reaction velocity. At this point the rate will be governed by one factor only, namely, the rate of conversion of substrate molecules to product molecules. Thus at low [S] the enzyme not only has to act on the substrate but must also seek it out in a medium made up of miscellaneous molecules such as those of the buffer and water. At high [S] the rate-limiting step is the enzymatic reaction proper; adding more substrate will not increase the velocity to a measurable degree. These considerations are beautifully set forth in an article by Van Slyke (1).

If the conversion to product occurs on the enzyme, then there ought to be an area on the enzyme molecule which will attach the product as well as the substrate. We will later have an opportunity to see that enzyme-substrate compounds, EnS, have been detected with substances which are regarded as *either* substrates or products.

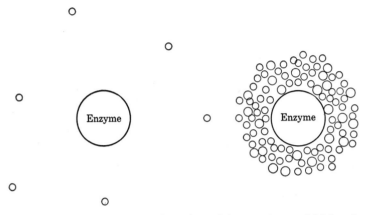

Fig. 8.1. Diagrammatic representation of conditions at low and high substrate concentration.

Non-reversibility simply means that an unfavorable equilibrium exists, that a reactant has been lost as a gas, and so forth. In general, the extent of reversibility will depend on the free-energy change of the reaction and will be independent of the catalytic properties of the enzyme. What we observe as the "product" of enzyme reaction is therefore that member of the reaction whose accumulation is favored by the K_{eq}.

Moreover, the phenomenon of "competitive inhibition" reinforces the concept of the EnS compound. In studying phosphatases, care must be taken not to wash the glassware in trisodium phosphate or to attempt the reaction in phosphate buffer. We will have an opportunity in Chapter 9 to discuss the quantitative effects of these competitive inhibitors on the velocity of reactions.

The existence of EnS compounds has now been directly demonstrated by Chance (7), and special consideration will be given to his work in Chapter 14.

2. The Michaelis Constant

The first satisfactory mathematical analysis of the diphasic activity curve was carried out by Michaelis and Menten in 1913 (8) and by Van Slyke and Cullen in the following year (9). Michaelis and Menten assumed that the intermediate complex EnS was reversibly formed according to the mass law

$$En + S \underset{k_2}{\overset{k_1}{\rightleftharpoons}} EnS$$

They believed that the rate of breakdown of EnS to form product P was small in relation to the rate of establishment of the equilibrium described by k_1 and k_2. The constant which they derived is therefore the *dissociation constant* of the EnS compound, i.e., k_2/k_1.

However, Briggs and Haldane (10) pointed out that the catalyzed reaction may deplete EnS at a substantial rate and that the Michaelis constant measured experimentally from kinetic curves is in fact $(k_2 + k_3)/k_1$, where

$$En + S \underset{k_2}{\overset{k_1}{\rightleftharpoons}} EnS \overset{k_3}{\rightleftharpoons} P + En$$

In the following derivation of the Michaelis constant, K_m, we will not restrict ourselves to a single EnS compound since the actual reaction may be complex and represent a many-step process.

$$\overbrace{En + S \rightleftharpoons EnS \rightleftharpoons EnS^1 \rightleftharpoons EnS^{11} \text{-----} EnP^{11} \rightleftharpoons EnP^1 \rightleftharpoons EnP}^{A} \rightleftharpoons En + P$$

Hence all intermediate EnS and EnP species will be designated as A. The other terms are En_t and En referring to the total and free enzyme concentrations, respectively. If, as may be true in the initial phase of the reaction, the substrate concentration is infinitely high and the product is essentially absent, the rate of formation of A will be governed by the rate of its decomposition. In this so-called "steady state"

$$En + S \underset{k_2}{\overset{k_1}{\rightleftharpoons}} A \underset{k_4}{\overset{k_3}{\rightleftharpoons}} En + P$$

the rate at which A is decomposing is equal to the rate at which it is formed.

The steady state can be thought to resemble the state of Minnesota. There is an infinitely high population around its borders hoping to find space to enter. If 10 people leave per day, they will be replaced immediately, so that the internal population remains in a steady state! With the aid of the concepts outlined above, the Michaelis-Menten equation may be developed as follows:

$$\underset{\substack{\text{Net velocity of} \\ \text{formation of A}}}{k_1[En][S] - k_2[A]} = \underset{\substack{\text{Net velocity of} \\ \text{decomposition of A}}}{k_3[A] - k_4[En][P]}$$

F. G. Hopkins   O. Warburg

L. Michaelis   O. Mayerhof

J. H. Northrop   H. Theorell

By transposition and grouping,

$$k_4[\text{En}][\text{P}] + k_1[\text{En}][\text{S}] = k_2[\text{A}] + k_3[\text{A}]$$

$$[\text{A}](k_2 + k_3) = [\text{En}](k_4[\text{P}] + k_1[\text{S}])$$

$$\frac{[\text{A}]}{[\text{En}]} = \frac{k_4[\text{P}] + k_1[\text{S}]}{k_2 + k_3} = \frac{[\text{P}](k_4)}{k_2 + k_3} + \frac{[\text{S}]k_1}{k_2 + k_3}$$

Since during the initial stages of the reaction [P] is infinitesimally small, the whole term containing this quantity can be dropped. Employing the symbol K_m as equivalent to $(k_2 + k_3)/k_1$ we have

$$\frac{[\text{En}]}{[\text{A}]} = \frac{[\text{En}]_t - [\text{A}]}{[\text{A}]} = \frac{[\text{En}]_t}{[\text{A}]} - 1 = \frac{K_m}{[\text{S}]}$$

The maximum velocity, V, will be proportional to $[\text{En}]_t$. However, any actual velocity,[1] v, will be proportional to the active enzyme or [A].

Thus $V = k_3[\text{En}]_t$ and $v = k_3[\text{A}]$. Hence

$$\frac{[\text{En}]_t}{[\text{A}]} = \frac{V}{v} = \frac{K_m}{[\text{S}]} + 1$$

Multiplying each side of the last two terms by [S] and rearranging yields the familiar Michaelis-Menten equation

$$v = \frac{V[\text{S}]}{K_m + [\text{S}]} = \frac{V}{1 + (K_m/[\text{S}])}$$

Both K_m and V are constants for the enzyme although they may vary independently of each other under different conditions.

3. Significance of K_m

A very practical definition of the Michaelis constant is that it is *the substrate concentration at half maximum velocity.* This is shown algebraically by

$$0.5 = \frac{1.0[\text{S}]}{K_m + [\text{S}]}$$

$$0.5K_m + 0.5[\text{S}] = 1.0[\text{S}]$$

$$K_m = [\text{S}]$$

Points of interest about this most fundamental of all enzyme constants and its derivation are:

A. K_m has the dimensions of concentration, i.e., moles/liter.

B. If $[\text{S}] = K_m$, $v = \tfrac{1}{2}V$.

C. K_m is not the dissociation constant of the EnS compound. This

[1] This is the "initial" velocity of the reaction.

would be k_2/k_1. K_m is the dissociation constant of a complicated equilibrium involving compound A.

D. $1/K_m$ is not the affinity constant of the EnS compound for the same reasons given above in C.

E. The equation has been derived for negligible [P].

F. K_m is a constant for the enzyme only under rigidly specified conditions.

G. Once K_m is known, the per cent v can be calculated at any [S].

H. The Michaelis constant is by far the most fundamental constant used in enzyme chemistry.

The reader is referred to the works of Haldane (2), Wilson (3), and Alberty (4) for a more complete discussion of this equation.

4. Relationship between K_m, [S], and Reaction Order

In the Michaelis-Menten equation there is an obvious dependence of the velocity on the relative magnitude of K_m and [S]. If [S] is very large in relation to K_m, the expression becomes $v = \dfrac{V[S]}{[S]}$, and the velocity is maximum, independent of [S], and therefore one of zero order. If the converse is true, and K_m is large constrated to [S], the relation becomes $v = \dfrac{V[S]}{K_m}$, v depends on [S], and the reaction is first order.

5. Relationship between K_m and the Dissociation or Affinity Constants

It was noted above that K_m is equal to $(k_2 + k_3)/k_1$. Where k_3 is large compared to k_2, K_m remains significantly larger than the dissociation constant of EnS. In any event, the K_m measured by kinetic studies of the activity *must always be at least equal to or larger than* the dissociation constant. In some instances it has been possible to measure the dissociation constant directly, e.g., by the sensitive spectrophotometric techniques of Chance (11). Theorell and Chance (12) found, for the alcohol dehydrogenase-reduced diphosphopyridine nucleotide compound, a dissociation constant of 10^{-7} while K_m was of the order of 10^{-5} M. The same method has been applied to lactic dehydrogenase (13).

The reversible combination of enzyme and substrate can be described by an affinity constant which is equal to the reciprocal of the dissociation constant or k_1/k_2. Hence $1/K_m$ is not the affinity constant of ES, as is often assumed. Rather, it is equal to the expression $k_1/(k_2 + k_3)$. Therefore, $1/K_m$ is always lower than the affinity constant, but, where k_3 is much smaller than k_2, then $1/K_m$ approaches the affinity constant.

6. Relationship between k_3, V, and Turnover Number

The velocity constant k_3 describes the rate of product formation from A, the active intermediate. The velocity of formation of product is then $v = k_3[A]$. At the start of the reaction the substrate concentration is high, all the enzyme is present as A, the velocity will be maximal, and $V = k_3[En]_t$. Now if concentrations of both enzyme and product are quoted in moles and the time unit is in minutes, k_3 will be the maximum turnover number of the enzyme.

For example, Theorell and Bonnichsen (14) measured k_3 for DPNH in the alcohol dehydrogenase system to be 39 sec^{-1}. Converting to minutes, this comes to 2340 min^{-1}. However, since ADH can bind 2 equivalents of reduced coenzyme, the equivalent weight of the protein is one-half of its molecular weight, and the maximum turnover number is therefore 4700. A direct determination of the dissociation constant for the enzyme and one substrate (e.g., the coenzyme) is difficult but not impossible (12, 13), and we must anticipate that in the future methods will be available for kinetic characterization of the entire reaction sequence by direct experimentation.

Indeed, Slater (26) has shown that for certain cases where K_m and V can be varied (by altering k_3), values for k_2 and k_1 can be derived. Since $K_m = (k_2 + k_3)/k_1$ then

$$K_m = \frac{k_2[En]_t + k_3[En]_t}{k_1[En]_t} = \frac{k_2[En]_t + V}{k_1[En]_t}$$

A plot of K_m *versus* V as illustrated in Fig. 8.2 will yield k_2/k_1 as the intercept, since at this point $V = 0$. Individual values of k_2 and k_1 can be derived in the following way: At the point where the extra-

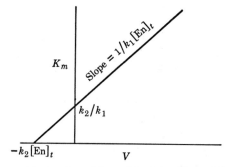

Fig. 8.2. Evaluation of k_2 and k_1 from K_m and V (26).

polated line cuts the V axis we find

$$K_m = 0 = \frac{k_2[\text{En}]_t + V}{k_1[\text{En}]_t} \quad \text{and} \quad V = -k_2[\text{En}]_t$$

The slope of the line will be $(k_2/k_1)/k_2[\text{En}]_t$ or $1/k_1[\text{En}]_t$.

7. Relationship between K_{eq}, K_m, and V

In 1930 Haldane (2) derived an important equation which, unfortunately, lay dormant in the literature for many years. The Haldane equation relates the kinetic constants for the forward and back reactions to the equilibrium constant for the catalyzed reaction. Thus,

$$K_{eq} = \frac{[\text{P}]}{[\text{S}]} = \frac{k_1 k_3}{k_4 k_2}$$

and multiplying numerator and denominator by $[\text{En}]_t(k_2 + k_3)/k_1 k_4$ leads to

$$K_{eq} = \frac{k_1 k_3 [\text{En}]_t \left[\dfrac{k_2 + k_3}{k_1 k_4}\right]}{k_4 k_2 [\text{En}]_t \left[\dfrac{k_2 + k_3}{k_1 k_4}\right]} = \frac{V_f\, K_{m,r}}{V_r\, K_{m,f}},$$

where the subscripts f and r refer to forward and reverse reaction, respectively.

The Haldane equation must be obeyed. For example, Frieden and Alberty (27) found that for fumarase, $V_{\text{fumarate}}/V_{\text{malate}} = 10.9 \times 10^4/7.9 \times 10^4$. The Michaelis constants were 2.6 and 8.6 μM for fumarate and malate, respectively. From these data the calculated equilibrium constant is $\dfrac{10.9}{7.9} \times \dfrac{8.3}{2.6} = 4.4$, a figure in exact agreement with the experimental value. The relative simplicity of the chemical reaction and the fact that the equilibrium constant is not too far from unity were two of the main reasons why Alberty and his associates chose fumarase for their study of forward and reverse kinetics.

8. Determination of K_m

Table 8.1 is taken from an early paper by Kuhn (15); it can be said to be typical of the effect of [S] on v. The units of v used in such a plot are immaterial. They may represent simply degrees of optical rotation (as used by Kuhn), milliequivalents of acid produced, and so forth, per unit of time for a milliliter, milligram, or other unit of crude enzyme. Or, for pure enzymes, they may be quoted in moles of product/mole enzyme^{-1} min^{-1}, i.e., the turnover number. The v should, however, represent the "initial" reaction velocity measured

over the period when the substrate concentration remains essentially
constant.

**Table 8.1.   Effect of Sucrose Concentration on Its Velocity of
Hydrolysis by Sucrase.   Kuhn (15)**

[S], M	Relative Velocity, measured from optical rotation at 15 minutes
0.1370	22.0
0.0995	20.5
0.0676	19.0
0.0262	12.5
0.0136	9.0
0.0100	7.0
0.0079	6.0

The estimation of V and hence K_m is exceedingly cumbersome from
the data in Table 8.1.   This is occasioned by the fact that v never ap-

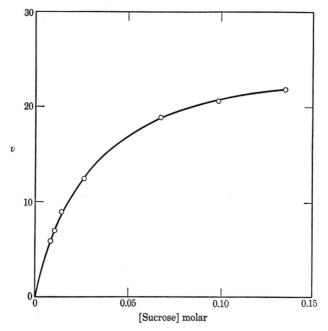

Fig. 8.3.   The relationship between sucrose concentration and its velocity of hydrolysis by sucrase; data from Kuhn (15).

pears to reach a maximum but is still creeping up even after relatively
concentrated substrate solutions are offered to the enzyme.   In Kuhn's

experiments, in which he studied the splitting of sucrose by yeast sucrase, the highest [S] was 0.137 M, or close to 5%. This is a relatively concentrated solution in which to ask the enzyme to perform. Even when the data are plotted, as in Fig. 8.3, we might guess that V is in the range 25–30, but it is impossible to say what the actual figure may be.

The Michaelis-Menten equation is related to the Henderson-Hasselbalch treatment of the dissociation of weak electrolytes. Rearranging the usual form of the Michaelis equation, we obtain

$$K_m + [S] = \frac{V[S]}{v}$$

$$K_m = \frac{V[S]}{v} - [S] = [S]\left(\frac{V}{v} - 1\right)$$

$$[S] = \frac{K_m}{(V/v) - 1} = \frac{K_m}{(V/v) - (v/v)} = K_m \frac{v}{V - v}$$

or

$$\log [S] = \log K_m + \log \frac{v}{V - v}$$

and

$$-\log [S] = -\log K_m + \log \frac{V - v}{v}$$

When $v = 50\%$,

$$\log \frac{V - v}{v} = 0 \quad \text{and} \quad [S] = K_m$$

Table 8.2 contains the same data as Table 8.1 except that the substrate concentration has also been expressed as $-\log [S]$. These data

Table 8.2. **Effect of the Negative Logarithm of Sucrose Concentration on Its Velocity of Hydrolysis by Sucrase. Kuhn (15)**

[S], M	$-\log [S]$	Relative Velocity, measured from optical rotation at 15 minutes
0.1370	0.86	22.0
0.0995	1.00	20.5
0.0676	1.17	19.0
0.0262	1.58	12.5
0.0136	1.87	9.0
0.0100	2.00	7.0
0.0079	2.10	6.0

have been plotted in Fig. 8.4. Kuhn actually employed these sigmoid curves for the estimation of K_m, corresponding to the maximum slope of the curve. It should be cautioned however that the ionization con-

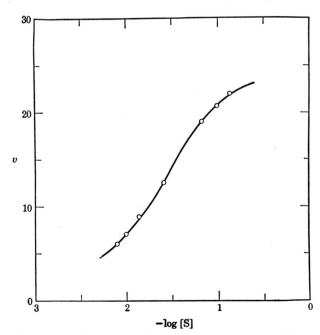

Fig. 8.4. The relationship between the negative logarithm of the sucrose concentration and its velocity of hydrolysis by sucrase; data from Kuhn (15).

stant in the Henderson-Hasselbalch equation is a thermodynamic equilibrium constant whereas K_m is derived from kinetic data.

In 1934[2] Lineweaver and Burk (16) pointed out that these constants could be more accurately determined if the data were presented in the form of a straight line. They showed that the Michaelis equation could be rearranged in a manner which yielded a straight line. Taking the reciprocal of each side,

$$\frac{1}{v} = \frac{K_m + [S]}{V[S]} = \frac{K_m}{V[S]} + \frac{[S]}{V[S]}$$

$$\frac{1}{v} = \frac{K_m}{V}\left(\frac{1}{[S]}\right) + \frac{1}{V}$$

This is equivalent to the expression

$$y = ax + b$$

where a is the slope and b the intercept of a straight line. Figure 8.5 shows Kuhn's data, rearranged as in Table 8.3, plotted in this so-called

---

[2] Several investigators had apparently introduced this treatment of enzyme kinetic data at an earlier date (28).

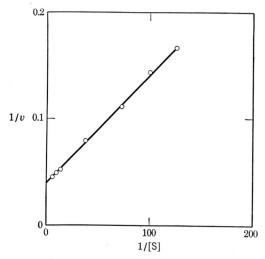

Fig. 8.5. Data from Kuhn (15) on the effect of substrate concentration on the velocity of sucrose hydrolysis by sucrase. The data are plotted in the *double reciprocal* manner (see Table 8.3).

"double reciprocal" manner. The intercept $1/V$ is 0.037, and so $V = 27$. The slope K_m/V is 0.00104, and hence $K_m = 0.028\ M$.

Table 8.3. Relationship between Reciprocal of Sucrose Concentration and Reciprocal of Its Velocity of Hydrolysis by Sucrase. Data of Kuhn (15)

[S], M	$\dfrac{1}{[S]}$	Relative Velocity, measured from optical rotation at 15 minutes	$\dfrac{1}{\text{Relative Velocity}}$
0.1370	7.3	22.0	0.046
0.0995	10.0	20.5	0.049
0.0670	14.8	19.0	0.053
0.0262	38.2	12.5	0.080
0.0136	73.5	9.0	0.111
0.0100	100	7.0	0.143
0.0079	127	6.0	0.167

The advantages are obvious when it is considered that measurements need not be done in very concentrated solutions; i.e., the [S] can be extrapolated to the value $1/S = 0$, where [S] is infinitely great.

Although the form of the Michaelis equation given above is the one generally employed for estimation of V and K_m, several other linear plots may be employed. For example, multiplying through by [S] gives

$$\frac{[S]}{v} = \frac{1}{V} \cdot [S] + \frac{K_m}{V}$$

in which the slope is $1/V$, and the intercept is K_m/V. This method results in a little less scatter of the experimental points. More recently, there have been further refinements of these methods: Eadie (17); Hofstee (18). For instance, the third possibility for a linear plot, i.e., $V = v + \dfrac{v}{[S]} \cdot K_m$ is less apt to obscure deviations from linearity and is strongly favored by Hofstee (18, 29, see Fig. 8.6).

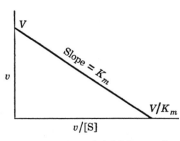

Fig. 8.6. Plot of initial reaction rate, v, versus v/substrate concentration.

Dixon (19) has suggested that the straight line in Fig. 8.5 be extrapolated across the $1/v$ axis until it intersects the $1/[S]$ axis. At this point $1/v$ is zero, and so

$$\frac{K_m}{V[S]} + \frac{1}{V} = 0 \qquad \frac{K_m}{V[S]} = -\frac{1}{V} \qquad \frac{1}{S} = -\frac{1}{K_m}$$

Thus, for two double reciprocal plots which have the same intercept on the $1/v$ axis but different slope, the line of greater slope will represent the larger K_m and will intersect the horizontal axis closer to the origin.

The accurate determination of K_m is a really formidable task. Data should be obtained over as wide a range of [S] as possible. Kuhn was actually able to achieve a seventeenfold range in the work cited above; a range of several hundred fold is desirable.

Instead of straight lines in the double reciprocal plot, conditions resembling those shown in Fig. 8.7 may actually be observed. In A and B the velocity becomes abnormally slow and fast, respectively, as the [S] is increased. This may mean choking of the active site by two molecules of the substrate or, in B, the enzyme may require two substrate molecules, and the attachment of one facilitates the rate of reaction of the second molecule. The abnormalities here are taking place in concentrated solutions of S. In C and D, where the departure from linearity is in dilute [S], the difficulties might be attributed to analytical errors.

Of course, it is not surprising that substrates such as hydrogen peroxide and urea should denature their own enzymes. Attention is directed to the paper of Howell and Sumner (20) on the effect of pH and urea concentration on the activity of urease. These investigators found a more or less normal velocity: [S] relationship at pH values

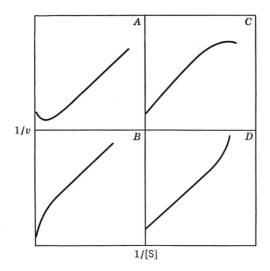

Fig. 8.7. Anomalies in the *double reciprocal* plot (see p. 106).

up to about 6; above this pH the velocity was much greater in dilute than in more concentrated substrate solutions.

9. The Magnitude of K_m for Enzymes

Although generalizations cannot be made, K_m for respiratory enzymes is often lower than for hydrolytic enzymes. Table 8.4 shows some representative data for enzymes whose K_m ranges from 10^{-1} to

Table 8.4. The K_m for Various Enzymes

Enzyme	Substrate	K_m, M
Maltase	Maltose	2.1×10^{-1}
Sucrase	Sucrose	2.8×10^{-2}
Phosphatase	Glycerophosphate	3.0×10^{-3}
Lactic dehydrogenase	Pyruvate	3.5×10^{-5}

10^{-5} M. At pH 7.0 the K_m for glucose dehydrogenase is 0.15 M for glucose but only 1.5×10^{-5} M for the coenzyme diphosphopyridine nucleotide (25).

10. Effect of pH on K_m and V

The profound effect of acidity on the rate of the catalyzed reaction was one of the first observations to be made with enzymes. Chapter 11 will deal with this aspect of enzyme kinetics.

It was stated above that the determination of K_m for an enzyme represents considerable labor. Usually, therefore, this constant has been evaluated only under a single set of conditions. Dixon (21), in a very interesting communication, has drawn attention to the possibilities of studying the nature of the ionizing group in enzymes by examining the value of K_m as a function of pH.[3]

The curve shown in Fig. 8.8 is drawn from the data of Greenberg and Mohamed (22) on arginase (21). Greenberg and Mohamed rea-

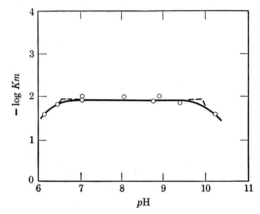

Fig. 8.8.   Change in Michaelis constant with pH for arginase (21, 22). Reproduced from *Biochemical Journal*, Cambridge University Press, London and New York.

soned that in the neutral range of pH the positively charged amino group of the arginine combined with a negatively charged group in the enzyme. In alkaline solution the amino group lost its charge, and K_m consequently increased. K_m increases also in acidic solution, owing to the loss of the negative charge on the enzyme.

The effect of pH on the K_m for ethanol in the alcohol dehydrogenase system has been determined by Theorell and Bonnichsen (14). They found K_m to be 1.2, 0.5, 0.7, and 2.0 mM at pH 6.8, 8.2, 9.0, and 9.8, respectively.

11. Practical Value of K_m

The K_m is useful in estimating the substrate concentration necessary to give maximal velocity. The form of the Michaelis equation is such that approximately 10 and 90% of V is achieved at [S] corresponding to $K_m \times 10^{-1}$ and $K_m \times 10$, respectively.[4] (See Fig. 8.4.)

[3] Dixon's theory is too simple to apply to fumarase because he does not consider buffer effects (24). In the case of fumarase, the K_m is directly proportional to the phosphate buffer concentration.

[4] The similarity between the Michaelis-Menten and the Henderson-Hasselbalch equations has been pointed out on p. 103.

For enzymes which attack a variety of substrates, those with the smallest K_m have often been regarded as the "natural" substrate. Meister (23) examined the K_m for a number of α-keto acids on lactic dehydrogenase, and pyruvic was found to have the lowest value.

The K_m for enzymes isolated from different sources may be compared in order to provide information on their possible identity.

References

General

1. D. D. Van Slyke, *Advances in Enzymology, 2,* 33 (1942).
2. J. B. S. Haldane, *Enzymes,* Longmans, Green and Co., London, 1930.
3. P. W. Wilson, in *Respiratory Enzymes,* Burgess Publishing Co., Minneapolis, Minn., 1949.
4. R. A. Alberty, *Advances in Enzymology, 17,* 1 (1956).

Bibliography

5. V. Henri, *Lois générales de l'action des diastases,* Paris, 1903.
6. A. J. Brown, *Trans. Chem. Soc., 81,* 373 (1902).
7. B. Chance, *Advances in Enzymology, 12,* 153 (1951).
8. L. Michaelis and M. L. Menten, *Biochem. Z., 49,* 333 (1913).
9. D. D. Van Slyke and G. E. Cullen, *J. Biol. Chem., 19,* 141 (1914).
10. G. E. Briggs and J. B. S. Haldane, *Biochem. J., 19,* 338 (1925).
11. B. Chance, *Rev. Sci. Instruments, 22,* 619 (1951).
12. H. Theorell and B. Chance, *Acta Chem. Scand., 5,* 1127 (1951).
13. B. Chance and J. B. Neilands, *J. Biol. Chem., 199,* 383 (1952).
14. H. Theorell and R. K. Bonnichsen, *Acta Chem. Scand., 5,* 1105 (1951).
15. R. Kuhn, *Z. physiol. Chem., 125,* 28 (1923).
16. H. Lineweaver and D. Burk, *J. Am. Chem. Soc., 56,* 658 (1934).
17. G. S. Eadie, *Science, 116,* 688 (1952).
18. B. H. J. Hofstee, *Science, 116,* 329 (1952).
19. M. Dixon, *Biochem. J., 55,* 170 (1953).
20. S. F. Howell and J. B. Sumner, *J. Biol. Chem., 104,* 619 (1934).
21. M. Dixon, *Biochem. J., 55,* 161 (1953).
22. D. M. Greenberg and M. S. Mohamed, *Arch. Biochem., 8,* 365 (1945).
23. A. Meister, *J. Biol. Chem., 184,* 117 (1950).
24. R. A. Alberty et al., *J. Am. Chem. Soc., 76,* 2485 (1954).
25. H. J. Strecker and S. Korkes, *J. Biol. Chem., 196,* 769 (1952).
26. E. C. Slater, in *The Physical Chemistry of Enzymes, Discussions Faraday Soc.,* No. 20 (1955).
27. C. Frieden and R. A. Alberty, *J. Biol. Chem., 212,* 859 (1955).
28. G. E. Briggs, *Nature, 179,* 1256 (1957).
29. B. H. J. Hofstee, *Enzymologia, 17,* 273 (1956).

9

Action of Inhibitors

1. Introduction (References 1–5)

The subject of inhibition is of sufficient importance to require special consideration in any review dealing with the general chemistry of enzymes.

The most potent poisons of living organisms exert their action by inhibiting enzymes. Cyanide combines with many natural substances, but specifically it is its reaction with the active metallic center of cytochrome oxidase that makes cyanide such a powerful poison. Carbon monoxide attaches itself to the iron atom of hemoglobin in such a manner that this pigment cannot perform its oxygen-carrying role. We may properly regard hemoglobin as catalyzing a partial enzymatic reaction; it only combines with rather than transforms its substrate oxygen. Arsenate exerts a poisonous effect because it chemically resembles phosphate and is thus able to block certain enzymatic reactions in which phosphate takes part (arsenolysis). The dialkyl halogenophosphates, such as the "nerve gases" developed during the war (e.g., diisopropyl fluorophosphate), are powerful inhibitors of esterases and certain proteolytic enzymes. Many similar examples could be cited.

For obvious reasons, inhibition reagents are of great practical interest in pharmacology and medicine. Much work has been done on the possibility of utilizing these principles in treating disease. It should be very helpful if we could use the method of selective enzymatic inhibition in the cancer problem; however, as Potter has pointed out (6), we still know all too little about the enzymatic machinery of the normal cell.

Although the mechanism of action of antibiotics is still obscure, it is safe to reason from the enzyme-trace substance hypothesis of Green (7) that many of them poison essential enzymes of microorganisms. Albert (8) has proposed that certain antibiotics function by chelation with metals. He thinks that it is not a deprivation of the essential metal but rather a direct toxicity of the intact chelate which causes those substances to be poisonous. Perhaps the metal chelate is too closely similar to an essential prosthetic group of an enzyme. Heavy metals are known to inhibit many enzymes, so that here again we can relate the poisonous activity of some substance to its effect on enzymes. Great excitement has been generated over the subject of "antienzymes" in toothpaste!

The judicial use of inhibitors in whole cells, extracts, homogenates, tissue slices, and the like has provided a large volume of detailed information on the intimate mechanism of action of complex enzyme systems. Most of the data for the complicated metabolic schemes such as the glycolytic and Krebs cycles have been so obtained.

Inhibitors may provide valuable clues as to which chemical bonds are involved in linking the substrate to the enzyme. A glance at the chemical structure of a new compound is all that is necessary in order to make an intelligent guess as to which if any enzymes it might inhibit. The functional group reagents which are useful in studying enzymes have been reviewed elsewhere (9), and more will be said of them later (see Table 9.2).

The above reasons are sufficient to indicate the necessity of studying briefly the various types of enzymatic inhibition known to occur. For comprehensive treatment of the subject the reader is referred elsewhere (1, 2).

2. Competitive Inhibition

This type of inhibition is often referred to as "reversible" although, as we shall see, this designation is inadequate since non-competitive inhibition may also be reversed. Competitive inhibition depends on the lack of absolute specificity of the chemical reactivity on the active site. The active site combines more or less loosely with the inhibitor, which is very possibly structurally related to the substrate, thus preventing access of the substrate to the enzyme surface.

The historical example of this type of inhibitor is malonic acid. This compound specifically and powerfully poisons succinic dehydrogenase.

$$HOOC\ CH_2\ CH_2\ COOH \qquad HOOC\ CH_2\ COOH$$

Succinic acid   Malonic acid

Apparently the enzyme cannot distinguish between the two acids,[1] so that both are capable of reaction with it. However, there is no

---

[1] At physiological pH both acids would bear two full negative charges.

opportunity for dehydrogenation in malonic acid. The degree of inhibition is dependent on the ratio malonate/succinate; sufficiently large concentrations of succinate are able to displace malonate completely from the enzyme (10). There are many further examples of this type in the literature, e.g., the inhibition of malic dehydrogenase by adenine (11). Here the inhibitor competes with the coenzyme for the active site on the protein.

The hallmark of competitive inhibition is the fact that *the velocity depends on the inhibitor concentration, the substrate concentration, and the relative affinities of inhibitor and substrate for the enzyme.*

The case for competitive inhibition will now be treated mathematically. The enzyme will combine with the inhibitor to form a complex EnI which may possess a true dissociation constant Ki. The intermediate enzyme-substrate

$$Ki = \frac{[En][I]}{[EnI]}$$

complex will again be designated as A, the total enzyme as En_t, and the velocity in the presence of the inhibitor will be v^1. The free enzyme will be written as En.

$$En + S \underset{k_2}{\overset{k_1}{\rightleftharpoons}} A \underset{k_4}{\overset{k_3}{\rightleftharpoons}} En + P$$

We have determined before that (see p. 98)

$$\frac{[En]}{[A]} = \frac{k_2 + k_3}{[S]k_1}$$

Since $[En] = [En]_t - [EnI] - [A]$ and $(k_2 + k_3)/k_1 = K_m$, we may divide by $[A]$ and equate the terms to give

$$\frac{[En]_t}{[A]} - \frac{[EnI]}{[A]} - \frac{[A]}{[A]} = \frac{K_m}{[S]}$$

$$\frac{[En]_t}{[A]} = \frac{K_m}{[S]} + \frac{[EnI]}{[A]} + 1$$

Substituting $\dfrac{[En][I]}{Ki}$ for $[EnI]$ we get

$$\frac{[En]_t}{[A]} = \frac{K_m}{[S]} + \frac{[En][I]}{Ki[A]} + 1$$

Since $[A] = \dfrac{[En][S]k_1}{k_2 + k_3} = \dfrac{[En][S]}{K_m}$, we may replace $\dfrac{1}{[A]}$ with $\dfrac{K_m}{[En][S]}$ to obtain

$$\frac{[En]_t}{[A]} = \frac{K_m}{[S]} + \frac{K_m[I]}{Ki[S]} + 1$$

The maximum velocity will be proportional to the total enzyme; the actual velocity will be proportional to [A]. Therefore,

$$\frac{[En]_t}{[A]} = \frac{V}{v^1}$$

$$\frac{V}{v^1} = \frac{KiK_m}{Ki[S]} + \frac{K_m[I]}{Ki[S]} + \frac{Ki[S]}{Ki[S]}$$

$$= \frac{KiK_m + K_m[I] + Ki[S]}{Ki[S]}$$

$$v^1 = \frac{V[S]Ki}{K_mKi + K_m[I] + [S]Ki}$$

Dividing by Ki gives

$$v^1 = \frac{V[S]}{K_m + (K_m[I]/Ki) + [S]}$$

$$= \frac{V[S]}{K_m\left(1 + \dfrac{[I]}{Ki}\right) + [S]}$$

It will be noted that the equation differs from the Michaelis expression only in the term $1 + ([I]/Ki)$. This factor is multiplied by K_m; therefore, *competitive inhibition increases the value of K_m so that an "apparent" K_m is actually measured.* If [S] is very large in relation to the term $K_m\left(1 + \dfrac{[I]}{Ki}\right)$, that term may be dropped, and the velocity is maximal and equal to the original value of V. If Ki is small and [I] large, there will be inhibition, the extent of which depends on [S].

The expression for competitive inhibition is readily put in linear form because it is formally similar to the Michaelis equation.

$$\frac{1}{v^1} = \frac{K_m + \dfrac{K_m[I]}{Ki} + [S]}{V[S]}$$

$$= \frac{K_m + \dfrac{K_m[I]}{Ki}}{V[S]} + \frac{[S]}{V[S]}$$

$$= \frac{1}{V}\frac{\left(K_m + \dfrac{K_m[I]}{Ki}\right)}{[S]} + \frac{1}{V}$$

$$= \frac{1}{V}\left(K_m + \frac{K_m[I]}{Ki}\right)\frac{1}{[S]} + \frac{1}{V} = \left(1 + \frac{[I]}{Ki}\right)\frac{K_m}{V} \cdot \frac{1}{[S]} + \frac{1}{V}$$

It will be recalled that in the Michaelis equation the slope in the double reciprocal plot is K_m/V. Here the slope, and consequently the apparent K_m, is increased by the quantity $1 + [I]/Ki$. This situation is illustrated in Fig. 9.1; i.e., the slope but not the intercept increases.

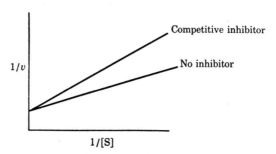

Fig. 9.1. Competitive inhibition shown by the *double reciprocal* plot.

3. Non-Competitive Inhibition

One type of inhibition which cannot be reversed by the simple expedient of raising the [S] is termed "non-competitive." The substrate is then unable to prevent the combination of the inhibitor with the enzyme. The amount of inhibition will accordingly depend on the [I] and Ki, and it will not be influenced by the [S]. Non-competitive inhibitors apparently combine with an enzyme at a point other than the attachment of S. They are then able to exert an effect on the active site even though they are situated some distance away.

Arginase is an enzyme which is competitively and non-competitively inhibited by lysine and monoamino acids, respectively (12). Non-competitive inhibitors thus often show less structural resemblance to the substrate than competitive inhibitors. Metal ions often act as non-competitive inhibitors.

The equation for non-competitive inhibition is derived algebraically in the following way. The symbols are the same as those used in describing competitive inhibition:

$$\text{En} + I \rightleftharpoons \text{EnI}$$

$$Ki = \frac{[\text{En}][\text{I}]}{[\text{EnI}]} = \frac{([\text{En}]_t - [\text{EnI}])[\text{I}]}{[\text{EnI}]}$$

$$Ki[\text{EnI}] = [\text{En}]_t[\text{I}] - [\text{EnI}][\text{I}]$$

$$Ki[\text{EnI}] + [\text{EnI}][\text{I}] = [\text{En}]_t[\text{I}]$$

$$[\text{EnI}](Ki + [\text{I}]) = [\text{En}]_t[\text{I}]$$

$$[\text{EnI}] = \frac{[\text{En}]_t[\text{I}]}{Ki + [\text{I}]}$$

The velocity in the absence of the inhibitor is proportional to the total enzyme concentration $[En]_t$; the velocity in the presence of the inhibitor is proportional to $[En]$, the free enzyme.

$$\frac{v}{v^1} = \frac{[En]_t}{[En]_t - [EnI]}$$

Substituting the above value of $[EnI]$

$$\frac{v}{v^1} = \frac{[En]_t}{[En]_t - \dfrac{[En]_t[I]}{Ki + [I]}}$$

$$\frac{v}{v^1} = \frac{1}{1 - \dfrac{[I]}{Ki + [I]}} = \frac{1}{\dfrac{Ki + [I] - [I]}{Ki + [I]}} = \frac{1}{\dfrac{Ki}{Ki + [I]}}$$

$$\frac{v^1}{v} = \frac{Ki}{Ki + [I]}$$

It is apparent from the above derivation that the velocity in the presence of the inhibitor depends on $[I]$ and Ki but not $[S]$. The V will be decreased because the system will behave as though it contained less enzyme; i.e., some has been chemically removed, and it is irretrievably lost so far as catalysis is concerned. Again, when Ki is small and $[I]$ large, the ratio v^1/v will be very small. When the reverse is true, the ratio becomes closer to 1, thus indicating lack of extensive inhibition.

Placing this equation in the double reciprocal form we have first

$$\frac{1}{v} = \frac{Ki}{v^1(Ki + [I])}$$

Substituting in $\dfrac{1}{v} = \dfrac{K_m}{V}\dfrac{1}{[S]} + \dfrac{1}{V}$ gives

$$\frac{Ki}{v^1(Ki + [I])} = \frac{K_m}{V}\frac{1}{[S]} + \frac{1}{V}$$

$$\frac{1}{v^1} = \left(1 + \frac{[I]}{Ki}\right)\left(\frac{K_m}{V} \cdot \frac{1}{[S]} + \frac{1}{V}\right)$$

Both the slope K_m/V and intercept $1/V$ are increased by the factor $\left(1 + \dfrac{[I]}{Ki}\right)$. Such a plot will have the form shown in Fig. 9.2.

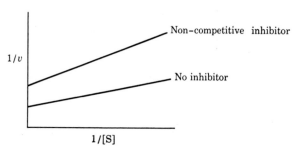

Fig. 9.2. Non-competitive inhibition shown by the *double reciprocal* plot.

4. Determination of *Ki*

The constant *Ki* should be measured in any exact work because it is a quantitative measure of the inhibition strength of the reagent. The equations given above were converted to straight lines in order to facilitate calculation of *Ki* (17).

Experiments should be carried out at two or more inhibitor concentrations while the [S] is varied over as wide a range as possible. On plotting $1/[S]$ versus $1/v$, a straight line should result from which it is possible to evaluate *Ki*. For example, in competitive inhibition the constant is given by the slope $= \dfrac{K_m}{V}\left(1 + \dfrac{[I]}{Ki}\right)$. For other types of inhibition the characteristics of the double reciprocal graph are given by Ebersole, Guttentag, and Wilson (15). Dixon (5) has suggested simpler graphical methods for calculating enzyme inhibition constants. Table 9.1 gives the equations for the different types of inhibition and

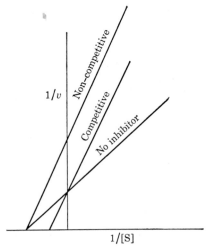

Fig. 9.3. Graphical representation of the equations given in Table 9.1.

Table 9.1. Calculation of Enzyme-Inhibitor Constants from Plots of Reciprocal Velocity versus Reciprocal Substrate Concentration

Type of Inhibition

	None	Competitive	Non-Competitive
Equation	$\dfrac{1}{v} = \dfrac{K_m}{V}\left(\dfrac{1}{[\mathrm{S}]}\right) + \dfrac{1}{V}$	$\dfrac{1}{v^1} = \left(1 + \dfrac{[\mathrm{I}]}{Ki}\right)\dfrac{K_m}{V}\cdot\dfrac{1}{[\mathrm{S}]} + \dfrac{1}{V}$	$\dfrac{1}{v^1} = \left(1 + \dfrac{[\mathrm{I}]}{Ki}\right)\left(\dfrac{K_m}{V}\cdot\dfrac{1}{[\mathrm{S}]} + \dfrac{1}{V}\right)$
Intercept on $1/v$ axis	$\dfrac{1}{V}$	$\dfrac{1}{V}$	$\dfrac{1}{V}\left(1 + \dfrac{[\mathrm{I}]}{Ki}\right)$
Intercept on $1/[\mathrm{S}]$ axis	$-\dfrac{1}{K_m}$	$-\dfrac{1}{K_m\left(1 + \dfrac{[\mathrm{I}]}{Ki}\right)}$	$-\dfrac{1}{K_m}$
Slope	$\dfrac{K_m}{V}$	$\dfrac{K_m}{V}\left(1 + \dfrac{[\mathrm{I}]}{Ki}\right)$	$\dfrac{K_m}{V}\left(1 + \dfrac{[\mathrm{I}]}{Ki}\right)$

Table 9.2. Some Representative Inhibitors of Enzymes*†

Inhibitor	Sensitive Group	Mechanism of Action	Type of Reaction	Representative Sensitive Enzyme
p-Chloromercuribenzoate	Sulfhydryl	$RS{:}H$ $\overline{Cl{:}}$ HgC_6H_4COOH or $RS{:}H$ $\overline{HO{:}}$ HgC_6H_4COOH	Mercaptide formation	Urease
Iodoacetamide (also iodoacetate)	Sulfhydryl (amino group also)	$RS{:}H$ $\overline{I{:}}$ CH_2CONH_2	Alkylation	Papain
N-Ethylmaleimide	Sulfhydryl	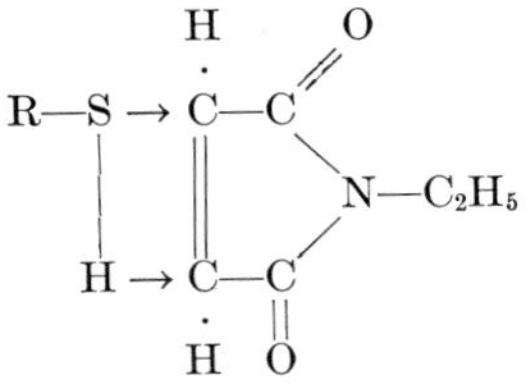	Addition	Myosin
Iodosobenzoate	Sulfhydryl	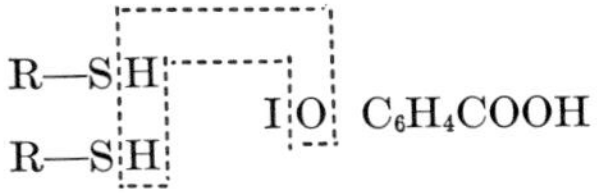 $R{-}S{:}H$ $\overline{I{:}O}$ C_6H_4COOH $R{-}S{:}H$	Oxidation	Triose phosphate dehydrogenase
Trivalent arsenicals	Sulfhydryl	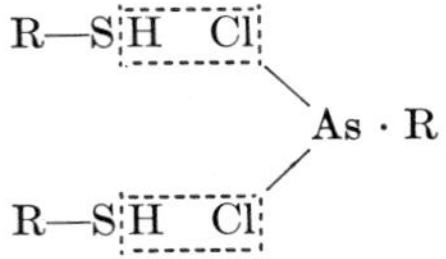 $R{-}S{:}H$ $\overline{Cl}$ $As \cdot R$ $R{-}S{:}H$ $\overline{Cl}$	Mercaptide formation	Succinoxidase
Ferricyanide	Sulfhydryl	$2RSH \rightarrow R{-}S{-}S{-}R$	Oxidation	β-Amylase

118

Iodine	(Sulfhydryl, aromatic residues)	$2RSH + I_2 \rightarrow R{-}S{-}S{-}R + 2HI$	Oxidation Iodination	Lactic dehydrogenase
Heavy-metal cations (Hg, Ag, etc.)	(Sulfhydryl, anions)	Mercaptylation $RCOO^- + Me^+ \rightarrow RCOO^- Me^+$	Mercaptide formation Salt formation	Glutamic dehydrogenase
Cyanide, azide	Metalloporphyrins; metals	Attachment to metals	Metal inactivation	Tyrosinase Catalase
Carbon monoxide	Metalloporphyrins	Attachment to metals (iron porphyrin complex is photodissociable)	Metal inactivation	Cytochrome oxidase
Chelating agents (citrate, oxalate, pyrophosphate, ethylenediamine tetraacetate; etc.)	Metals	Removal of metal	Metal inactivation	Aspartase
Fluoride	Metals; magnesium-protein complex	Mg-fluorophosphate or Mg-fluoride; Mg-protein	Metal inactivation	Enolase
Alkoxyhalogenophosphates (diisopropylfluorophosphate, DFP; etc.)	Serine or imidazole?	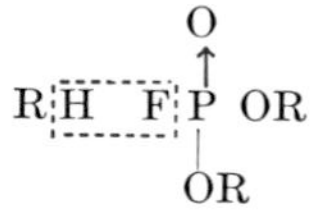 $R{:}\ddot{H}\ \overset{O}{\overset{\uparrow}{\underset{\cdots}{F}}}{:}P\ OR$ OR	Phosphorylation	Cholinesterase
Arsenate	Organic phosphate bond with $\Delta F_{hydrolysis} > 4000$ cal	Competitive acceptor against phosphate	Arsenolysis	Phospho transacetylase

* Further data are available in review articles (13, 14).
† The table does not include non-specific inhibitors such as the macroanionic and macrocationic substances (16).

shows the simplest means of calculating Ki (i.e., by use of the intercepts shown in Fig. 9.3) from plots of $1/v$ versus $1/[S]$. In each case the intercept on the $1/[S]$ axis is given by the relation: intercept on $1/v$ axis/slope. Solutions for the equations shown in Table 9.1 were obtained by alternately setting $1/v$ or $1/v^1$ and $1/[S]$ equal to zero.

5. Other Types of Inhibition

The inhibition types described above are those most commonly used in mechanism studies. Enzymes may, of course, be inhibited by any protein denaturant such as trichloroacetic acid, urea, heat, foaming, and so forth. These non-specific inhibitors are usually irreversible and give little information about the active site of the enzyme.

It cannot be emphasized too strongly that, when functional group reagents are used, they should be allowed sufficient time to react with the protein. This means that the inhibition and activity experiments should be separated. Also, it is preferable to use reactions which are reversible. Since inhibition by p-chloromercuribenzoate is commonly reversed with cysteine, it is reasoned that this compound reacts selectively with the SH group and that this is all that it does to the protein molecule. Inhibitors cannot in themselves be classified as either competitive or non-competitive because the type of inhibition will depend on the particular enzyme under investigation. Thus an SH group in one enzyme might be essential for activity, but in another it might be situated only near the point of substrate attachment. Wilson (15) and his associates have defined certain other types of inhibition. In "uncompetitive" inhibition the inhibitor combines with EnS but not with the free enzyme; in "quadratic" inhibition the inhibitor combines with some intermediate which makes EnS available in the reaction sequence. Segal, Kachmar and Boyer (3) have given one simple, general equation describing competitive, non-competitive and uncompetitive inhibition. The latter type is also known as "anti-competitive inhibition" and although relatively rare, has been studied in a number of cases (18).

6. Chemical Basis of Inhibition

As might be expected, any reagent which reacts with the functional groups of proteins is a potential enzyme inhibitor. Since a variety of reagents have been available for testing, it is not surprising to find that over the years almost every protein functional group has been implicated as necessary for the proper activity of a certain enzyme (2). In addition to chemical modification of the protein, any reagent which reacts with or displaces a substrate, coenzyme or required metal ion will similarly inhibit the catalyzed reaction. Table 9.2 shows the chemical reaction obtained with some common inhibitors and Table 9.3 gives a more complete list of the groups attacked but without reference to the mechanism of reaction.

Table 9.3. Functional Group Reagents* (2, 20)

Group	Reagent
Amino	Ketene, acetic anhydride, phenyl-isothiocyanate, formaldehyde, nitrous acid, fluorodinitrobenzene, aminopeptidase
Carboxyl	Esterification, carboxypeptidase
Phenolic	Iodine, nitrous acid, acylating agents, tyrosinase
Imidazole	Fluorodinitrobenzene, methylene blue photooxidation, 5-dimethylamino-1-naphthalene sulfonyl chloride
Sulfhydryl	(See Table 9.2)
Disulfide	Cysteine, thioglycollic acid, ascorbic acid, H_2S, 1,2-dimercaptopropanol (British Anti-Lewisite, BAL)
Peptide bonds	Proteolytic enzymes
Phosphate	Phosphatase

* Many of these are non-specific.

7. Relationship between Inhibition and Activation

Ogston (19) has directed attention to the fact that activation and inhibition can be regarded as two sides of the one coin. He and others have proposed that these two quantities can be treated as a simple general case involving a modifier, reactant and enzyme. He has also cautioned that in the chemical or mechanistic interpretation of competitive inhibition, identical kinetic consequences to that described on pp. 111–114 would follow were the inhibitor to combine at a site *remote* from that of the substrate and yet nevertheless affect the dissociation constant of the substrate. Since this type of effect would be reciprocal and since the modifier could either inhibit or activate, the result would be either competitive inhibition or "cooperative activation." Similarly, non-competitive inhibition might be attributed to (a) reaction of the inhibitor at the same site as the substrate but with $Ki \langle\langle K_{Dissoc., sub.}$ or (b) combination of the inhibitor at a site remote from that of the substrate affecting not the strength of binding of the substrate but rather a transient state in the catalyzed reaction.

References

General

1. P. W. Wilson, in *Respiratory Enzymes,* edited by H. A. Lardy, Burgess Publishing Co., Minneapolis, Minn., 1949.
2. I. W. Sizer, *Science, 125,* 54 (1956).
3. H. L. Segal, J. F. Kachmar, and P. D. Boyer, *Enzymologia, 15,* 187 (1952).
4. P. G. Scholefield, *Can. J. Biochem. and Physiol., 33,* 1003 (1955).
5. M. Dixon, *Biochem. J., 55,* 170 (1953).

Bibliography

6. Van R. Potter, in *Respiratory Enzymes,* edited by H. A. Lardy, Burgess Publishing Co., Minneapolis, Minn., 1949.
7. D. E. Green, *Advances in Enzymology, 1,* 177 (1941).
8. A. Albert, *Nature, 172,* 201 (1953).
9. H. S. Olcott and H. Fraenkel-Conrat, *Chem. Revs., 41,* 151 (1947).
10. F. G. Hopkins, E. J. Morgan, and C. Lutwak-Mann, *Biochem. J., 32,* 1829 (1938).
11. J. N. Williams, *J. Biol. Chem., 195,* 629 (1952).
12. A. Hunter and C. E. Downs, *J. Biol. Chem., 157,* 427 (1945).
13. W. D. McElroy, *Quart. Rev. Biol., 22,* 25 (1947).
14. F. P. Chinard and L. Hellerman, in *Methods of Biochemical Analysis,* edited by D. Glick, Interscience Publishers, N. Y., 1954.
15. E. R. Ebersole, C. Guttentag, and P. W. Wilson, *Arch. Biochem., 3,* 399 (1943).
16. P. C. Spensley and H. J. Rogers, *Nature, 173,* 1190 (1954).
17. H. Lineweaver and D. Burk, *J. Am. Chem. Soc., 56,* 658 (1934).
18. K. S. Dodgson, B. Spencer and K. Williams, *Nature, 177,* 432 (1956).
19. A. G. Ogston, in *The Physical Chemistry of Enzymes, Discussions Faraday Soc.,* No. 20 (1955).
20. H. Fraenkel-Conrat in *Methods in Enzymology, Vol. IV,* Academic Press, N. Y. (1957).

10

Effect of Temperature

1. "Optimum" Temperature (References 1–3)

The influence of temperature on enzymes and their activity has been reviewed by Sizer (1), Wilson (2), and Moelwyn-Hughes (3). At least over a certain range, enzymatic reactions behave like ordinary chemical reactions in that, as the temperature is increased, the rate increases.

With enzymes, however, a "point of diminishing returns" is reached, since the enzyme itself will begin to suffer thermal inactivation at higher temperatures. This fact caused considerable confusion before the protein nature of enzymes was realized. The optimum temperature was used as a constant, like a melting point, to characterize an enzyme. However, the actual temperature at which an enzyme passes through its maximum activity will depend on many factors such as the purity of enzyme and substrate and the presence of activators or inhibitors. Especially will it be influenced by the method of following the reaction. The so-called optimum temperature will, therefore, be clearly a function of the time chosen for the rate measurement.

If, as we have stated before, all measurements are made as initial reaction velocities, where the reaction is zero order, the curves will never cross. Here the activity is independent of product inhibition, denaturation effects, and so forth, and so it is more likely to be a true characteristic of the catalytic properties of the enzyme.

2. Activation Energy

The effect of temperature on the velocity of many reactions encountered in nature can be described by an equation which Arrhenius derived, empirically, many years ago.

$$\frac{d \ln k}{dT} = \frac{E}{RT^2}$$

That is to say, the change in the natural logarithm of the rate constant

k is inversely proportional to the square of the absolute temperature multiplied by R, the gas constant. The new quantity E is the "activation" energy. The Maxwell-Boltzmann law states that the energy distribution among molecules is such that, the greater the amount of energy required for their activation, the greater will be the fraction of molecules acquiring enough energy to react following a given increase in temperature. E may be regarded as the amount of energy needed for placing the molecules in a reactive state. If E is large, the rate of reaction will increase rapidly for a fixed increase in temperature. This is to say that E and the temperature coefficient or ratio of the rates at two temperatures are directly proportional. The symbol μ

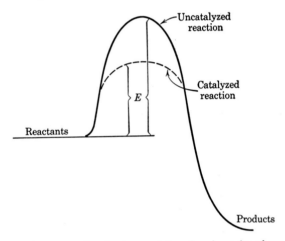

Fig. 10.1. The energy barrier in uncatalyzed and catalyzed reactions.

is often used instead of E in biological work in order to signify that the quantity measured may not be as rigorously defined as the "energy of activation."

Modern theories demand that in order for molecules to react they must first become activated (4). The molecules must first absorb the amount of energy, E, shown in Fig. 10.1; they can then react and be converted to products. At least part of the energy barrier shown in the figure is by-passed in catalytic reactions, and the agent responsible is believed to be the intermediate complex, the formation of which requires less energy (1).

The Arrhenius equation is rendered more useful by integration.

$$\ln k = \frac{-E}{R}\left(\frac{1}{T}\right) + \text{constant}$$

If the limits are selected, T_1 and T_2, corresponding to rate constants of k_1 and k_2,

$$\ln \frac{k_2}{k_1} = \frac{E}{R} \left(\frac{1}{T_1} - \frac{1}{T_2} \right)$$

or

$$\ln \frac{k_2}{k_1} = \frac{E(T_2 - T_1)}{RT_1T_2}$$

Converting to common logarithms and expressing R in calories

$$\log \frac{k_2}{k_1} = \frac{E(T_2 - T_1)}{2.3 \times 1.98 \times T_1T_2} = \frac{0.219E(T_2 - T_1)}{T_1T_2}$$

The usefulness of the Arrhenius equation will now be illustrated. By measuring the reaction rates at several temperatures the constant E can be evaluated by direct substitution (or graphically as below). Then, knowing E and the rate at one temperature, the rate at any other temperature can be predicted. Supposing that $E = 12,000$ calories and the temperature is increased from $22°$ to $32°C$,

$$\log \frac{k_2}{k_1} = \frac{0.219 \times 12,000(305 - 295)}{295 \times 305} = 0.29$$

$$k_2/k_1 = 2$$

Thus, under these conditions, the rate of the reaction is doubled.

Doubling or tripling the reaction rate, within certain temperature limits, for a $10°$ rise in temperature is frequently encountered. The activation energy is of value in interpreting reaction mechanisms. Crozier (5) has pointed out that the activation energy of biological reactions may be that of the "pacemaker" or slowest member in a complicated reaction sequence. The fact that the E for inactivation of enzymes and protein denaturation is high and of the same magnitude could, in the absence of pure enzymes, be taken as evidence that the pure enzymes are proteins. If a crude extract attacks several chemically related substrates, the question might arise whether the extract contains only one or several enzymes. If the activation energies of the extract on all substrates is constant, this may be taken as *preliminary* evidence that only one enzyme is present (1).

3. Determination of the Activation Energy

The equation

$$\ln k = \frac{-E}{R} \left(\frac{1}{T} \right) + \text{constant}$$

is obviously that of a straight line of $\ln k$ versus $1/T$ with slope $-E/R$. Again, expressing $-E/R$ as calories and using common logs

we obtain the relationship shown in Fig. 10.2, in which the slope of
the line is $-0.219E$. Such a plot is prepared by taking the reaction
rate at various temperatures.

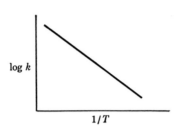

Most enzyme reactions follow the Arrhenius equation over "physiological" temperatures. The values of E obtained are of the order of magnitude of those for chemical reactions. However, when the same reaction is subjected to inorganic and enzymatic catalysis, the enzymatic reaction is found to have the lower activation energy. The value of E will be influenced by the constituents of the medium as far as these factors

Fig. 10.2. Graphical calculation of the activation energy.

alter the catalytic site of the enzyme. Sharp breaks in the line shown
in Fig. 10.2 indicate that the reaction possesses a critical temperature;[1]
Sizer (1) has suggested that this transition represents a shift in the
configuration of the enzyme molecule.

We have already seen (Chapter 8) that even in the simplest case
of Michaelis-Menten kinetics, where $v = V/(K_m/[S] + 1)$, the three
rate constants k_1, k_2, and k_3 are involved. However, at high $[S]$, v
becomes V and equal to $k_3[En]_t$. Thus, since k_3 should obey the
Arrhenius equation, a plot of $\log_{10} V$ *versus* $1/T$ should give a straight

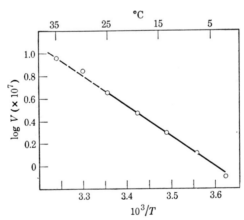

Fig. 10.3. Effect of temperature on the maximum rate of enzymatic dephosphorylation of ATP (8). Reproduced from *Archives of Biochemistry and Biophysics*, Academic Press, N. Y.

[1] Kistiakowsky and Lumry (7), who worked with urease, claim that such
breaks are artifacts and without significance to the reaction mechanism.

line corresponding to that shown in Figure 10.2. That this is actually the case can be seen from Figure 10.3 which represents the results of Ouellet, Laidler and Morales (8) on the effect of temperature on the V for the enzymatic dephosphorylation of ATP.

4. Thermal Inactivation

When there is any doubt about the thermal stability of an enzyme, the rule is always to use refrigeration. A few unhappy experiences are sufficient to develop in a research worker a fetish about refrigeration of enzymes. Instability is often encountered as low as 30°, and most enzymes are denatured above 60°. Complete denaturation following brief exposures, with very few exceptions, is to be anticipated in the range 80° to 100°. Soluble enzymes as a rule suffer no ill effects from low temperatures; e.g., they are often stored in ammonium sulfate solutions in the cold, lyophilized to dry powders, or simply frozen and kept at low temperatures.[2]

The activation energy for inactivation of the catalytic activity of an enzyme is characteristically high and lies in the range 40,000 to 100,000 calories/mole. A careful study by Northrop (6) has shown that the heat inactivation of several crystalline proteolytic enzymes closely follows the precipitation of the enzyme as denatured protein. Trypsin shows the remarkable ability to recover from its partial thermal inactivation.

References

General

1. I. W. Sizer, *Advances in Enzymology, 3,* 35 (1943).
2. P. W. Wilson, in *Respiratory Enzymes,* edited by H. A. Lardy, Burgess Publishing Co., Minneapolis, Minn., 1949.
3. E. A. Moelwyn-Hughes in *The Enzymes,* edited by J. B. Sumner and K. Myrbäck, Academic Press, N. Y., 1951.

Bibliography

4. S. Glasstone, K. J. Laidler, and H. Eyring, *The Theory of Rate Processes,* McGraw-Hill Book Co., N. Y., 1941.
5. W. J. Crozier, *J. Gen. Physiol., 7,* 189 (1924).
6. J. H. Northrop, *Crystalline Enzymes,* Columbia University Press, N. Y., 1939.
7. G. B. Kistiakowsky and R. Lumry, *J. Am. Chem. Soc., 71,* 2006 (1949).
8. L. Ouellet, K. J. Laidler and M. F. Morales, *Arch. Biochem., 39,* 37 (1952).

[2] The formation of ice crystals may inactivate the enzyme by surface denaturation.

11

Effect of Hydrogen-Ion Concentration

1. "Optimum pH" (References 1–4)

Temperature affects enzymatic activity in various ways; the number of factors controlling the effect of pH on enzymes is even greater. A rather complete discussion of these factors may be found in the article by Johnson (4). Again, as with temperature, the concept of "optimum pH" may have little real meaning. Thus variables such as temperature, type of buffer, substrate concentration, presence or absence of inhibitors or activators, type of substrate, and the ionic strength may have a bearing on the hydrogen ion activity at which the enzyme acts best. In changing the pH one must be particularly cognizant of a possible concommitant change in the ionic composition of the medium. Some effects of ionic environment on the velocity of the forward and reverse reactions catalyzed by ADH are shown in Table 11.1 (Theorell, 5).

Table 11.1. Influence of Some Sodium Salts, 0.15 M, on the Reaction Velocity V/e sec^{-1}, in the ADH + DPN + DPNH System; pH = 7.1, Phosphate Buffer Ionic Strength = 0.1, 23.55°. (Theorell, 5)

[ADH] = 0.13 μM		[ADH] = 0.13 μM	
[CH$_3$CHO] = 2100 μM		[C$_2$H$_5$OH] = 2300 μM	
[DPNH] = 9.6 μM		[DPN] = 8 μM	
Salt	V/e sec^{-1}	Salt	V/e sec^{-1}
Glycine	15	Glycine	0.32
Phosphate	8.7	Phosphate	0.26
Phosphate + versene	8.9	—	—
Chloride	3.5	Chloride	0.097
Sulfate	2.3	Sulfate	0.059
Nitrate	1.6	Nitrate	0.013
Bromide	0.13	Bromide	0.055
Formate	0.17	Formate	0
—	—	Acetate	0.059

2. Effect of pH on Substrate or Product

In dealing with the effect of pH on enzyme-catalyzed reactions one of the first points to be considered is that of ionizations in the substrate or product. Such ionizations will render the equilibrium constant pH dependent, and, as we have already seen, the Michaelis constant and the maximum velocity are related to the equilibrium

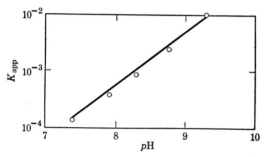

Fig. 11.1. Effect of pH on the apparent equilibrium constant for the oxidation of lactate by diphosphopyridine nucleotide and lactic dehydrogenase (6). Reproduced from *Journal of Biological Chemistry*, American Society of Biological Chemists, New Haven.

constant through the Haldane equation (see Chapter 8). We have mentioned the fact that, at physiological pH, 1 equivalent of acid is formed during the reduction of the pyridine nucleotides. Racker (6) studied such a reduction with lactic dehydrogenase, and Fig. 11.1 is reproduced from his paper. The equilibrium constant is given by

$$K_{eq} = \frac{[\text{DPNH}][\text{H}^+][\text{pyruvate}]}{[\text{DPN}^+][\text{lactate}]}$$

If we disregard the proton in the numerator, an apparent equilibrium constant may be written

$$K_{app} = \frac{[\text{DPNH}][\text{pyruvate}]}{[\text{DPN}^+][\text{lactate}]}$$

The K_{app}, which includes the compounds of interest, will theoretically increase tenfold for every unit of higher pH. The effect of buffering the reaction at a high pH, i.e., $\sim$10, is, to effectively remove one of the products, in this instance hydrogen ions. The result is that the reduction of the coenzyme tends to go to completion in basic solution.

It was pointed out previously that this generation of acid is made possible in the case of the pyridine nucleotides by the conversion of a charged, strongly basic quaternary N to an uncharged weakly basic tertiary N atom. At very low pH where the tertiary N would be charged, the reaction would be

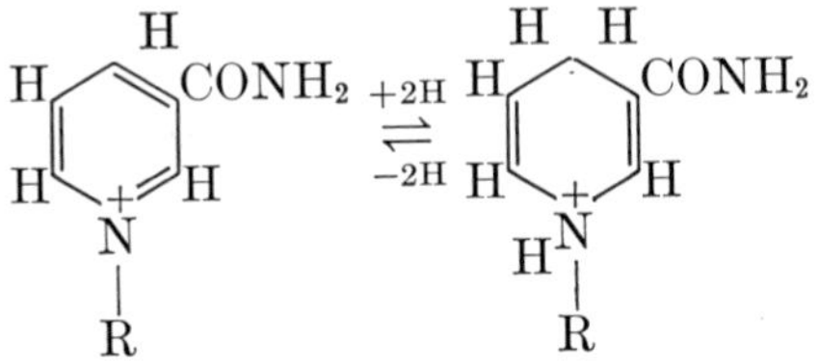

$$\text{H} \quad \text{CONH}_2 \overset{+2\text{H}}{\underset{-2\text{H}}{\rightleftharpoons}} \text{H} \quad \text{H} \quad \text{CONH}_2$$

so that no acid would be formed and the reduction would no longer be pH-dependent. The pKa of the tertiary N of reduced diphosphopyridine nucleotide is unknown; according to Krebs it lies below pH 4 to 5 (7).

If it is desired to determine diphosphopyridine nucleotide, or any compound oxidized by it, quantitatively (8), a high pH is preferred in order to pull the reaction over to the right. Similarly, in the preparation of solid reduced diphosphopyridine nucleotide, N sodium hydroxide may simply be added to keep the solution at pH 10 to 11 until the reduction is complete (9).

Undoubtedly the most numerous examples of pH dependence will be found with the various esterases. However, that the process is not at all restricted to these enzymes is apparent from the reactions cited below. The following are only a few of the additional reactions for which proton exchanges may be recorded at more or less physiological pH.

Esterases

  Acyl esters

$$\text{RCOOR}' + \text{H}_2\text{O} \rightleftharpoons \text{RCOO}^- + \text{H}^+ + \text{R}'\text{OH}$$

  Phospho esters

$$\overset{\text{O}}{\underset{\text{O}^-}{\text{RO}\overset{\uparrow}{\text{P}}\text{OR}'}} + \text{H}_2\text{O} \rightleftharpoons \overset{\text{O}}{\underset{\text{O}^-}{\text{RO}\overset{\uparrow}{\text{P}}\text{O}^-}} + \text{H}^+ + \text{R}'\text{OH}$$

The work of Alberty and his associates (10) shows that the hydrolysis of the terminal phosphate residue of ATP will produce acid at slightly alkaline but not at slightly acid pH. Similar participation of hydrogen ions could be illustrated for many other enzymes and coenzymes. The hydrolysis of acetyl coenzyme A would proceed as follows from acid to alkaline solution:

		Equivalents of Acid Produced

At low pH $\quad$ RSCOCH$_3$ + H$_2$O $\rightleftharpoons$ RSH + HOOCCH$_3$ $\qquad$ 0

At intermediate pH $\qquad\longrightarrow$ RSH + H$^+$ + $^-$OOCCH$_3$ $\qquad$ 1

At high pH $\qquad\longrightarrow$ RS$^-$ + 2H$^+$ + $^-$OOCCH$_3$ $\qquad$ 2

Acid is also formed during the reduction with hydrogen of certain inorganic atoms such as ferric iron.

$$Fe^{+++} + H \rightleftharpoons Fe^{++} + H^+$$

The principles and consequences enunciated above will apply equally well here.

As a general case, suppose, for example, a substrate A is converted to a product B and that both of the reactants may bind hydrogen ions.

$$\begin{array}{ccc} HA & & B + H^+ \\ \updownarrow & \rightleftharpoons & \updownarrow \\ A + H^+ & & HB \end{array}$$

$$K_{app} = \frac{[B]_{eq}}{[A]_{eq}} = K_{eq}\frac{(1 + [H^+]/Ka_B)}{(1 + [H^+]/Ka_A)}$$

In this equation the K_{eq} is modified by pH, i.e., the acid form of the reactant has been replaced by a term containing the H$^+$ and the acidic dissociation constant. The K_{eq} derived in this manner should be independent of pH.

If the substrate contains ionizable groups, there is, of course, a possibility that the enzyme will attack only the charged or uncharged species. Johnson (4) has given data for the effect of pH on the activity of intestinal aminopeptidase acting on triglycine. He studied the enzymatic activity in neutral and alkaline solutions and concluded that the enzyme attacked only the *Zwitterion* form of the tripeptide.

Nearly all naturally occurring substances contain acidic or basic groups of some type. The enzyme might be expected to show preference for the anion, cation, neutral, or, if the substrate contains both acidic and basic groups, the *Zwitterion form*. In such cases the pH will have a profound effect on the apparent K_m. For example, if the enzyme requires the anion form, less of the latter will be available in acidic solution and more substrate must be added in order to saturate the enzyme. Correspondingly, if the active form of the substrate were a *Zwitterion*, the apparent K_m would increase in both acidic and basic solution. If the enzyme itself is unaffected by pH changes in the

range of interest, the maximum initial velocity will be independent of
pH because of the possibility of extrapolation to infinite substrate
concentration.

The above discussion applies equally well to activators. For example, Johnson (4) found that leucyl peptidase, which is activated
by magnesium, decreases in activity sharply over pH 9.2 because of
loss of activator by precipitation as the hydroxide.

3. Effect of pH on the Enzyme or Enzyme-Substrate Complex

The most usual type of pH-activity relationship found for enzymes
is a bell-shaped curve of the type shown in Fig. 11.2. Such bell-

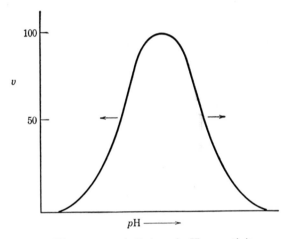

Fig. 11.2. The common bell-shaped pH vs. activity curve.

shaped curves may be the result of variation of either V or K_m with
pH or they may represent an irreversible inactivation at extremities
of pH. In 1911 Michaelis and Davidsohn (11) explained the bell-
shaped curve in terms of an isoelectric protein as the active form of
the enzyme. However, Haldane (12) could find little correlation between pH optimum and isoelectric point and proposed instead that
the activity depended upon the ionization of certain groups at the
active center.

The simplest interpretation of the bell-shaped pH curve is that of
an active site that is capable of binding two protons, the mono-
protonated form being the active enzyme.

$$H_2En_{inactive} \rightleftharpoons HEn_{active} \rightleftharpoons En_{inactive}$$

Derivations for the appropriate equations for such effects of pH have
been reported by Dixon (2), Waley (13), Alberty (1), and Laidler

(3). The following example is derived from the mechanism given by Alberty (1):

$$
\begin{array}{ccc}
\text{En} & \text{EnS} & \\
K_{bEn}\ \Updownarrow & \quad k_1 \quad \Updownarrow\ K_{bEnS} & \\
\text{EnH} + \text{S} \xrightleftharpoons[k_2]{} & \text{EnHS} \xrightarrow{k_3} \text{EnH} + \text{P} \\
K_{aEn}\ \Updownarrow & \quad \Updownarrow\ K_{aEnS} & \\
\text{EnH}_2 & \text{EnH}_2\text{S} &
\end{array}
$$

Thus the free enzyme and the enzyme-substrate complex are shown to have two ionizable groups and only the mono-protonated form is active. The total concentration of the enzyme $[\text{En}]_t$ is given by

$$[\text{En}] + [\text{EnH}] + [\text{EnH}_2] + [\text{EnS}] + [\text{EnHS}] + [\text{EnH}_2\text{S}]$$

$$= \frac{K_{bEn}[\text{EnH}]}{[\text{H}^+]} + [\text{EnH}] + \frac{[\text{EnH}][\text{H}^+]}{K_{aEn}} + \frac{K_{bEnS}[\text{EnHS}]}{[\text{H}^+]}$$

$$+ [\text{EnHS}] + \frac{[\text{EnHS}][\text{H}^+]}{K_{aEnS}}$$

$$= [\text{EnH}]\underbrace{\left\{\frac{K_{bEn}}{[\text{H}^+]} + 1 + \frac{[\text{H}^+]}{K_{aEn}}\right\}}_{x} + [\text{EnHS}]\underbrace{\left\{\frac{K_{bEnS}}{[\text{H}^+]} + 1 + \frac{[\text{H}^+]}{K_{aEnS}}\right\}}_{y}$$

$$= [\text{EnH}]x + [\text{EnHS}]y, \text{ or, by transposition,}$$

$$[\text{EnHS}] = \frac{[\text{En}]_t - [\text{EnH}]x}{y}$$

Since $[\text{S}]\rangle\rangle[\text{En}]_t$, the latter expression simplifies to

$$[\text{EnHS}] = [\text{En}]_t/y$$

At the start of the reaction the velocity, v (or $k_3[\text{EnHS}]$, see Chapter 8), will equal the maximum initial velocity, V.

$$v = k_3[\text{EnHS}] = V = \frac{k_3[\text{En}]_t}{\dfrac{K_{bEnS}}{[\text{H}^+]} + 1 + \dfrac{[\text{H}^+]}{K_{aEnS}}}$$

By similar algebraic manipulations (2) it can be shown that the equation for the pH dependence of the Michaelis constant is:

$$K_{m\,\text{app.}} = K_m \frac{f_{En}\,p\text{H} \cdot f_S\,p\text{H}}{f_{EnS}\,p\text{H}}$$

Kirkwood (14) has derived a theory of the effect of pH on reaction rate based on fluctuation forces between protein molecules arising from fluctuations in protonic charge and charge configuration. It should also be pointed out that Gutfreund (15) has found trypsin and chymotrypsin follow an S-shaped pH curve. This would signify that only a single ionizable group is involved in the activity of these enzymes.

References

General

1. R. A. Alberty, *J. Cell. Comp. Physiol., 47*, suppl. 1, 245 (1956).
2. M. Dixon, *Biochem. J., 55,* 161 (1953).
3. K. J. Laidler, *Trans. Faraday Soc., 51,* 528 (1955).
4. M. J. Johnson, in *Respiratory Enzymes,* edited by H. A. Lardy, Burgess Publishing Co., Minneapolis, Minn. (1949).

Bibliography

5. H. Theorell, in *Discussions of the Faraday Soc.,* No. 20, p. 224 (1955).
6. E. Racker, *J. Biol. Chem., 184,* 313 (1950).
7. E. G. Krebs, personal communication.
8. R. K. Bonnichsen, and H. Theorell, *Scand. J. Clin. Lab. Inv., 3,* 58 (1951).
9. R. K. Bonnichsen, *Acta Chem. Scand., 4,* 714 (1950).
10. R. A. Alberty, R. M. Smith, and R. M. Bock, *J. Biol. Chem., 193,* 425 (1951).
11. L. Michaelis and H. Davidsohn, *Biochem. Z., 35,* 386 (1911).
12. J. B. S. Haldane, *Enzymes,* Longmans, Green and Co., London, 1930.
13. S. G. Waley, *Biochem. Biophys. Acta, 10,* 27 (1953).
14. J. G. Kirkwood, in *Discussions Faraday Soc.,* No. 20, p. 78 (1955).
15. H. Gutfreund, in *Discussions Faraday Soc.,* No. 20, p. 255 (1955).

12

Energetics

1. Introduction (References 1–11)

The subject of biological thermodynamics or "energetics" has become of great importance in biochemistry. Several articles dealing exclusively with this subject have appeared (1, 2, 3). The older articles by Lipmann (4, 5) and Kalckar (6) are still classics in this field. Considerable information of a general nature is available in the articles by Krebs *et al.* (7), in the books by Bull (8) and Clark (9), and in the reviews by Oesper (10) and Kaplan (11).

Organisms are able to live and function solely as a result of a constant supply of energy from an outside source, i.e., in the form of "foodstuffs." The biological organism is not a heat engine, and it cannot convert temperature and pressure changes into useful work. For instance, utilization of energy from the chemical reaction

$$C_6H_{12}O_6 + 6O_2 \rightleftharpoons 6CO_2 + 6H_2O + energy$$

must be achieved by chemical reactions designed to trap the energy released. *The chemical reactions involved in this constant flow of energy are catalyzed by enzymes.* This statement holds true for plants, microorganisms, and animals. A study of the over-all energy changes occurring during biochemical reactions provides an intimate knowledge of metabolic pathways and life processes. A further association with enzymology lies, as we shall see, in the usefulness of the principles of energetics in predicting whether or not a particular reaction is thermodynamically probable. The energetic properties of a system give information on how completely a given reaction may proceed; the enzyme, in dilute solution, acts only as a catalyst to hasten attainment of the equilibrium dictated by the laws of thermodynamics. Enzymes cannot catalyze energetically unfavorable reactions; to do so would be to perform miracles!

135

2. Fundamental Concepts and Terms

The first law of thermodynamics will be useful in the following discussion. It states that *the sum of all energies in an isolated system remains constant.*

Energy may be expressed in several different quantities, such as heat and work. However, whereas work can be completely converted to heat, heat cannot be converted completely to work. It has become the custom to express all forms of energy in terms of heat units, or calories.

Heat that is released or absorbed by a reaction at constant pressure is termed the *heat of reaction,* ΔH. It is equal to: ΣH products $-\Sigma H$ reactants. When the products contain less heat than the reactants, the sign of the ΔH is negative. Thus the burning of carbohydrate has a negative heat of reaction, $-\Delta H$.

The energy of a reaction which is available for the performance of useful work is designated as *free energy,* or ΔF. Energetically, reactions may be classed as either *exergonic* or *endergonic.* *Exergonic reactions have a negative ΔF and tend to proceed spontaneously, such as hydrolytic reactions.* On the other hand, *an endergonic reaction, with a positive ΔF, must be coupled with an exergonic (i.e., with a negative ΔF) reaction in order to proceed spontaneously. Many synthetic reactions fall into this category.*

At first glance it might appear that a reaction with a positive ΔF cannot take place at all. Many such reactions, however, are known to occur in nature. The reason they can occur lies in the fact that living organisms provide a coupling mechanism whereby the energy of an exergonic process "drives" a normally endergonic reaction. Another means whereby endergonic reactions might proceed as written would be the selective separation of the product, perhaps behind a membrane, or compartment, from the site of the reaction. Still another device used by nature may be the formation of stable enzyme-substrate compounds with the product. The last possibility has been implicated by Theorell (12) in his studies on ethanol oxidation. A large negative value for ΔF does not imply a rapid reaction since the actual rate is modified by other properties of the system and by the catalyst.

The difference between ΔH and ΔF for the oxidation of 1 mole of glucose under approximately physiological conditions is some 15,000 calories (8). This additional energy resulting from the completely efficient oxidation of the glucose is termed the *reversible heat of reaction* since it represents the additional calories which pass into or out of a reaction proceeding at maximum efficiency. For the oxidation of glucose, ΔF has a negative value some 15,000 calories greater than the ΔH. The reversible heat of reaction divided by the absolute temperature is equal to the change in *entropy*, ΔS. Entropy has been defined as "a measure of the number of possible configurations of a system having a given energy" (8).

The relationship between ΔF, ΔH, and ΔS is given by

$$\Delta F = \Delta H - T \,\Delta S$$

Sometimes the entropy factor $T \,\Delta S$ is negligible so that the magnitude of ΔH approaches that of ΔF. This approximation is of historical interest in enzymology since certain compounds with very large heats of hydrolysis were discovered during the intensive research on muscle contraction around 1930. See Section 7, Chapter 12.

3. Relationship between the Equilibrium Constant and Free-Energy Change

In any reaction, such as $A + B \rightleftharpoons C + D$, the free-energy change at a given temperature is described by the relation

$$\Delta F = \Delta F^{\circ} + RT \ln \frac{[C][D]}{[A][B]}$$

where the concentrations are those in the steady state.[1] The term ΔF°, a constant for the reaction, is named the *standard free-energy change*. When the reactants are all present at "unit" concentration (molal for solutes, 1 atmosphere for gases, pure liquids, or solids), $\Delta F = \Delta F^{\circ}$. The necessity for having such a constant for any reaction is apparent, since we cannot record ΔF for all possible concentrations of reactants and products.

A reaction which has reached the equilibrium point is interchanging reactant and product molecules at the same rate. At equilibrium there is no change in concentration, and ΔF is zero. From the equation

$$\Delta F^{\circ} = -RT \ln K_{eq}$$

[1] That is, this is the change in free energy when 1 mole of A and 1 mole of B react to form 1 mole of C and 1 mole of D without changing the concentrations of any of these substances. If A, B, C, and D are in equilibrium, $\Delta F = 0$, and this equation reduces to

$$0 = \Delta F^{\circ} + RT \ln \frac{[C]_{eq}[D]_{eq}}{[A]_{eq}[B]_{eq}}$$
$$= \Delta F^{\circ} + RT \ln K_{eq}$$
$$\Delta F^{\circ} = -RT \ln K_{eq}$$

if we change to common logs and select 25°, we obtain

$$\Delta F^\circ = -1.98 \times 298 \times 2.3 \times \log_{10} K_{eq}$$

$$= -1370 \log_{10} K_{eq}$$

This simple expression provides a convenient way to obtain ΔF° from an experimentally measurable quantity, K_{eq}. The relationship of K_{eq} to ΔF° at 25° is seen from the tabulated figures. Some of the

K_{eq}	ΔF°
100	−2740
10	−1370
1	0
0.1	+1370
0.01	+2740

experimental conditions and pitfalls will be discussed in Section 9, Chapter 12.

4. Relationship between pH and Free-Energy Change

We have already noted several instances in which the equilibrium position of a reaction is dependent on pH. Such reactions will similarly exhibit a pH dependent-free energy change. As an illustration, we might consider the hydrolysis of ethyl acetate as a function of pH.

At pH < 3

$$CH_3COOC_2H_5 \quad + H_2O \rightleftharpoons CH_3COOH + C_2H_5OH$$

But at pH > 7

$$CH_3COOC_2H_5 + H_2O \rightleftharpoons CH_3COO^- + H^+ + C_2H_5OH$$

Thus at values greater than about pH 7 one full equivalent of acid is produced and, at 25°, some −1370 calories must be added to the apparent free energy change for every unit increase in pH.

In the biochemical literature many values quoted as ΔF° have been calculated through the use of apparent equilibrium constants, the latter sometimes measured at an unspecified pH. Since ΔF° refers to the standard state of 1 molal, this symbol should, strictly speaking, be reserved for a pH of zero. Since this pH is physiologically unrealistic, the symbol $\Delta F'$ is used to indicate that all solutes are in the standard state except the hydrogen ion. Thus $\Delta F'$, which is the *apparent free-energy change*, should always bear the additional designation of pH.

Carpenter (73) has suggested the use of what he has named the "un-ionized compound convention" as a designation for the free-energy

change in hydrolytic reactions. Fig. 12.1 depicts the strong pH dependence of the free-energy change of hydrolysis of ATP in the region
of physiological hydrogen ion concentration.

The possible binding of cations other than the hydrogen ion should

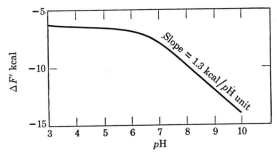

Fig. 12.1. Free energy of hydrolysis of ATP as a function of pH. Adapted from
Alberty *et al.* (37).

not be overlooked. Many of the enzymes which act on phosphorus-
containing substrates require magnesium for activity. In kinase reactions, for example, the presence of this cofactor will affect the equilibrium of the reaction since the metal ion binds much more strongly
to ATP than to ADP.

5. Relationship between the Oxidation-Reduction Potential and Free-Energy Change

The work performed by a reaction in which a transfer of electrons
occurs may be described in terms of the potential difference or electromotive force. All oxidation-reduction reactions, of which there are
many in nature, may be so described. The equation relating ΔF to
electromotive force is $\Delta F = -n\mathrm{F}E$ where n is the number of electrons
taking part in the reaction and F is the faraday (23,068 calories per
volt equivalent). E is the potential or experimentally measured
quantity. More will be said about the fundamental concepts of oxidation-reduction reactions in Chapter 13.

6. The Coupling Mechanism

All animals and many other living organisms depend on the oxidation of carbohydrate as their main source of energy. We have seen
that there must be a chemical method for trapping the energy of this
reaction since organisms must function under conditions of constant
temperature and pressure. The question we wish to examine here is

how energy can be trapped from an exergonic process and made to do useful work. (See Chapter 24.)

The only manner in which chemical energy can be transferred from one reaction to another is via a common reactant (1). Consider the reactions

I $A \rightleftharpoons B$ $K_{eq\ I}$ = 1000, $\Delta F°$ = -4110 cal

II $B \rightleftharpoons C$ $K_{eq\ II}$ = 0.1, $\Delta F°$ = $+1370$ cal

In the discussion that follows we will assume that the catalysts for these two reactions are present. Considering first the *separate reactions*, it will be seen that for the first reaction the ratio [B]/[A], i.e., in any concentration units such as number of molecules, will be 1000/1 at equilibrium. In the second reaction the ratio [C]/[B] will be 1/10 or 100/1000 at equilibrium. Thus for each molecule of A there will be 100 of C, and the equilibrium constant of the *mixed reaction*, [C]/[A], will be 100. This is more succinctly shown by

$$K_{eq}\ \text{over-all} = K_{eq\ I} \times K_{eq\ II} = 1000 \times 0.1 = 100$$

The $\Delta F°$ for the over-all reaction is, at 25°, -1370×2, or -2740 cal. The reaction is exergonic, and A is thereby converted into C. Here we have employed the common reactant B as a bridge over which the energy of the exergonic process $A \rightleftharpoons B$ has been used to "drive" the endergonic reaction $B \rightleftharpoons C$. That reaction could not proceed to any great extent in the absence of the reaction $A \rightleftharpoons B$.

This is certainly the main mechanism used by nature to carry out the many endergonic reactions required in life. However, suppose that, in the separate reaction II above, 22 molecules of B were initially present, and C was totally absent. At equilibrium there would be 2 molecules of C per 20 of B. If a molecule of C diffused through a membrane impermeable to B, the equilibrium constant would demand that approximately one further molecule of B should be converted to C. The possible spatial separation of reactants and products *in vivo* has not received sufficient attention in the past.

7. Nature of the Coupling Mechanism

In 1927 Eggleton and Eggleton (13) and two years later Fiske and Subbarow (14) isolated creatine phosphate from muscle. Meyerhof and Suranyi (15) measured the heat of enzymatic decomposition of this compound and found it to be large. This fact indicated that the free energy of hydrolysis might also be large.

$$\begin{array}{c} \text{O} \\ \text{H} \uparrow \\ \text{HN}{=}\text{CN}{\sim}\overset{|}{\text{P}}\text{OH} \\ \overset{|}{\text{NH}} \quad \overset{|}{\text{OH}} \quad \overset{|}{\text{NH}_2} \\ \overset{|}{\text{CH}_2}\text{CH}_2\text{CH}_2\overset{|}{\text{CH}}\text{COOH} \\ \text{Arginine phosphate} \end{array} \qquad \begin{array}{c} \text{O} \\ \text{H} \uparrow \\ \text{HN}{=}\text{CN}{\sim}\overset{|}{\text{P}}\text{OH} \\ \overset{|}{\text{OH}} \\ \overset{|}{\text{N}}{-}\text{CH}_3 \\ \overset{|}{\text{CH}_2}\text{COOH} \\ \text{Creatine phosphate} \end{array}$$

The next important development, due to Lundsgaard (16), showed that iodoacetate-poisoned muscle tissue is still capable of contraction. Iodoacetate is believed to act by alkylation of the sulfhydryl groups of glyceraldehyde phosphate dehydrogenase. The poison is so tightly bound that the reaction goes essentially to completion (17). This

$$\underset{\text{Active enzyme}}{\text{RSH}} + \underset{\text{Iodoacetate}}{\text{I CH}_2\text{COOH}} \rightleftharpoons \underset{\text{Inactive enzyme}}{\text{RSCH}_2\text{COOH}} + \text{HI}$$

enzyme catalyzes one of the main energy-yielding steps in glycolysis, and the question at once arose as to the source of energy for contraction of the iodoacetate-poisoned muscle. Lundsgaard then showed that creatine phosphate disappeared from the iodoacetate-poisoned muscle during the contraction process. This experiment indicated that the mysterious energy source resided in the new phosphorus-containing compound itself.

The key compound was isolated in 1929. In that year Lohmann (18) obtained adenosine triphosphate, ATP, from muscle. In subsequent years he proved its structure and demonstrated its stepwise degradation to adenosine diphosphate and adenylic acid. *This substance has proved to be the common reactant which appears in plants, microorganisms, and animals to trap the energy of exergonic reactions. The energy acquired is used to drive endergonic processes of life.*

The ATP which is formed, for example, in the oxidation of carbohydrate, is not stored as such. Rather it is placed in a reserve pool of energy-rich compounds known as the "phosphagens." These substances are phosphocreatine in vertebrates and arginine phosphate in the invertebrates. The reaction for the synthesis of a phosphagen is

Adenosine–5′– triphosphate, ATP
Less 1 phosphate, adenosine–5′– diphosphate, ADP
Less 2 phosphates, adenosine–5′– monophosphate, AMP

known as the "Lohmann reaction," since Lohmann first demonstrated these substances to exist in equilibrium with ATP. The equilibrium constant of this reaction is not far from unity (64), and hence

$$\text{Creatine} + \text{ATP} \rightleftharpoons \text{ADP} + \text{Creatine phosphate}$$

$\Delta F°$ is also small. This means that the energy of ATP has been smoothly transferred over to creatine phosphate. It also means that the reaction can be tipped back and forth with relative ease, depending on the concentration of the reaction partners. *In this manner the energy of metabolism is stored in the phosphagen and doled out through ATP for direct utilization in a myriad of endergonic reactions.*

Other phosphagens of as yet unknown structure may perhaps be uncovered (19). The metaphosphate of certain microorganisms may serve this purpose (20).

In 1954 a new series of nucleoside pyrophosphates was discovered. In 1949, James T. Park and M. J. Johnson (21, 22) had found that labile phosphate compounds accumulated in the cells of *Staphylococcus aureus* grown in the presence of penicillin. Leloir and others have implicated derivatives of these compounds, the uridine-5′-phosphates, as important components of coenzymes (23–25) and as intermediates in nucleic acid biosynthesis (26), energy transfer (27), and photosynthesis (28). The isolation of uridine-5′-triphosphate from yeast has been achieved by Lipton, Morell, Frieden, and Bock (29). The chemical properties of these compounds in many ways resemble those of the adenosine phosphates, but full details on their biological properties are not yet complete.

Cytidine-5′-triphosphate, CTP
Less one phosphate, cytidine-5′-diphosphate, CDP
Less two phosphates, cytidine-5′-monophosphate, CMP

Uridine-5′-triphosphate, UTP
Less 1 phosphate, uridine-5′-diphosphate, UDP
Less 2 phosphates, uridine-5′-monophosphate, UMP

The mono-, di-, and triphosphates of adenosine, cytidine, guanosine and uridine have been found in natural materials (57). The Pabst Brewing Co. of Milwaukee has prepared an attractive brochure (Circular OR-10, January 1956) which sets forth the spectral and other properties of these important substances. In summary it might

OH

$$\text{HOP}\!\sim\!\text{OP}\!\sim\!\text{OP}\!-\!\text{OCH}_2$$

(with O, O, O above the three P atoms with downward arrows, and OH, OH, OH below)

Guanosine-5′-triphosphate, GTP
Less one phosphate, guanosine-5′-diphosphate, GDP
Less two phosphates, guanosine-5′-monophosphate, GMP

be stated that although ATP appears to be the most usual common reactant, specific roles for UTP, CTP and GTP have been found in sugar metabolism in plants, in phospholipid biosynthesis and in the oxidation of α-keto glutarate, respectively.

The essential role of phosphorus as a nutrient for living organisms had been recognized for many years. Its connection with energy-transferring mechanisms dates from around the turn of the century, when the Büchner brothers first became interested in obtaining protein from yeast for therapeutic purposes. They elected to preserve their cell-free extracts in concentrated sugar solutions and were surprised to observe that the extracts fermented the sugar. This extraction of the fermentation enzymes from yeast was important in that it refuted Pasteur's "vitalistic" theory that life and fermentation were inseparable. Harden and Young (30) in 1905 found that fermentation of sugar by Büchner extracts of yeast could be greatly accelerated by the addition of phosphoric acid, and they were able to prove that the inorganic phosphate became esterified. In the years that followed, a large number of sugar esters of phosphate, bearing the name of their discoverer, appeared in the biochemical literature.

8. Free-Energy Levels

It will be noted that the pyrophosphate bonds in ATP were designated as $\sim$, indicating them to be different from ordinary phosphate ester bonds. This symbol was introduced by Lipmann (4) to show that such chemical bonds liberate relatively large amounts of free energy on hydrolysis; i.e., they are "high-energy bonds." The symbol is now also used for other high-energy bonds not involving phosphate. Although Lipmann's original classification is an oversimplification, it is still of great help in segregating metabolic intermediates according to their energy levels. The following discussion will be concerned with bond hydrolysis energies of the low, intermediate, and high types.

It should be stressed that this method of referring to bond energy is opposite to that in common usage in physical chemistry. Since the energy level is a property of the whole molecule rather than a single bond it might be preferable to designate a compound such as ATP an "energy-rich" material. Biochemists have been reluctant to abandon these terms, in spite of the confusion which their use engenders, and hence there is a constant appearance of new designations for this concept. Klotz (3), for example, prefers the term "group transfer potential."

Extensive tables of free-energy data for biologically important compounds are given in the papers by Krebs and his associates (61, 7).

A. *Compounds of Low Hydrolysis Energy.* An "ordinary" ester such as that between an alcohol and a carboxylic or phosphoric acid belongs to the low-energy class. Such esters are relatively stable to heat, acid, and the usual laboratory manipulations. It may seem somewhat anomalous that such stable compounds should be regarded as low in energy. However, we are interested here in how much energy is released from the *hydrolysis* of such substances, and if much work has to be done on them to initiate this hydrolysis, the net gain in work will be small.

The following reaction is slightly exergonic, owing mostly to the

$$\text{Ordinary ester} + H_2O \rightleftharpoons \text{Alcohol} + \text{Acid}$$

large concentration of water normally present. The $-\Delta F'$ for such a reaction at neutral pH is of the order of 2000 to 3000 calories. Table 12.1 lists some of the naturally occurring ordinary phosphate esters

Table 12.1.   Some Naturally Occurring Phosphate Esters and Their $\Delta F'$ of Hydrolysis (31, 44, 7)

Compound	Synonym	$\Delta F'$, kcal (pH 8.5)
α-Glycerophosphate	Karrer ester	-2.2 (38°)
Glyceric acid-2-phosphate	Meyerhof-Kiessling ester	-4 (30°)
Glyceric acid-3-phosphate	Nilsson ester	-3 (30°)
Glucose-6-phosphate	Robison ester	-3 (38°)
Fructose-6-phosphate	Neuberg ester	-3 (38°)

the $\Delta F'$ of hydrolysis of which has been recorded. These measurements were made by Meyerhof with the aid of a phosphatase enzyme (31, 44). Although chemically rather stable, these esters are subject to hydrolysis by the phosphatase enzymes, which are ubiquitous in nature (Chapter 18). The physiological role of the ordinary or low-energy phosphate esters is no doubt manifold. The attachment of phosphate to the carbohydrate molecule during fermentation alters a specificity phenomenon whereby ordinary unphosphorylated carbohydrate remains quite stable in tissues. Once the carbohydrate is phosphorylated it is easily attacked by enzymes and fermented. The union of phosphorus with the carbohydrate molecule mobilizes the phosphate group and places it in the "ready" position to receive the energy of carbohydrate oxidation. This is probably the main function of the phosphate esters listed in Table 12.1.

Phosphorylation of substances is known to affect their selectivity to diffusion through cell walls and membranes, an important aspect of metabolic reactions. The water solubility of compounds containing phosphorus is exceedingly great; e.g., Zetterström and Ljunggren (32) have been able to bring vitamin D into aqueous solution by making the ester.

Mono- and diester phosphates will have two and one ionizable hydroxyl groups, respectively. When only one acid group is present, it will have a pKa between 1.5 and 2.5 while the secondary phosphates will have a dissociation around pH 6.5. The ionization of these compounds may be of significance in their electrostatic attraction for positively charged groups. Thus the presence of phosphate may be important in the attachment of these esters to enzyme proteins. It is noteworthy that they are all stronger acids than the parent orthophosphate (Table 12.2). Thus the free energy of hydrolysis will always be to some extent pH dependent in the region of the secondary phosphoryl ionization.

Table 12.2. Secondary Phosphoryl Dissociation Constants of Some Phosphate Esters

Compound	pKa, secondary	Reference
Phosphoric acid	6.81	33
α-Glycerophosphate	6.44	33
2-Phosphoryl D-glyceric acid	6.48	34
3-Phosphoryl D-glyceric acid	5.98	33
Glucose-1-phosphate	6.13	35
Glucose-6-phosphate	6.11	36
Fructose-6-phosphate	6.11	36
Adenosine diphosphate	6.26	37
Adenosine triphosphate	6.48	37
Pyridoxal-5-phosphate	6.20	56

The dissociation constants of phosphate vary somewhat with salt concentration, and hence the data in Table 12.2 are satisfied only under specified conditions. Table 12.3 gives some pKa values obtained by Alberty (74) for the titration of adenosine phosphates with a variety of bases.

Table 12.3.   pKa′ Values for the Terminal Phosphate Group of the Adenosine-5′-Phosphates at 25° and 0.2 Ionic Strength (74)

Cation Compound	$(C_3H_7)_4N^+$	$(C_2H_5)_4N^+$	$(CH_3)_4N^+$	K^+	Na^+	Li^+
AMP	6.45 ± 0.02	6.45 ± 0.02	6.40 ± 0.02	6.32 ± 0.02	6.29 ± 0.02	6.19 ± 0.02
ADP	6.68 ± 0.02	6.68 ± 0.02	6.02 ± 0.02	6.40 ± 0.02	6.36 ± 0.02	6.10 ± 0.02
ATP	6.95 ± 0.02	6.91 ± 0.02	6.76 ± 0.02	6.48 ± 0.02	6.41 ± 0.02	5.98 ± 0.02
AQP	7.26 ± 0.12	7.14 ± 0.12	6.84 ± 0.12	6.57 ± 0.12	6.43 ± 0.12	5.92 ± 0.12
predicted						
AQP	7.27 ± 0.02	7.23 ± 0.02	7.06 ± 0.02	6.58 ± 0.02	6.46 ± 0.02	6.04 ± 0.02
experimental						

It has become apparent that the phosphate radical is capable of intramolecular migration from one alcohol group to another, probably through the cyclic intermediate (38).

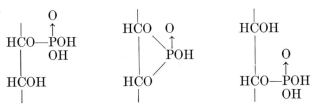

B. *Compounds of Intermediate Hydrolysis Energy.*   The common representatives of this class are the hemiacetal C—O—P containing glucose-1-phosphate and the glycosides. Data for this class are given in Table 12.4. Glycosides are of very general occurrence in nature,

Table 12.4.   The Free Energy of Hydrolysis of Some Compounds of Intermediate Energy

Compound	Synonym	pH	Temperature, °C	ΔF, kcal	Reference
Glucose-1-phosphate	Cori ester	—	—	−5.0	10
D-Glucose-1-fructoside	Sucrose	6.6	30°	−6.5	39

but the ΔF of hydrolysis has been measured for only a few such compounds. The experiments of Doudoroff, Barker, and Hassid (40) with bacterial sucrose phosphorylase have introduced the concept of a higher-energy enzyme-substrate intermediate. The series of reactions postulated by them is

Glucose-1-phosphate + Enzyme ⇌ Glucosyl · Enzyme + H_3PO_4

Glucosyl · Enzyme + Fructose ⇌ Sucrose + Enzyme

The energy of the glucose-1-phosphate bond is preserved in the glucosyl·enzyme complex, and this is subsequently used in the formation of the intermediate-energy glycosidic bond of sucrose. Several monosaccharides could be used in place of fructose as the glucose acceptor.

This reaction is referred to as a "transglucosidation," and the enzymes that promote these catalyses are termed "transglucosidases" (Chapter 18).

C. *Compounds of High Hydrolysis Energy.* Several compounds are now known which have bond energies of the order of −10,000 or more calories. Most, but not all, of these compounds contain phosphorus. They are in general quite unstable to dilute alkali, heat, and acid. Their large −ΔF of hydrolysis is in some ways associated with this lability. For example, the vigorous acetylating agents acetic anhydride and acetyl chloride are similarly unstable. Table 12.5 sum-

Table 12.5. The Approximate Free Energy of Hydrolysis of Some Compounds of Higher Energy (10, 7)

Compound	Bond Type	pH	Temperature, °C	$\Delta F'$,* kcal	Reference
Adenosine triphosphate	Pyrophosphate	7.0	30	−7 to −8	60
Adenosine diphosphate	Pyrophosphate	—	—	similar to ATP?	7
Pyrophosphate, inorganic	Pyrophosphate	7.5	—	−8.9	7
Creatine phosphate	Guanidino phosphate	7.7 to 9.8	20	−9†	10
Acetyl phosphate	Acyl phosphate	—	37	−12†	10
1,3-diphosphoryl D-glyceric acid	Acyl phosphate	6.9	25	−12†	10
Phosphoryl enolpyruvate	Enol phosphate	8.5	25	−12†	5
Acetyl coenzyme A	Thiol ester	7.2	22	−8.2	41, 63
Carbamyl phosphate		—	—		65
Adenyl carbonate	Acid anhydride	—	—	Comparable to ATP?	70
Adenyl acetate		—	—		66
Adenyl amino acids		—	—		67, 68
Adenyl sulfate		—	—		69

* Unless otherwise designated, a physiological pH is to be assumed.
† Corrected by use of $\Delta F'$, pH 7, of −7 to −8 kcal for ATP.

marizes the bond hydrolysis energies of compounds of the high-energy class.

Inorganic pyrophosphate itself contains a high-energy grouping, and this fact suggests that the accumulation of metaphosphate in certain organisms is an energy-storing mechanism (20). ATP contains two such pyrophosphate bonds and a third ordinary ester phosphate bond. Under conditions of high-carbohydrate and low-nitrogen nutrition, yeast can be made to accumulate relatively large amounts of ATP. Pabst Brewing Company employs this approach in its commercial preparation of the compound. Although the dry powder is relatively stable, dilute alkali at 100° rapidly splits the pyrophosphate bonds. In 1 N HCl at 100° the pyrophosphate bonds of ATP and ADP are broken in 7 minutes; this is the so-called "7-minute phosphorus." The ordinary ester bond of the AMP is considerably more stable and belongs to the low-energy grouping.

A discussion of the high energy content of the pyrophosphate bonds will be reserved for the following section. It should be noted that this bond is present in several coenzymes such as the pyridine nucleotides, coenzyme A, and thiamine pyrophosphate.

The guanidino phosphates have already been discussed to some extent. Proof that the hydrolysis energy of creatine phosphate is close to that of ATP was provided by the equilibrium measurements of Lehmann (42) for the Lohmann reaction. He found the equilibrium constant to be close to unity, so that the reaction as written is slightly endergonic, and creatine phosphate therefore contains of the order of 1000 calories more energy than ATP. It is generally conceded that, from the standpoint of their mechanism of action, the hydrolysis energies of the phosphagens must be close to that of ATP.

Acetyl phosphate, which was discovered by Lipmann during his study of the bacterial oxidation of pyruvate (5), and 1,3-diphosphoryl D-glyceric acid are of somewhat higher energy than the phosphagens or the adenosine polyphosphates. The high energy content of acetyl phosphate is readily apparent from a comparison of the equilibria of the (I) *hydroclastic* and (II) *phosphoroclastic* splitting of pyruvic acid. The first reaction is exergonic and proceeds to the right with a large $-\Delta F'$. The phosphoroclastic reaction on the other hand, is only

I $\quad$ CH₃COCOOH + H₂O ⇌ CH₃COOH + HCOOH

II $\quad$ CH₃COCOOH + H₃PO₄ ⇌ CH₃C(=O)O~P(=O)(OH)OH + HCOOH

slightly exergonic because the energy is preserved in the acyl phosphate compound. A further indication of the higher energy of acetyl phosphate is the fact that $\Delta F'$ at neutral pH for the reaction

CH₃—C(=O)—O~P(=O)(OH)—OH + ADP ⇌ CH₃COOH + ATP

is about -3000 calories (5). This would place the $\Delta F'$ for acetyl phosphate this amount over ATP.

With regard to the other acyl phosphate, the Negelein-Brömel ester, similar considerations hold. Bücher (43) crystallized phosphoglyceric acid transphosphorylase from yeast in 1947. This enzyme transfers the phosphate from the acyl compound to ADP.

1,3-Diphosphoryl D-glyceric acid + ADP ⇌

$\qquad$ 3-Phosphoryl D-glyceric acid + ATP

The K_{app} is 3300, corresponding to $\Delta F' = -4600$ calories. The diphosphoryl D-glyceric acid apparently yields this quantity of energy over that in ATP.

Phosphoryl enolpyruvate, often called the Lohmann-Meyerhof ester, may also be equilibrated with ADP according to the reaction

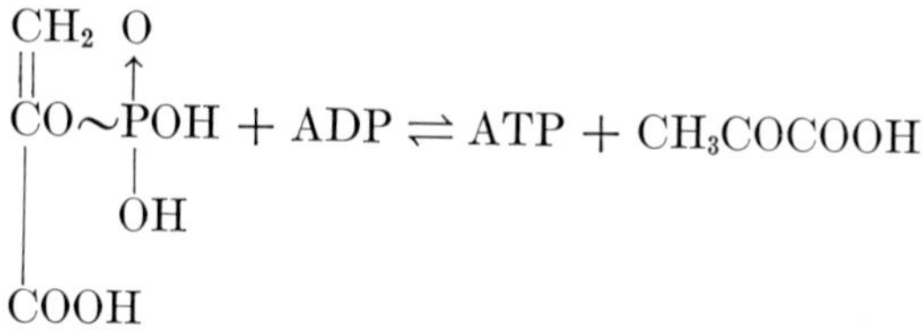

$$
\begin{array}{c}
CH_2 \quad O \\
\| \quad \uparrow \\
CO{\sim}POH + ADP \rightleftharpoons ATP + CH_3COCOOH \\
| \\
OH \\
| \\
COOH
\end{array}
$$

The $\Delta F'$ of -4300 calories suggests that it contains about this much more free energy than ATP (44).

The acetylation coenzyme, CoA (F. Lipmann, Nobel Prize 1953), was isolated in its acetylated form by Lynen (45). He suggested that the compound, acetyl CoA, was a new high-energy substance of the type CoAS $\sim$ COCH$_3$. Stadtman (46) studied the reaction

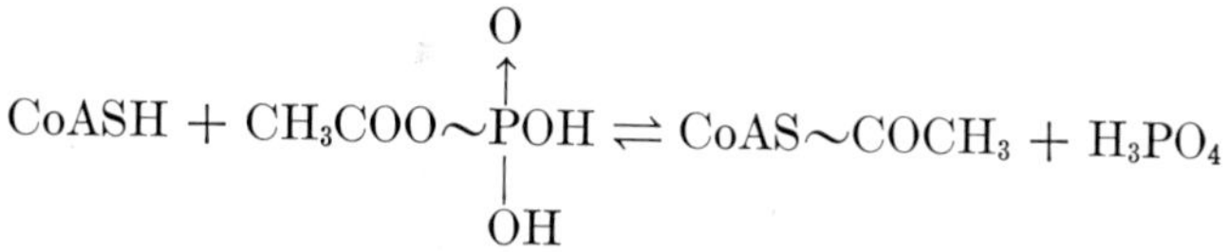

$$
\begin{array}{c}
O \\
\uparrow \\
CoASH + CH_3COO{\sim}POH \rightleftharpoons CoAS{\sim}COCH_3 + H_3PO_4 \\
| \\
OH
\end{array}
$$

with the enzyme phosphotransacetylase. Under the experimental conditions used the K_{eq} was 60 M, corresponding to $\Delta F'$ of -3000 calories. Assuming the value of about 12,000 calories for acetyl phosphate, about 9000 calories must have been retained in the acetyl CoA compound.

According to the Lipmann report (47), acetyl imidazole, thiamine, and certain other compounds are on the energy-rich level. Lipmann et al. (65) registered yet another important advance when they identified carbamyl phosphate

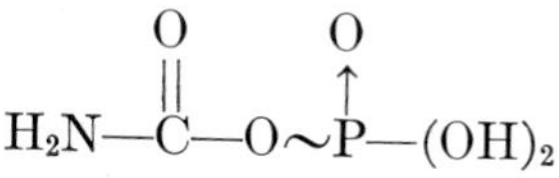

$$
\begin{array}{c}
O \qquad O \\
\| \qquad \uparrow \\
H_2N{-}C{-}O{\sim}P{-}(OH)_2
\end{array}
$$

as an "energy rich" compound. Also, several adenyl anhydrides of the structure shown below have been prepared from ATP. Binkley (62) has synthesized S-phosphocysteine. Compounds of this type may occur as intermediates during the action of such enzymes as the phosphokinases.

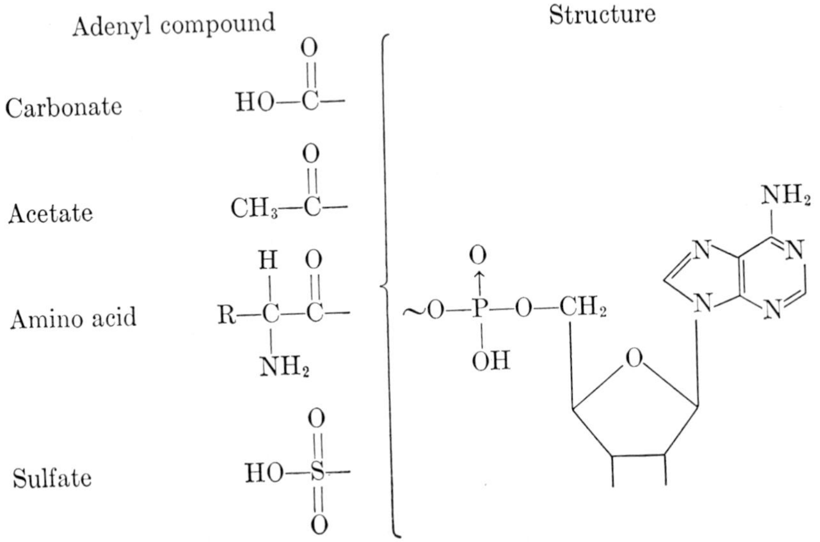

Adenyl compound	Structure

Carbonate $HO-\overset{\overset{\displaystyle O}{\|}}{C}-$

Acetate $CH_3-\overset{\overset{\displaystyle O}{\|}}{C}-$

Amino acid $R-\underset{\underset{\displaystyle NH_2}{\|}}{\overset{\overset{\displaystyle H}{\|}}{C}}-\overset{\overset{\displaystyle O}{\|}}{C}-$

$\sim O-\overset{\overset{\displaystyle O}{\uparrow}}{\underset{\underset{\displaystyle OH}{\|}}{P}}-O-CH_2$

Sulfate $HO-\overset{\overset{\displaystyle O}{\|}}{\underset{\underset{\displaystyle O}{\|}}{S}}-$

9. Determination of Free Energy of Hydrolysis

The $\Delta F°$ of hydrolysis of the low-energy-type compounds may be measured directly from the equilibrium constant. Kay (48) studied the hydrolysis of glycerol phosphate with phosphatase. The equilibrium constant was found to be close enough to unity to permit it to be measured directly from the catalyzed reaction. Here the convention

$$\text{Glycerophosphate} + H_2O \rightleftharpoons \text{Glycerol} + H_3PO_4$$

$$K_{eq} = \frac{[\text{Glycerol}][H_3PO_4]}{[\text{Glycerophosphate}][H_2O]}$$

is to multiply the equilibrium constant by 55.5 or 55.6, the molar concentration of pure water (see Section 10, this chapter, and reference 31). This amounts to omitting $[H_2O]$ from the equilibrium expression.

There are obvious experimental difficulties in the determination of very large or small values of K_{eq}, and in practice it will not be possible to measure values greater or less than about 10^5 or 10^{-5}. The use of isotopically labeled reactants has an advantage in that radioactivity measurements are more sensitive than other forms of analysis.

The investigation of the free energy of hydrolysis of the "energy-rich" compounds is therefore inherently more difficult. If we had a good and reliable method for obtaining a value on only one compound with $\Delta F°$ of 8 to 12 kilocalories then this substance could be equilibrated with all of the unknown "energy rich" compounds (provided of course that the proper enzymes were available). We have seen that

and therefore experimentally determinable. That is, once we have reliable data on the free energy of one high-energy compound, data on other high-energy compounds can be obtained provided that we have some means of equilibrating the reactants. We have already seen how this principle has been applied in measuring $\Delta F'$ for 1,3-diphosphoryl D-glyceric acid and other phosphorus-containing compounds which were equilibrated with a "standard," in this case ATP.

Values for the free energy of hydrolysis of ATP have ranged from an early estimate of -12 kcal at pH 7.8 to -7 kcal at pH 7.0 (59). Recently, Robbins and Boyer (60) made a relatively direct measurement through the use of the hexokinase reaction.

$$\text{ATP} + \text{Glucose} \overset{\text{Hexokinase}}{\rightleftharpoons} \text{Glucose-6-phosphate} + \text{ADP}$$

$$\text{Glucose-6-phosphate} + \text{H}_2\text{O} \overset{\text{Phosphatase}}{\rightleftharpoons} \text{Glucose} + \text{H}_3\text{PO}_4$$

Sum: $\qquad \text{ATP} + \text{H}_2\text{O} \rightleftharpoons \text{ADP} + \text{H}_3\text{PO}_4$

Robbins and Boyer measured the apparent equilibrium constant of the hexokinase reaction at pH 6.0, in the presence and absence of Mg^{++}, through the use of isotopic dilution techniques. The best values were obtained with ADP and glucose-C^{14}-6-phosphate as initial reactants. Estimation of K_{app} at pH 7 for the hexokinase reaction gave a $\Delta F'$ value which, when added to that for the phosphatase reaction, amounted to -7.6 kcal for $\Delta F'$ for ATP at pH 7 and zero Mg^{++} concentration. This is considered the best value currently available for ATP and agrees quite well with other independent measurements (72).

Conversion of an acyl phosphate to a thiol ester is a mildly exergonic process. Thus:

$$\overset{\displaystyle \text{O}}{\underset{\displaystyle \text{OH}}{\overset{\uparrow}{\underset{|}{\text{CH}_3\text{COO}\sim\text{P}}}}}\text{OH} + \text{CoASH} \rightleftharpoons \text{CoAS}\sim\text{COCH}_3 + \text{H}_3\text{PO}_4$$

This reaction, catalyzed by phosphotransacetylase, has a K_{app} of 60 M corresponding to $\Delta F'$ of -3000 calories. Hence $\Delta F'$ for acetyl CoA must be about -12 kcal (the value for acetyl phosphate) less this amount, or roughly -9 kcal calories (46).

A related equilibrium method is the coupling of the unknown, very exergonic reaction to a very endergonic process involving a common reactant. This technique has also been used to obtain the $\Delta F'$ of the acetyl mercaptide bond of acetyl CoA, $\text{CoAS} \sim \text{COCH}_3$ (41).

It was stated in section 12.5 that the free-energy change could be estimated from potential measurements and the equation $\Delta F = -n\text{F}\,\Delta E$. Such determinations are, of course, restricted to oxidation-reduction reactions. Kaplan (11) has given the oxidation of pyruvic acid as an example of this method for obtaining free-energy data.

Meyerhof (50) has determined the pyrophosphate bond hydrolysis energy of ATP by an interesting method in that it involves the principles of equilibrium, thermal, and oxidation-reduction data. He studied the oxidation of glyceraldehyde-3-phosphate with the simultaneous accumulation of ATP. The reaction

Glyceraldehyde-3-phosphate $+$ DPN$^+$ $+$ ADP $+$ H$_3$PO$_4$ $\rightleftharpoons$

3-Phosphoryl d-glycerate $+$ DPNH $+$ ATP $+$ 2H$^+$

was split, for purposes of calculation, into the oxidation of the aldehyde, the reduction of DPN$^+$, and the phosphorylation of ADP. The $\Delta F'$ for the various part reactions was found as follows: glyceraldehyde phosphate oxidation by thermal data, reduction of DPN$^+$ by oxidation-reduction potential calculations, and the phosphorylation of ATP by difference from the equilibrium constant of the over-all reaction measured.

10. Theory of Hydrolysis Energy

That the energy released from the hydrolysis of a stable phosphate bond is largely a result of the driving force of water may be illustrated from the original data of Kay (48). In measuring the hydrolysis of glycerol phosphate with intestinal phosphatase he obtained the following results. With an initial phosphate concentration of $7.1 \times 10^{-3}\,M$ the per cent phosphate esterified was 28 and 46 at 50% and 75% glycerol, by volume. The molar concentrations of water are 27.8 and 13.9 for the two concentrations of glycerol. This reaction will be only pH dependent in the region between pH 6 and 7 where there is a difference in the pKa_2 of glycerophosphate and H$_3$PO$_4$.

At 50% glycerol $\quad K_{eq} = \dfrac{6.84 \times 5.11 \times 10^{-3}}{1.99 \times 10^{-3} \times 27.8} = 0.63$

At 75% glycerol $\quad K_{eq} = \dfrac{10.24 \times 3.83 \times 10^{-3}}{3.27 \times 10^{-3} \times 13.9} = 0.86$

$K_{eq\,(average)} = 0.75$

From $\Delta F^\circ = -RT \ln K_{eq}$ we get, at 38°, $-4.58 \times 311 \times \log 0.75 =$ $+200$ calories. Calculated in this way the hydrolysis would be slightly endergonic as written. By correcting for the aqueous medium we obtain $\Delta F^\circ = -4.58 \times 311 \times \log (0.75 \times 55.6) = -2280$ calories. This energy is not stored in the phosphate ester; rather it represents the driving action of water.

The higher bond energies are believed to be the result of several separate effects. One factor is clearly the difference in stability between the compound and its split products. If the products are much more stable than the reactant, then the ΔF° will be a large negative value (6). Inorganic phosphate is capable of resonance between a wide variety of structures:

$$\begin{array}{ccc}
\text{O} & \text{O}^- & \text{O}^- \\
\uparrow & | & | \\
\text{HOPO}^- & \text{HOP}{\rightarrow}\text{O} & \text{HOPO}^- \\
| & | & \downarrow \\
\text{O}^- & \text{O}^- & \text{O}
\end{array}$$

and the opportunity for resonance is also very great in the ordinary phosphate esters. However, the number of resonating structures is greatly reduced in the case of pyrophosphates

$$\begin{array}{cccc}
\text{O} & \text{O} & \text{O}^- & \text{O}^- \\
\uparrow & \uparrow & | & | \\
\text{ROPO}{\sim}\text{PO}^- & & \text{ROPO}{\sim}\text{PO}^- & \\
| & | & \downarrow & \downarrow \\
\text{O}^- & \text{O}^- & \text{O} & \text{O}
\end{array}$$

Such effects are also known as "opposing resonance" (6, 51).

Hill and Morales (52) have pointed out that the instability of the pyrophosphates may in some measure be occasioned by electrostatic repulsion from the negatively charged acid groups. Still a third effect is the free energy of ionization of the groups released during hydrolysis. Phosphoryl enolpyruvate owes its instability mainly to the fact that the enolpyruvate formed can revert to the stable keto form after hydrolysis. The energy of this change is estimated to be in the range 5500 to 9000 calories. Smaller effects of opposing resonance and electrostatic repulsion are to be noted for phosphoryl enolpyruvate.

$$\begin{array}{cc}
\text{NH}_2 & \text{O} \\
\overset{+}{\underset{|}{\text{H}_2\text{N}}}{=}\text{CNH}_2 & \overset{+}{\text{H}_2\text{N}}{=}\overset{\overset{\text{H}}{|}}{\text{C}}\text{N}{\sim}\overset{\uparrow}{\underset{|}{\text{PO}^-}} \\
 & \overset{}{\underset{|}{\text{NH}}}\ \ \text{O}^- \\
 & \overset{}{\underset{}{\text{R}}}
\end{array}$$

Guanidinium   Guanidinium
ion   phosphate

The amino and guanidino phosphates are unstable by virtue of opposing resonance. The free guanidinium ion has a double bond which can exist in any one of three positions whereas in the guanido phosphates this bond is excluded from the position holding the phosphate. The acyl mercaptide bond bears a formal relation to the pyrophosphates, enolphosphates, and acyl phosphates in that all these compounds may be regarded as acid anhydrides. Again, all these substances may form acid during hydrolysis.

11. Chemical Synthesis of Some Compounds Important in Biological Energetics

The chemical synthesis of these compounds is of special interest to workers in intermediary metabolism for at least two reasons. In the first place, chemical synthesis often, but not always, places these compounds on the market at a lower cost than the natural material. Secondly, chemical synthesis is of interest from the standpoint of exact isotopic labeling and proof of structure.

As an example of the synthesis of an ordinary ester, the work of Lampson and Lardy (53) on the preparation of glucose-6-phosphate will be cited. The acetone compound of 5,6-anhydroglucose is treated with secondary potassium phosphate in aqueous solution. Hydrolytic elimination of the acetone group is achieved with HBr. This method, although perhaps not the method of choice for the synthesis of glucose-6-phosphate, is useful for placing radioactive phosphorus in the sugar molecule without first having to synthesize an organic derivative of the radioactive material.

As might be expected, synthesis of the high-energy compounds requires special approaches. After years of painstaking research, Todd (54) and his group at Cambridge succeeded in synthesizing adenosine triphosphate. In this remarkable achievement, they obtained a substance identical in every respect with the compound isolated from muscle by Lohmann some twenty years earlier. Dibenzylchlorophosphonate was used as the phosphorylating reagent, and selective intermediary partial debenzylation was obtained with the quaternizing agent N methyl morpholine. If the monodebenzylation had occurred on the adenylic acid phosphate, a branched ATP would have resulted with the following structure:

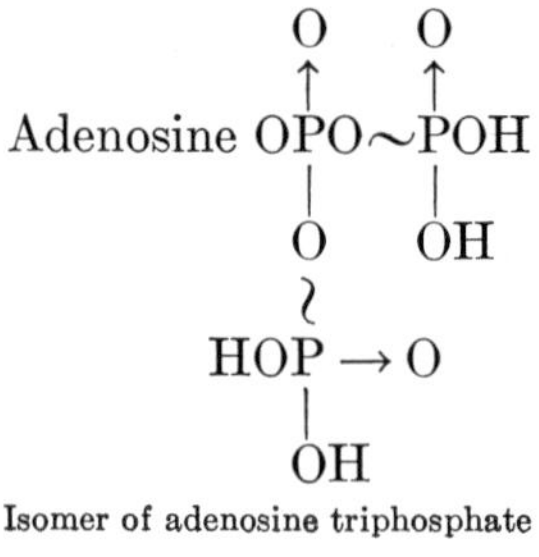

$$
\begin{array}{ccc}
& O & O \\
& \uparrow & \uparrow \\
\text{Adenosine} & OPO{\sim}POH \\
& | & | \\
& O & OH \\
& \wr & \\
& HOP & \to O \\
& | & \\
& OH & \\
\end{array}
$$

Isomer of adenosine triphosphate

This compound would have two primary and two secondary phosphoryl dissociations whereas adenosine triphosphate has only a single secondary phosphoryl dissociation. Electrometric titration of the product showed it to have the correct structure.

Khorana (55) has developed a brilliant new method for introducing a pyrophosphate group under very mild conditions. The reagent is a mixture of commercial aqueous H_3PO_4 and dicyclohexyl carbodiimide. The solvent is aqueous pyridine. The reaction is written to show the formation of a possible intermediate. This novel reaction has already

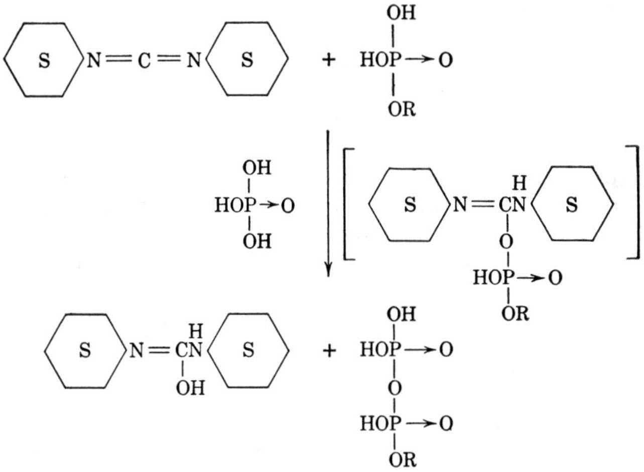

yielded ADP and ATP and should be useful in preparing coenzymes containing the pyrophosphate bond, such as flavin adenine dinucleotide, which cannot be readily obtained by isolation methods.

In seeking better yields of nucleoside pyrophosphates, both Chambers and Khorana (58) and Todd et al. (71) have adopted the use of phosphoramidic esters.

$$R\!-\!O\!-\!\overset{\displaystyle O}{\underset{\displaystyle OH}{\overset{\uparrow}{P}}}\!-\!NH_2 + HO\!-\!\overset{\displaystyle O}{\underset{\displaystyle OH}{\overset{\uparrow}{P}}}\!-\!OH \rightarrow R\!-\!O\!-\!\overset{\displaystyle O}{\underset{\displaystyle OH}{\overset{\uparrow}{P}}}\!-\!O\!-\!\overset{\displaystyle O}{\underset{\displaystyle OH}{\overset{\uparrow}{P}}}\!-\!OH + NH_3$$

References

General

1. M. J. Johnson, in *Respiratory Enzymes,* edited by H. A. Lardy, Burgess Publishing Co., Minneapolis, Minn., 1949.

2. A. B. Pardee, in *Chemical Pathways of Metabolism,* edited by D. M. Greenberg, Academic Press, N. Y., 1954.

3. I. M. Kiotz, *Energetics in Biochemical Reactions*, Academic Press. N. Y., 1957, p. 27.

4. F. Lipmann, *Advances in Enzymology, 1,* 99 (1941).

5. F. Lipmann, *Advances in Enzymology, 6,* 231 (1946).

6. H. Kalckar, *Chem. Revs., 28,* 71 (1941).

7. K. Burton and H. A. Krebs, *Biochem. J., 54,* 94 (1953); H. A. Krebs and H. L. Kornberg, *Ergebnisse der Physiologie,* III (1957).

8. H. B. Bull, *Physical Biochemistry,* second edition, John Wiley & Sons, N. Y., 1951.

9. W. M. Clark, *Topics in Physical Chemistry,* Williams and Wilkins, Baltimore, Md., 1948.

10. P. Oesper, in *Phosphorus Metabolism,* 1, edited by W. D. McElroy and B. Glass, Johns Hopkins Press, Baltimore, Md., 1951.

11. N. O. Kaplan, in *The Enzymes,* edited by J. B. Sumner and K. Myrbäck, Academic Press, N. Y., 1951.

Bibliography

12. H. Theorell and R. K. Bonnichsen, *Acta Chem. Scand., 5,* 1105 (1951).

13. P. and G. P. Eggleton, *Biochem. J., 21,* 190 (1927).

14. C. H. Fiske and Y. Subbarow, *J. Biol. Chem., 81,* 629 (1929).

15. O. Meyerhof and J. Suranyi, *Biochem. Z., 191,* 106 (1927).

16. E. Lundsgaard, *Biochem. Z., 217,* 162 (1930).

17. H. L. Segal and P. D. Boyer, *J. Biol. Chem., 204,* 265 (1953).

18. K. Lohmann, *Naturwiss., 17,* 624 (1929).

19. E. Baldwin and W. H. Yudkin, *Proc. Roy. Soc., B136,* 614 (1950).

20. B. Ingelman, in *The Enzymes,* edited by J. B. Sumner and K. Myrbäck, Academic Press, N. Y., 1952.

21. J. T. Park and M. J. Johnson, *J. Biol. Chem., 179,* 585 (1949).

22. J. T. Park, *J. Biol. Chem., 194,* 877, 885, 897 (1952).

23. E. Cabib, L. F. Leloir, and C. E. Cardini, *J. Biol. Chem., 203,* 1055 (1953).

24. R. Caputto, L. F. Leloir, C. E. Cardini, and A. C. Paladini, *J. Biol. Chem., 184,* 333 (1950).

25. G. J. Dutton and I. D. E. Storey, *Biochem. J., 53,* xxxvii (1953).

26. R. B. Hurlbert, *Federation Proc., 12,* 222 (1953).

27. A. Kornberg, in *Phosphorus Metabolism,* 1, edited by W. D. McElroy and B. Glass, Johns Hopkins Press, Baltimore, 1951.

28. J. G. Buchanan, V. H. Lynch, A. A. Benson, D. F. Bradley, and M. Calvin, *J. Biol. Chem., 203,* 935 (1953).

29. S. H. Lipton, S. A. Morell, A. Frieden, and R. M. Bock, *J. Am. Chem. Soc., 75,* 5449 (1953).

30. A. Harden and W. Young, *J. Chem. Soc., 21,* 189 (1905).

31. O. Meyerhof and H. Green, *J. Biol. Chem., 178,* 655 (1949).

32. R. Zetterström and M. Ljunggren, *Acta Chem. Scand., 5,* 283 (1951).

33. W. Kiessling, *Biochem. Z., 273,* 103 (1934).

34. W. Kiessling, *Ber., 68,* 243 (1935).

35. C. Cori, S. Colowick, and G. Cori, *J. Biol. Chem., 121,* 465 (1937).

36. O. Meyerhof and K. Lohmann, *Biochem. Z., 185,* 113 (1927).

37. R. A. Alberty, R. M. Smith, and R. M. Bock, *J. Biol. Chem., 193,* 425 (1951).

38. D. M. Brown and A. R. Todd, *J. Chem. Soc., 1952,* 44.

39. W. Z. Hassid, in *Phosphorus Metabolism*, 1, edited by W. D. McElroy and B. Glass, Johns Hopkins Press, Baltimore, 1951.

40. M. Doudoroff, H. A. Barker, and W. Z. Hassid, *J. Biol. Chem., 168,* 725 (1947).

41. J. R. Stern, S. Ochoa, and F. Lynen, *J. Biol. Chem., 198,* 313 (1952).

42. H. Lehmann, *Biochem. Z., 286,* 336 (1935).

43. T. Bücher, *Biochim. et Biophys. Acta, 1,* 292 (1947).

44. O. Meyerhof and P. Oesper, *J. Biol. Chem., 179,* 1371 (1949).

45. F. Lynen and E. Reichert, *Angew. Chem., 63,* 47 (1951).

46. E. R. Stadtman, *J. Biol. Chem., 196,* 535 (1952).

47. F. Lipmann, *Federation Proc., 12,* 673 (1953); E. R. Stadtman, in *Mechanism of Enzyme Action,* edited by W. D. McElroy and B. Glass, Johns Hopkins Press, Baltimore, 1954.

48. H. D. Kay, *Biochem. J., 22,* 855 (1928).

49. G. S. Parks and H. M. Huffman, *Free Energies of Some Organic Compounds,* Chemical Catalog Co., N. Y., 1932.

50. O. Meyerhof, *Ann. N. Y. Acad. Sci., 45,* 377 (1944).

51. P. Oesper, *Arch. Biochem., 27,* 255 (1950).

52. T. L. Hill and M. F. Morales, *J. Am. Chem. Soc., 73,* 1656 (1951).

53. G. P. Lampson and H. A. Lardy, *J. Biol. Chem., 181,* 693 (1949).

54. J. Baddiley, A. M. Michelson, and A. R. Todd, *J. Chem. Soc., 1949,* 582.

55. H. G. Khorana, *Chem. Revs., 53,* 145 (1953); *J. Am. Chem. Soc., 76,* 3517 (1954).

56. V. R. Williams and J. B. Neilands, *Arch. Biochim. et Biophys.,* 1954.

57. H. Schmitz, R. B. Hurlbert, and V. R. Potter, *J. Biol. Chem., 209,* 41 (1954).

58. R. W. Chambers and H. G. Khorana, *Chem. Ind.* 1022 (1956).

59. M. F. Morales et al., *Physiol Rev., 35,* 1 (1955).

60. E. A. Robbins and P. D. Boyer, *J. Biol. Chem., 224,* 121 (1957).

61. H. A. Krebs et al., *Biochem. J., 54,* 78–117 (1953).

62. F. Binkley, *J. Biol. Chem., 195,* 283 (1952).

63. K. Burton, *Biochem. J., 59,* 34 (1955).

64. L. Noda, S. A. Kuby and H. A. Lardy, *J. Biol. Chem., 210,* 83 (1954).

65. M. E. Jones, L. Spector and F. Lipmann, *J. Am. Chem. Soc., 77,* 819 (1955).

66. P. Berg, *J. Biol. Chem., 222,* 1015 (1956).

67. P. Berg, *J. Biol. Chem., 222,* 1025 (1956).

68. M. B. Hoagland, E. B. Keller and P. C. Zamecnik, *J. Biol. Chem., 218,* 345 (1956).

69. R. Bandurski, unpublished. H. Hilz and F. Lipmann, *Proc. Natl. Acad. Sc., 41,* 880 (1955).

70. B. K. Bachhawat and M. J. Coon, *J. Am. Chem. Soc., 79,* 1505 (1957).

71. V. M. Clark, G. W. Kirby and A. Todd, *J. Chem. Soc.,* 1497 (1957).

72. T. H. Benzinger and R. Hems, *Proc. Natl. Acad. Sc., 42,* 896 (1956).

73. F. H. Carpenter, Personal communication.

74. R. M. Smith and R. A. Alberty, *J. Phys. Chem., 60,* 180 (1956).

13

Oxidation-Reduction

1. Introduction (References 1–4)

The fundamental role of oxygen in animal life was recognized by Lavoisier about 1770, and a concept believing it to be indispensable for all living things dates to this period. Although we now recognize that many species of microorganisms and plants can thrive without oxygen, this gas is indispensable for the vast number of biological species which oxidize foodstuffs according to the general reaction[1]

$$C_6H_{12}O_6 + 6O_2 \rightleftharpoons 6H_2O + 6CO_2 + \text{Energy}$$

The substrate need not necessarily be sugar, for certain bacteria can derive their energy from the oxidation of many types of organic and even inorganic compounds. Species that must have oxygen in order to liberate energy from foodstuffs are termed *obligate aerobic* organisms.

Methods for culturing microorganisms in the pure state were sufficiently advanced by 1920 so that their oxygen requirements could be quantitatively evaluated. It became apparent that some bacteria did not require oxygen; moreover, the presence of the slightest amount of this gas was sufficient to stop their growth. Such organisms as the *Clostridia* make up the important group of bacteria known as the *obligate anaerobes*.

Pasteur had recognized the dramatic changes in the metabolism of yeast occasioned by the presence or absence of oxygen. He found that fermentation, the production of alcohol, was inhibited by oxygen but that the organism grew better and consumed more sugar in the presence of an adequate supply of oxygen. This phenomenon has become known as the "Pasteur effect," or the inhibition of fermentation by oxygen. The Pasteur effect is of common occurrence in the *facultative* aerobic or anaerobic species.

---

[1] This reaction does not apply for the microorganisms which obtain energy by oxidation of non-carbohydrate material such as sulfur or iron.

Although the above discussion has dealt exclusively with oxygen gas, the scope of our modern concept of oxidation has been broadened to include many reactions in which molecular oxygen plays no direct part whatsoever. The types of reactions now designated as oxidations may be summarized as follows:

A. Gain of oxygen: e.g., oxidation of an aldehyde

$$R \cdot CHO + \tfrac{1}{2}O_2 \rightleftharpoons R \cdot COOH$$

B. Dehydrogenation: e.g., oxidation of an alcohol

$$R \cdot CH_2OH \rightleftharpoons R \cdot CHO + 2H$$

C. Loss of electrons: e.g., oxidation of a metal

$$Fe^{++} \rightleftharpoons Fe^{+++} + e$$

It is important to remember that oxidations and reductions cannot proceed via the above "half-reactions." *Every substance undergoing oxidation must be accompanied by a substance undergoing reduction, and vice versa.*

The following discussion will cover the concepts of oxidation-reduction judged to be the most useful in work with enzymes. Derivation of the equations from thermodynamic considerations may be found in the book by Clark (1). Much useful information is contained in the stimulating articles by Johnson (2) and Michaelis (3).

2. Theory

All forms of oxidation-reduction reactions can be written in a manner that will show the participation of electrons. The term "hydrogen transport" is formally identical to "electron transport," which is somewhat more general and exact. Since the hydrogen atom can dissociate into a proton and an electron, $\tfrac{1}{2}H_2 \rightleftharpoons H^+ + e$, electrons may be transported by the carrier systems while the H^+ is temporarily absorbed by the buffer medium of the cell.

Substances which take part in oxidation-reduction reactions will have an electron-escaping or electron-attracting tendency which is directly proportional to their strength as reducing and oxidizing agents, respectively. A quantitative measure of this tendency is necessary in order to compare the effectiveness of different agents. Such measurements are made possible through the capacity of metallic wires to conduct electrons. Further, a matter of great technical importance is the existence of suitable meters (potentiometers) which will measure the "electron pressure," potential, or tendency for electrons to flow.

Electrical potentials can be measured only in terms of the difference measured between two electrodes. Noble or "inert" metals are used in practice on the electrodes in order to insure that they will not take part in the chemical reaction under study. Both electrodes may be dipped into the same solution, or they may be dipped into different solutions connected by a suitable bridge, thus allowing the migration of ions without actual physical mixing of the solutions.

The hydrogen electrode provides a primary standard for the measurement of oxidation-reduction potentials. The potential of this electrode is given by the expression

$$E_h = \frac{RT}{n\mathbf{F}} \ln \frac{[\mathrm{H^+}]}{P_{\mathrm{H_2}}^{\frac{1}{2}}}$$

where E_h is the voltage, R is the gas constant or 8.314 absolute joules $\times$ degree^{-1} $\times$ mole^{-1}, T is the absolute temperature, $[\mathrm{H^+}]$ is the hydrogen-ion activity, $P_{\mathrm{H_2}}$ is the pressure of hydrogen gas, $\mathbf{F}$ is the quantity of electricity or faraday (96,496 absolute joules $\times$ absolute volt equivalent^{-1}), and n is the number of electrons transferred. If we arbitrarily fix both $[\mathrm{H^+}]$ and $P_{\mathrm{H_2}}^{\frac{1}{2}}$ as unity, then $E_h = 0$. *This, there-*

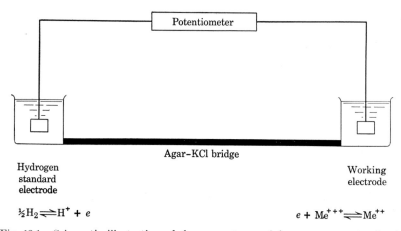

Fig. 13.1. Schematic illustration of the apparatus used for measurements of oxidation-reduction potentials.

fore, is the definition of the hydrogen electrode. It has a potential of zero at all temperatures. The hydrogen electrode provides a standard against which unknown systems can be measured. In practice, it may be more convenient to replace the hydrogen electrode with some other electrode of known potential (by reference to the hydrogen electrode), such as the calomel electrode.

The experimental arrangement for oxidation-reduction potential measurements is shown in Fig. 13.1. In the example shown, one "half-cell" is the hydrogen electrode and the other half-cell contains a mixture of oxidized and reduced metal ion (Me^{+++}, Me^{++}) in solution. The working cell will be further assumed to be "electromotively active"; i.e., the metallic ions are able to remove or donate electrons to the inert electrode. The potential difference between the working cell and the hydrogen electrode finds expression in the fundamental equation

$$E_h = E_0 + \frac{RT}{n\mathbf{F}} \ln \frac{[Ox]}{[Red]}$$

The concentrations, or, more precisely, the activities, of the oxidized and reduced forms are expressed as $[Ox]$ and $[Red]$. Using $30°C$ and converting to common logarithms, the above equation simplifies to

$$E_h = E_0 + \frac{0.06}{n} \log \frac{[Ox]}{[Red]}$$

It will be seen at once that this equation is very similar to the Henderson-Hasselbalch expression for the dissociation of weak electrolytes. When $[Ox] = [Red]$, $E_h = E_0$. The constant E_0 is thus defined as the potential of the 50% oxidized, 50% reduced system. Just as the constant pKa gives a quantitative measure of the tendency for acids and bases to expel or accept protons, so the constant E_0 describes quantitatively the ability of an oxidation-reduction reaction to expel or accept electons. The E_0 values of various systems are recorded as the "normal oxidation-reduction potentials" since they are the E_h of a half-reduced or -oxidized system at pH zero.

A simple, but highly effective method of determination of E_0 is through the use of oxidation-reduction buffers (Fig. 13.2). For example, if the unknown exhibits a highly characteristic color change on addition or loss of electrons, a mixture of ferro- and ferricyanide ions may serve as the buffer. In this type of experiment one starts with a trace of the unknown dissolved in a solution containing one valency state of the buffer, e.g., ferricyanide. The pH should be con-

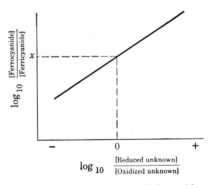

Fig. 13.2. Determination of the oxidation-reduction potential of an unknown by the use of ferrocyanide-ferricyanide buffer. The value x and the E_0 for ferrocyanide–ferricyanide are inserted into the electrode equation.

trolled. After the addition of various aliquots of standard ferrocyanide solution the extent of reduction of the unknown is measured either colorimetrically or spectroscopically. When the ratio [reduced]/[oxidized] unknown = 1.0 the potential of the solution can be ascertained by inserting the known ratio of [ferrocyanide]/[ferricyanide] and the E_0 for this couple into the electrode equation. Davenport and Hill (12) have employed this method for determination of E'_0 for various types of cytochrome c.

Figure 13.3 records the electrometic titration curves for two reac-

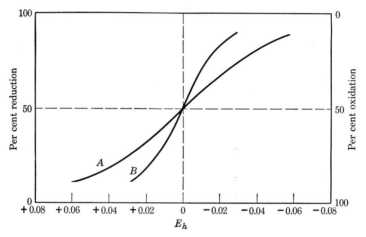

Fig. 13.3. Oxidation-reduction titration curves for systems involving two (curve B) and one (curve A) electron transfer.

tions, A and B, which involve one- and two-electron transfers, respectively. The E_0's for both reactions are assumed to be zero. The reason that a two-electron transfer gives a steeper slope of the curve is that here the ratio log $\dfrac{[Ox]}{[Red]}$ is multiplied by 0.03 (at 30°C) rather than 0.06. For a single-electron transfer the approximately 90% oxidized system will be described by

$$E_h = E_0 + 0.06 \log \tfrac{10}{1} = E_0 + 0.06$$

At about 10% oxidation, the E_h is equal to $E_0 - 0.06$ volt. At the same levels of oxidation the potentials for the two-electron transfer reaction are $+$ and $- 0.03$ volt from the E_0.

3. Univalent and Bivalent Electron Transfers

The example cited above, that of the oxidation and reduction of a metallic ion, can be illustrated by the ferric $\rightleftharpoons$ ferrous iron transformation. This is the type of reaction that occurs during the single-electron transport by the iron atom of the cytochrome enzymes. However, many biochemical oxidations involve the transfer of two electrons.

$$\text{Ethanol} \rightleftharpoons \text{Acetaldehyde} + 2H^+ + 2e$$

$$\text{Lactate} \rightleftharpoons \text{Pyruvate} + 2H^+ + 2e$$

$$\text{Succinate} \rightleftharpoons \text{Fumarate} + 2H^+ + 2e$$

Michaelis (3) has championed the concept that most electron transfers proceed via a single-step process.[2] For example, a careful study of the oxidation of tetraphenyl-*p*-phenylenediamine by Michaelis (4) revealed the existence of an intermediate. This intermediate, or semi-

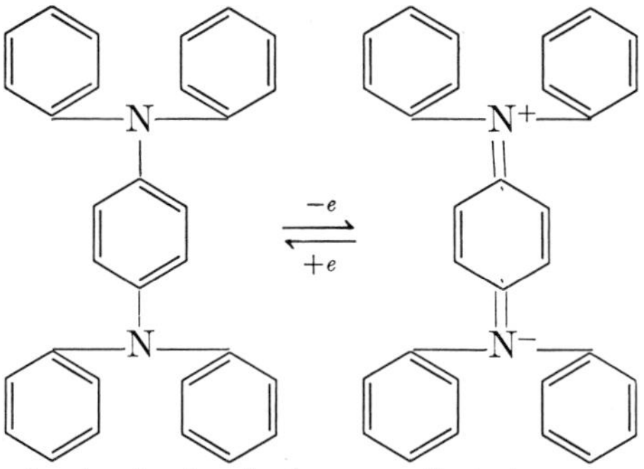

Tetraphenyl-*p*-phenylenediamine   Semiquinone

quinone, is stabilized by resonance, and hence it can be detected under practical laboratory circumstances. The over-all transfer of two electrons is a clear instance of two successive single-electron transfers. A further example of this phenomenon may be cited. The microorganism *B. pyocyaneus* forms a pigment, pyocyanine, which undergoes the following reduction steps:

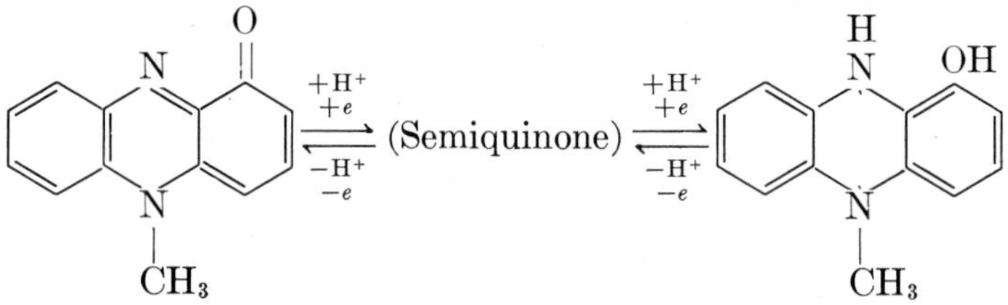

Pyocyanine (oxidized)   Pyocyanine (reduced)

Accordingly, the entire titration curve for pyocyanine shows three equivalent points, the central one of which represents complete formation of the semiquinone (5).

[2] A discussion of this subject appears in the article by Westheimer (10).

4. Effect of pH on Oxidation-Reduction Potentials

From the equation for the hydrogen electrode, it may be observed that if $P_{H_2} \frac{1}{2}$ is maintained at unity, the E_h will be proportional to the $[H^+]$, and, at 30°C, $E_h = 0.06 \log [H^+] = -0.06 \, pH$. The potential of the hydrogen electrode will, therefore, vary with pH in a manner such that at pH 7.0 it is equal to $(-0.06 \times 7) = -0.42$ volt.

The comparison of systems at pH 7.0 is of greater usefulness in biological work, and it has become customary to designate measurements at a pH other than zero as E_0'. Most of these measurements have been made at pH 7.0. The ratio $\Delta E_0'/\Delta pH$ will depend on the value of n. It happens to be -0.06 volt for the hydrogen electrode (30°), since here $n = 1$. The figure is -0.03 volt for $n = 2$ electrons.

5. Effect of Ionization on Oxidation-Reduction Reactions

A large number of naturally occurring oxidants and reductants are weak electrolytes. Therefore, it is necessary to consider the effect of ionization on the oxidation-reduction potentials. This is of particular significance in those reactions where new acidic or basic groups are formed during the reaction. For example, oxidation of DPNH or TPNH creates a new basic group, whereas oxidation of acetaldehyde to acetic acid generates a new acid group.

To illustrate the principles involved, we may consider a weak dibasic acid which can undergo both oxidation and ionization. The total concentration of the reduced form $[\text{Red}]_t$ will be equal to the sum of all the ionized and un-ionized species.

$$[\text{Red}]_t = [\text{Red H}_2] + [\text{Red}^- \text{H}] + [\text{Red}^=]$$

The degree of ionization will depend on the pH and will be described quantitatively by the ionization constants

$$Ka_1 = [\text{Red}^- \text{H}][\text{H}^+]/[\text{Red H}_2]$$

and

$$Ka_2 = [\text{Red}^=][\text{H}^+]/[\text{Red}^- \text{H}]$$

Substitution to remove the common term $[\text{Red}^- \text{H}]$ yields

$$Ka_1 = [\text{H}^+]^2[\text{Red}^=]/[\text{Red H}_2]Ka_2$$

Since

$$[\text{Red}^=] = [\text{Red}]_t - [\text{Red H}_2] - [\text{Red}^- \text{H}]$$

then

$$Ka_1 = [\text{H}^+]^2([\text{Red}]_t - [\text{Red H}_2] - [\text{Red}^- \text{H}])/ [\text{Red H}_2]Ka_2$$

$$Ka_1Ka_2[\text{Red H}_2]/[\text{H}^+]^2 = [\text{Red}]_t - [\text{Red H}_2] - [\text{Red}^- \text{H}]$$

$$[\text{Red}]_t = (Ka_1Ka_2[\text{Red H}_2]/[\text{H}^+]^2) + [\text{Red H}_2] + [\text{Red}^- \text{H}]$$

Since

$$[\text{Red}^- \text{H}] = Ka_1[\text{Red H}_2]/[\text{H}^+]$$

$$[\text{Red}]_t = ([\text{Red H}_2]Ka_1Ka_2/[\text{H}^+]^2)$$

$$+ Ka_1[\text{Red H}_2]/[\text{H}^+] + [\text{Red H}_2]$$

$$= [\text{Red H}_2](Ka_1Ka_2/[\text{H}^+]^2 + Ka_1/[\text{H}^+] + 1)$$

$$[\text{Red H}_2] = [\text{Red}]_t/(Ka_1Ka_2/[\text{H}^+]^2 + Ka_1/[\text{H}^+] + 1)$$

Substituting this value of [Red H$_2$] in the electrode equation

$$E_h = E_0 + RT/2\text{F} \ln [\text{Ox}][\text{H}^+]^2/[\text{Red H}_2]$$

we obtain

$$E_h = E_0 + RT/2\text{F} \ln [\text{Ox}](Ka_1Ka_2 + Ka_1[\text{H}^+] + [\text{H}^+]^2)/[\text{Red}]_t$$

$$= E_0 + RT/2\text{F} \ln [\text{Ox}]/[\text{Red}]_t$$

$$+ RT/2\text{F} \ln (Ka_1Ka_2 + Ka_1[\text{H}^+] + [\text{H}^+]^2)$$

When the [H$^+$] is high, the terms containing the dissociation constants can be removed to give, at 30°

$$E_h = E_0 + 0.03 \log \frac{[\text{Ox}]}{[\text{Red}]_t} + 0.03 \log [\text{H}^+]^2$$

$$= E_0 + 0.03 \log \frac{[\text{Ox}]}{[\text{Red}]_t} - 0.06 \, p\text{H}$$

The last equation shows that, at 50% oxidation or reduction, the potential will decrease by 0.06 volt per unit increase in pH. This behavior is the same as that of the hydrogen electrode. At intermediate pH where the term $Ka_1[\text{H}^+]$ is predominant the change will be -0.03 volt, and at very high pH where only Ka_1Ka_2 is important there will be no effect of pH.

Conant's (see reference 1) early work on anthroquinone-2,6-disulfonate is often quoted as an example of the change in half-oxidation potential with pH. This compound ionizes as follows in the reduced state:

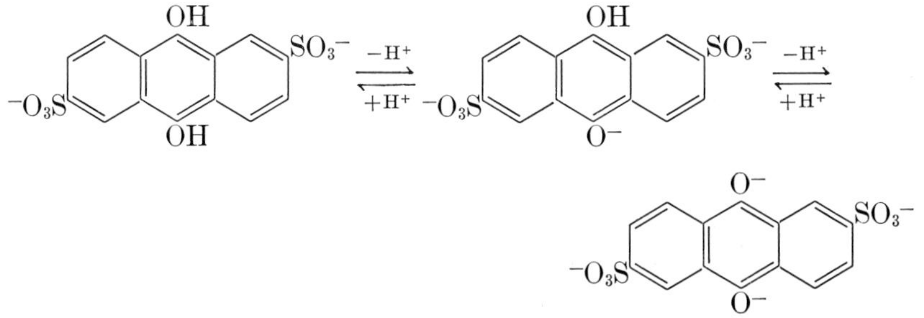

The oxidation of the reduced, ionized form is

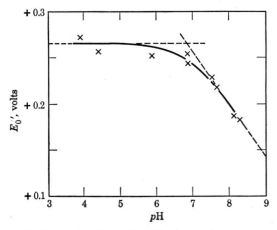

The sulfonic acid groups are strong enough to be completely ionized at all physiological values of pH. The plot of half-oxidation potential versus pH for this compound gives a straight line with a slope of -0.06 volt from 0 to about pH 8.0. Above pH 8.0 the slope becomes less and reaches zero at about pH 10.5. Between these pH values the slope is -0.03 volt. The dissociation constants of each of the ionizing groups may be found by extrapolation of the two lines of -0.06 volt and zero slope against the line of -0.03 volt slope. The points of intersection correspond to pKa_1 and pKa_2 for the stepwise ionization.

Fig. 13.4. The oxidation-reduction potential of cytochrome c as a function of pH (6). Reproduced from *Archives of Biochemistry*, Academic Press, New York.

Figure 13.4 is taken from the data of Paul (6) on the variation in E_0' with pH for cytochrome c. The break close to pH 7 results in the formation of a line with slope of about 0.06, indicating a monovalent ionization.

6. Relation between Free Energy and Oxidation-Reduction Potentials

Tables of oxidation-reduction potentials, such as those found in Lardy's book (2), may be used to predict the direction and extent of oxidation-reduction reactions. These potentials have been established by means of the potentiometric method. However, there is another, less accurate manner of obtaining this information. Certain dyes are highly colored in the oxidized state and colorless in the reduced state. Such dyes can be used as oxidation-reduction indicators in the same manner as pH indicators are used. A favorite dye in biological work is methylene blue (MeB^+). The E_0' of MeB^+ at pH 7.0 is close to zero;

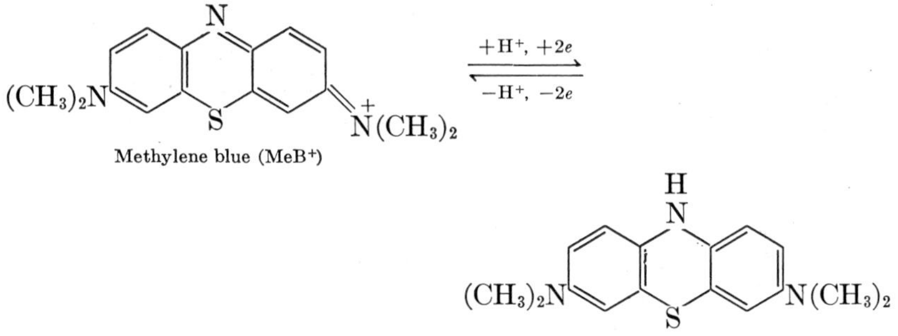

Methylene blue (MeB⁺)

Leucomethylene blue (MeBH)

hence all systems more negative than zero will tend to reduce it. Neutral red is a dye of much lower potential, and fewer enzymatic reactions will reduce it. It is possible to construct a rather complete scale of dyes of known E_0' values and then test the unknown system with each dye. In the illustration shown, the unknown system would reduce dyes 1 and 2 but not 3 and 4. The E_0' of the unknown would, therefore, lie somewhere between that of dyes 2 and 3.

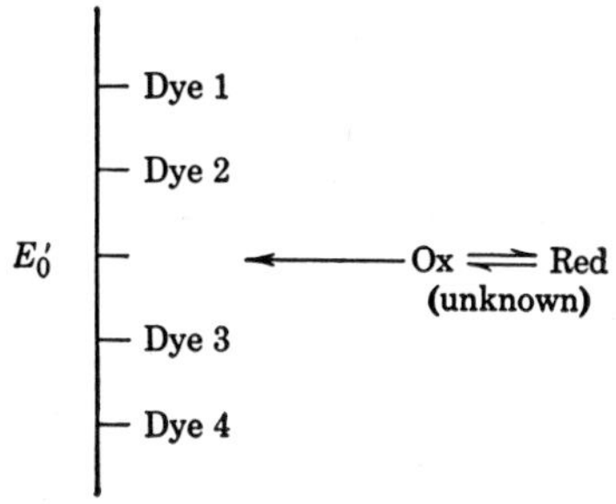

The use of relatively non-toxic dyes such as MeB^+ has yielded a vast amount of qualitative data on respiratory enzymes. These experiments usually necessitate the use of a special vessel known as the Thunberg tube. (Figure 13.5.) This is an ordinary test tube with a hollow ground-glass stopper. A side arm is provided for evacuation in order that the dye can be protected from air autoxidation. The enzyme (or, e.g., bacterial suspension) and substrate can be separated by placing one in the tube and one in the stopper. Mixing is done after evacuation. If desired, the *rate* of dye reduction may be followed colorimetrically to give an indication of the enzyme concentration. This provides the opportunity for testing for activators and inhibitors.

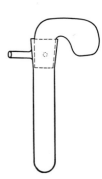

Fig. 13.5. The Thunberg tube.

The scale of oxidation-reduction potentials contains the strongly oxidizing systems at the higher voltage and the reducing systems at the lower voltages. The potential difference between any pair of reactions on the scale is a measure of the driving force of the reaction between them. This is best illustrated by reference to an example. If two reactions, 1 and 2, with characteristic E_0' values, are mixed,

$$\text{Red}_1 \rightleftharpoons \text{Ox}_1 \tag{1}$$

$$\text{Red}_2 \rightleftharpoons \text{Ox}_2 \tag{2}$$

the over-all reaction will be

$$\text{Red}_1 + \text{Ox}_2 \rightleftharpoons \text{Ox}_1 + \text{Red}_2$$

and the equilibrium constant will be

$$K_{eq} = \frac{[\text{Ox}_1][\text{Red}_2]}{[\text{Red}_1][\text{Ox}_2]}$$

Also, at equilibrium, the potential will be a function of the concentration of the oxidized and reduced species present.

$$E_h = E'_{0(1)} + \frac{RT}{n\mathbf{F}} \ln \frac{[\text{Ox}_1]}{[\text{Red}_1]} = E'_{0(2)} + \frac{RT}{n\mathbf{F}} \ln \frac{[\text{Ox}_2]}{[\text{Red}_2]}$$

$$E'_{0(2)} - E'_{0(1)} = \frac{RT}{n\mathbf{F}} \ln \frac{[\text{Ox}_1]}{[\text{Red}_1]} - \frac{RT}{n\mathbf{F}} \ln \frac{[\text{Ox}_2]}{[\text{Red}_2]}$$

$$= \frac{RT}{n\mathbf{F}} \left(\ln \frac{[\text{Ox}_1]}{[\text{Red}_1]} - \ln \frac{[\text{Ox}_2]}{[\text{Red}_2]} \right)$$

$$= \frac{RT}{n\mathbf{F}} \ln \left(\frac{[\text{Ox}_1][\text{Red}_2]}{[\text{Red}_1][\text{Ox}_2]} \right) = \frac{RT}{n\mathbf{F}} \ln K_{eq}$$

or

$$\Delta E_0' = \frac{RT}{n\mathbf{F}} \ln K_{eq} \qquad \Delta E_0' n\mathbf{F} = RT \ln K_{eq}$$

Since

$$\Delta F^\circ = -RT \ln K_{eq}$$

$$\Delta F^\circ = -n\mathbf{F} \, \Delta E_0'$$

The faraday is expressed in calories, i.e., 23,063 calories per volt equivalent. When a single electron is transferred, ΔF is equal to -2306 calories per 0.100 volt change in potential at 30°.

If, in the example given, $E'_{0(1)}$ is -0.150 volt and $E'_{0(2)}$ is -0.050 volt, then

$$\Delta E_0' = -0.050 - (-0.150) = 0.100 \text{ volt}$$

This reaction is, therefore, exergonic to the extent of -2306 calories per transferred electron.

7. Relationship between Binding Activity of Enzymes and the Oxidation-Reduction Potential

Simply because a certain system has a slightly lower potential than another system does not mean that the former cannot oxidize the latter. The driving force in the reaction will depend on the actual concentrations or activities of the reactants, and these may be sufficient to overcome an unfavorable potential difference.

A further manner in which E_0' data may be misleading is in the effect of binding of substrates or coenzymes to the protein. Work by Theorell (7) on the reaction

Ethanol + Diphosphopyridine nucleotide$_{ox}$ $\rightleftharpoons$

Acetaldehyde + Diphosphopyridine nucleotide$_{Red}$ + H$^+$

has shown that the catalyst, alcohol dehydrogenase, can combine much more tightly with the reduced than with the oxidized coenzyme. As a consequence of this binding the apparent equilibrium constant at high enzyme concentration will be higher than at lower concentrations of the enzyme. This is because in the lower concentrations the enzyme is not present in sufficient quantity to enter into a stoichiometric reaction with the coenzyme. Since the logarithm of the equilibrium constant and oxidation-reduction potentials are directly proportional (see above), an increase in the former is accompanied by an increase in the latter. The brief summary of potentials is taken from Theorell

	E_0', volts
Cytochrome b	-0.04
Old yellow ferment	-0.06
Free riboflavin	-0.185
Alcohol dehydrogenase · DPNH	-0.21
DPNH	-0.32 (11)

and Bonnichsen's (7) paper. This shift in potential through coupling with the protein may be a technique used by nature to overbridge high potential gaps. Similar experiments with hemochromes have been carried out by Clark (8).

8. The *rH* Scale

Dixon (9) has developed a system of quantitatively expressing oxidation-reduction potential data. The new scale is termed *rH* and is defined as

$$rH = -\log [H_2]$$

The *rH* is zero at a hydrogen pressure of 1 atmosphere, and it extends up to a value of 41 at 1 atmosphere of oxygen. The range of biological interest, however, lies between 0 and 25.

The equilibrium constant may be replaced by *rH* in the familiar relationship between ΔF and K_{eq} for a mixture such as $AH_2 + A$ in reaction with H_2.

$$\Delta F = -2.3RT \, rH$$

at 30°C $\Delta F = -1380 \, rH$ cal

In the oxidation-reduction reaction

$$AH_2 \rightleftarrows A + H_2$$

the dissociation constant may be formulated by

$$K = \frac{[A][H_2]}{[AH_2]}$$

and $rH = -\log K - \log \dfrac{[AH_2]}{[A]}$. This expression is closely similar to

the *p*H equation of Henderson-Hasselbalch since plotting *rH* versus the

ratio $\dfrac{[AH_2]}{[A]}$ gives a sigmoid curve with a span of exactly 2 *rH* units for

a two-electron transfer over the range of 0.1 to 10 for $\dfrac{[AH_2]}{[A]}$. The

corresponding span is 4 *rH* units for $n = 1$. At 50% oxidation or reduction, $rH = rH_0$. Dixon (9) claims several other simplifying relationships for the new system.

9. Summary of Biological Significance

The biological import of the oxidation-reduction potential is summarized in Fig. 13.6. Electrons are transferred from the substrate (foodstuff) through a series of carriers, each functioning at a characteristic oxidation-reduction potential level, to the ultimate acceptor, oxygen. A rather complete list of E_0' values for systems of biological interest may be found in Lardy's book (2).

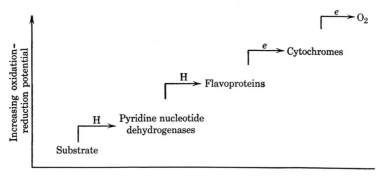

Fig. 13.6. The electron transport system in relation to the oxidation-reduction potential.

References

General

1. W. M. Clark, *Topics in Physical Chemistry,* Williams and Wilkins Co., Baltimore, Md., 1948.
2. M. J. Johnson, in *Respiratory Enzymes,* edited by H. A. Lardy, Burgess Publishing Co., Minneapolis, Minn., 1949.
3. L. Michaelis, in *The Enzymes,* edited by J. B. Sumner and K. Myrbäck, Academic Press, N. Y., 1951.
4. L. Michaelis, *Chem. Revs., 16,* 243 (1935).

Bibliography

5. E. A. H. Friedheim and L. Michaelis, *J. Biol. Chem., 91,* 355 (1931).
6. K. G. Paul, *Arch. Biochem., 12,* 441 (1947).
7. H. Theorell and R. K. Bonnichsen, *Acta Chem. Scand., 5,* 1105 (1951).
8. W. M. Clark et al., *J. Biol. Chem., 135,* 543 (1940).
9. M. Dixon, *Multi-Enzyme Systems,* Cambridge University Press, Cambridge, 1949.
10. F. H. Westheimer, in *The Mechanism of Enzyme Action,* edited by W. D. McElroy and B. Glass, Johns Hopkins Press, Baltimore, Md., 1954.
11. K. Burton and T. H. Wilson, *Biochem. J., 54,* 86 (1953).
12. H. E. Davenport and R. Hill, *Proc. Roy. Soc. London,* Ser. B., *139,* 327 (1952).

14

Enzyme-Substrate Compounds

1. Introduction (References 1–5)

The typical sigmoid curve observed in kinetic studies on the effect of the log of the substrate concentration on the activity of enzymes satisfies the theory that an intermediate compound of the enzyme with its substrate is formed. Although the kinetic data agree with the theory, this in no way constitutes a proof of the enzyme-substrate complex hypothesis.

A direct physical or chemical demonstration of the enzyme-substrate complex, EnS, is desirable not only to prove the Michaelis theory but also to give information on the more intimate mechanism of the reaction, i.e., which groups in the enzyme and substrate take part in the bond formation. Thus possibilities are opened up for the splitting of the complex with specific protein functional group reagents. Quantitative studies on EnS give the dissociation or affinity constants. These are thermodynamic constants, and as such they are much more useful than the kinetic constant, K_m, for interpretation of the reaction mechanisms.

2. Methods of Study

The study of EnS compounds has several fundamental difficulties. In the first place, such compounds are too unstable to permit their isolation. Hence they are not easily adapted to the usual type of organic-chemical manipulation. Generally, they must be studied in solution by some physical technique.

A major obstacle is the acquisition of the pure enzyme. Even after this has been obtained, one is faced with the vast difference in molecular size between the enzyme and substrate. For example, if an enzyme has a molecular weight of 100,000, a 1% solution of it corresponds to a

10^{-4} *M* solution. On mixing equimolar concentrations of the enzyme and substrate one seeks to find a change in the properties of a group on the enzyme or substrate which is present at, say, 10^{-4} *M* concentration. To detect this minute difference a very sensitive apparatus is needed, and this means that some form of light-absorption measurement must generally be employed.[1] The procedures used in spectrophotometry are very gentle, and photocells are available which are sensitive to very small changes in light intensity.

In general, two variations of the spectrophotometric technique are possible:

A. *Rapid-Flow Apparatus.* A machine for mixing solutions with great rapidity was developed by Hartridge and Roughton (1) and later greatly modified and improved by Chance (2). In this technique it is attempted to identify spectrophotometrically the fleeting intermediate formed when enzyme and substrate are rapidly mixed. There are many technical difficulties in this approach, such as the development of a rapid-mixing technique, and the method has not been extensively used by workers other than Chance.

B. *Static, Sensitive Apparatus.* Chance (2) has pioneered the development of supersensitive recording spectrophotometers suitable for enzyme work. These machines permit the investigation of "half" enzyme-substrate compounds. The concept that nearly all enzymes require two substrates has been clearly enunciated by several workers, in particular by LuValle and Goddard (3). Very often the second substrate is simply water, as, for example, with peptidases and esterases. It is customary to regard the half EnS formed with an enzyme with only one of its substrates as a true EnS compound. Obviously, these compounds cannot be studied with the static technique when water participates in the reaction.

The procedure in the static method is to add to a dilute solution of the enzyme a high micromolar excess of the substrate. The real problem is then to measure the presence of 1 micromole of complex in the presence of many micromoles of free substrate. Some of the difficulty is removed when more than 1 mole of the substrate is attached per mole of enzyme. An example of this approach is the study of the lactic dehydrogenase-DPNH compound [Chance and Neilands (8)]. Here the complete "titration" of a dilute solution of the protein with DPNH gave an optical density change of only a little more than 0.0100. (See Fig. 14.1.)

[1] An alternative method is the use of the ultracentrifuge to determine the extent of binding (24).

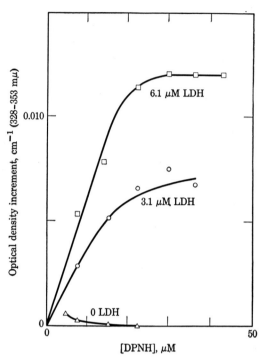

Fig. 14.1. The titration of lactic dehydrogenase with reduced diphosphopyridine nucleotide (8). Reproduced from *Journal of Biological Chemistry,* American Society of Biological Chemists, New Haven.

3. Substrate Compounds with Hydroperoxidases

The iron porphyrin enzymes are, for several reasons, remarkably suited for the study of EnS compounds. In the first place, it happens that some of these enzymes (e.g., catalase) are very easy to crystallize. All of them have intense absorption spectra, contributed by the iron-porphyrin prosthetic group. One band, the so-called "Soret" band in the region of 400 mμ, has a molar extinction coefficient of the order of 140,000 in base-coordinated hematin. In fact, the spectra of the cytochromes are so characteristic that it may be possible to study their EnS compounds in living cells. This is a fortunate circumstance because the cytochromes, with the exception of the component c, have generally resisted isolation procedures.

One of the first conclusions to be drawn from the work on catalase and peroxidase is that their mechanism of action is similar enough to classify them under a single name, the *hydroperoxidases.* The initial spectroscopic observations in this field were made many years ago by

Stern (4). More recently, the peroxide compounds of the hydroperoxidases have been extensively investigated by Chance (5).

The initial compound of catalase or peroxidase with hydrogen peroxide has been termed complex I by Chance. It has the type of spectrum shown in Fig. 14.2. It is significant that complex I is not formed by those iron porphyrin proteins that are without enzymatic activity, the hemoglobins and myoglobins. Complex II is a secondary

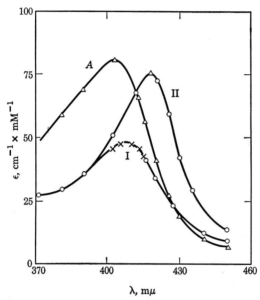

Fig. 14.2. Spectra of the Soret band of free horseradish peroxidase (*A*), complex I (I), and complex II (II) with hydrogen peroxide (5). Reproduced from *Advances in Enzymology*, Interscience Publishers, New York.

compound derived from complex I; it may be either active or inactive, depending on the enzyme.[2] The exact structure of these complexes is unknown, although we may note that the only manner in which the Soret band is reduced in intensity is through opening of the tetrapyrrole ring or detachment of the heme and protein. The reader is referred to the review by Chance (5) which deals specifically with this subject.

4. Substrate Compounds with Dehydrogenases

Theorell and Bonnichsen (6) made the interesting discovery that the spectrum of reduced diphosphopyridine nucleotide, DPNH, is al-

[2] George (27) has suggested that complex II should not be regarded as an enzyme-substrate compound since it apparently does not contain either hydrogen peroxide or the anion O_2H^-.

tered in the presence of equimolar proportions of the crystalline liver
alcohol dehydrogenase (ADH). Figure 14.3 is taken from their classical paper (6). It may be seen that the absorption band of the free
reduced coenzyme with a broad maximum at 340 mμ is shifted to the
ultraviolet on coupling with alcohol dehydrogenase. There is an isos-
bestic point at 328 mμ. The concentration of ADH giving maximum
effect is $\frac{1}{2}$ mole, corresponding to a complex of the type ADH·
(DPNH)$_2$.

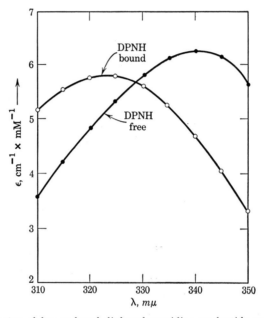

Fig. 14.3. Spectra of free reduced diphosphopyridine nucleotide and the alcohol-
dehydrogenase-reduced diphosphopyridine nucleotide compound (6). Reproduced
from *Acta Chemica Scandinavia,* Scandinavian Chemical Societies, Stockholm.

The ADH·(DPNH)$_2$ complex can be split under very mild conditions with the sulfhydryl-binding reagent p-chloromercuribenzoate.
When this is done, the spectrum of the free DPNH is regenerated.
Since the absorption in the region of 340 mμ is contributed solely by
the reduced pyridine ring of the coenzyme, it is logical to conclude
with Theorell and Bonnichsen that an —SH group of the enzyme is
combined in "one way or another" with this part of the coenzyme
molecule. Finally, the kinetic studies of Theorell and Chance (7)
have shown this complex to be a true Michaelis intermediate with a
dissociation constant of about 10^{-7} M.

In view of the close similarity in action of ADH and lactic dehydrogenase, LDH, it was of interest to test LDH for possible complex formation with DPNH. The results show that DPNH also attaches to the apoenzyme, but there are some significant differences between the DPNH complex with ADH and LDH. The LDH·DPNH compound is extremely difficult to detect, and Chance and Neilands (8) were forced to use especially sensitive techniques in their study of the properties of this compound. (See Fig. 14.1) The LDH·DPNH compound is much more highly dissociated than its ADH analog. The higher apparent dissociation constant for the LDH·DPNH compound, 7×10^{-6} *M*, may account for the much higher turnover number of LDH over ADH. Neilands (23) found LDH to be inhibited by *p*-chloromercuribenzoate, but the mercurial reacts very, very slowly with this enzyme.

Glyceraldehyde-3-phosphate dehydrogenase is one of the most colorful enzymes of the glycolytic cycle. It is a relatively stable enzyme which can be rather easily isolated from different sources (11, 12). Warburg and Christian (9) obtained it from yeast, and the Coris isolated it from rabbit muscle in good yield (10). A unique property of the muscle enzyme is the fact that the protein crystallizes in combination with a quantity of DPN⁺. Several workers have studied its mechanism of action. Most of the data are summarized in a paper by Segal and Boyer (13). The particular reaction sequence which they prefer is as follows:

$$R{-}\overset{\overset{\textstyle O}{\|}}{C}{-}H + HS{\cdot}En{\cdot}DPN^+ \rightleftharpoons \left[R{-}\overset{\overset{\textstyle H}{|}}{\underset{\underset{\textstyle H}{|}}{C}}(O){-}S{\cdot}En{\cdot}DPN^+ \right]$$

$$\left[R{-}\overset{\overset{\textstyle H}{\overset{\textstyle O}{|}}}{\underset{\underset{\textstyle H}{|}}{C}}{-}S{\cdot}En{\cdot}DPN^+ \right] \rightleftharpoons R{-}\overset{\overset{\textstyle O}{\|}}{C}{\sim}S{\cdot}En{\cdot}DPNH + H^+$$

$$R{-}\overset{\overset{\textstyle O}{\|}}{C}{\sim}S{\cdot}En{\cdot}DPNH + DPN^+ \rightleftharpoons DPNH + R{-}\overset{\overset{\textstyle O}{\|}}{C}{\sim}S{\cdot}En{\cdot}DPN^+$$

$$R{-}\overset{\overset{\textstyle O}{\|}}{C}{\sim}S{\cdot}En{\cdot}DPN^+ + HR' \rightleftharpoons R{-}\overset{\overset{\textstyle O}{\|}}{C}{-}R' + HS{\cdot}En{\cdot}DPN^+$$

The substrate may be glyceraldehyde-3-phosphate, glyceraldehyde, or

even acetaldehyde. The first step visualizes the formation of a hemi-
mercaptal which is oxidized by the DPN$^+$, the latter being firmly
attached to the crystalline enzyme. The reduced coenzyme-enzyme-
thiol ester complex is then oxidized by the DPN$^+$ that it is necessary
to add in order to make the reaction proceed. The oxidized complex
is then free to transfer the acyl compound to different acceptors, designated as HR'. These may be inorganic phosphate, simple thiol compounds such as coenzyme A, or arsenate. The enzyme therefore has
the dual role of oxidizing aldehydes and transferring the acyl compound to suitable acceptors.

Harting and Chance (14) have spectrophotometrically identified the

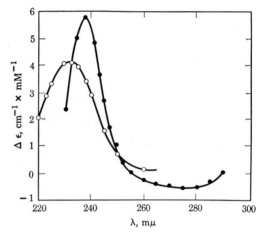

Fig. 14.4. Spectra of acetyl glutathione (—O—O—) and the triose phosphate
dehydrogenase-acetyl compound (14). Reproduced from *Federation Proceedings,*
Federation of American Societies for Experimental Biology, Washington.

acyl derivative of the enzyme. It has an absorption band in the ultraviolet with a maximum similar to but not identical with the known
acyl thiol esters such as acetyl glutathione. The spectra are shown in
Fig. 14.4. The site in the protein responsible for this effect has not
been definitely shown to be a sulfhydryl group. The data in the figure
indicate a considerable difference in the spectra of the simple acyl
thiol compounds and the acyl enzyme.

Both Racker (15) and Velick (16) have found a broad band with a
maximum around 360 mμ which they attribute to the formation of an
enzyme·DPN$^+$ compound. It should be recalled that the reduced
intact enzyme has the maximum at 340 mμ characteristic of free
DPNH (17).

As regards the coenzyme binding it must therefore be concluded that there are substantial differences in the mechanism of its attachment to the alcohol, lactic, and triose phosphate dehydrogenases.[3]

Beinert (30) has found that the acyl CoA dehydrogenases Y_1, Y_2, and G form very stable complexes with their respective substrates. The bound substrates remain associated with the protein on dialysis, ultracentrifugation and ammonium sulfate precipitation.

5. Substrate Compounds with Phosphorylases

Although there has been no direct demonstration of EnS compound formation by carbohydrate-splitting enzymes, the possible existence of such compounds has been rendered highly probable by the evidence at hand. Lagenbeck (18) attributed the hydrolysis of glycosides to the following series of reactions:

$$-\overset{|}{C}-O-\overset{|}{C}- + \text{EnOH} \rightleftharpoons -\overset{|}{C}-O-\text{En} + \text{HO}-\overset{|}{C}-$$

Glycoside	Enzyme	EnS compound	First product

$$-\overset{|}{C}-O-\text{En} + H_2O \rightleftharpoons -\overset{|}{C}-OH + \text{EnOH}$$

Enzyme glycoside (EnS)		Second product	Enzyme

Doudoroff, Barker, and Hassid (19, 20) have provided excellent evidence that an intermediate glucosyl enzyme exists in the action of bacterial sucrose phosphorylase (a transglucosidase). According to their scheme,

$$\text{Glucose-1-phosphate} + \text{En} \rightleftharpoons \text{Glucosyl·En} + H_3PO_4$$

$$\text{Glucosyl·En} + \text{Monosaccharide} \rightleftharpoons \text{Disaccharide} + \text{En}$$

The criteria for such a scheme are: (a) exchange of the phosphate of the phosphate ester with radioactive inorganic phosphate; (b) arsenolysis of the phosphate ester; (c) transfer of the glucosyl group to a variety of acceptors. The mode of attachment of the glucosyl part to the enzyme is unknown.

6. Substrate Compounds with Proteolytic Enzymes

The formation of stable enzyme-inhibitor compounds by reaction of certain proteolytic enzymes with DFP has been alluded to in a

[3] Studies with deutero-labeled reactants show that the alcohol (28), lactic (28), and malic dehydrogenases (29) all catalyze a *direct* transfer of hydrogen from substrate to coenzyme. This can only mean that substrate and coenzyme are adsorbed at adjacent sites on the enzyme.

previous section. A. K. Balls and his associates (31) have demonstrated the essential worth of this approach by preparing acetyl chymotrypsin. Evidence at hand indicates that acylation occurs at

$$\text{Chymotrypsin} + \begin{cases} \text{Acid anhydride} \\ \text{Acid chloride} \\ p\text{-nitrophenylacetate} \end{cases}$$

$$\Updownarrow \qquad\qquad \text{Acid} + \text{Chymotrypsin}$$

$$\text{Acyl-chymotrypsin} \nearrow$$

$$\searrow$$

$$\text{Ester} + \text{Chymotrypsin}$$

a catalytically reactive site in the enzyme (32). The acyl group is then transferred to a co-substrate which may be either water or an alcohol (33). The chemical nature of the reactive site, or sites, has not been defined but both "reactive" serine and histidine side chains are under suspicion (34).

7. Miscellaneous Enzyme-Substrate Compounds

Since Johnson and co-workers (21) discovered the activating effect of metal ions on peptidases, theories have been advanced for the structure of the enzyme-metal-substrate complexes presumably involved. The work in this field has been summarized by Smith (22).

Since we know of more than 70 enzymes that can be obtained in the crystalline state, there is obviously still a great opportunity for fundamental research in the field of enzyme-substrate compounds.

8. Denaturation Reactions and Enzyme Precursors

Enzyme-substrate compounds are studied primarily to give information on the chemistry of the active site of the enzyme molecule and to reveal the intimate mechanism of the catalyzed reaction. It is appropriate to outline at this time some of the other techniques available for such a study.

It is a common experience that denatured proteins generally are without catalytic activity. A careful study of the subtle differences that exist between the native and denatured enzyme molecules should therefore provide data on the structural features necessary for activity. This subject has been treated at some length by Laidler (25).

Zymogens are enzyme precursors. Comparison of the properties of the zymogen and the enzyme should make it possible to determine what changes are necessary in order to develop enzymatic activity. The studies of Neurath and his associates (26) on the activation of zymogens indicate that this particular reaction may involve the loss of a peptide fragment.

References

General

1. H. Hartridge and F. J. W. Roughton, *Proc. Roy. Soc. London, A104,* 376 (1923).
2. B. Chance, *Rev. Sci. Instruments, 22,* 619 (1951). See also *Technique of Organic Chemistry,* edited by S. L. Friess and A. Weissberger, Interscience Publishers, N. Y., *Vol. VIII,* 1953.
3. J. E. LuValle and D. R. Goddard, *Quart. Rev. Biol., 23,* 197 (1948).
4. K. G. Stern, *J. Biol. Chem., 114,* 473 (1936).
5. B. Chance, *Advances in Enzymology, 12,* 153 (1951).

Bibliography

6. H. Theorell and R. Bonnichsen, *Acta Chem. Scand., 5,* 1105 (1951).
7. H. Theorell and B. Chance, *Acta Chem. Scand., 5,* 1127 (1951).
8. B. Chance and J. B. Neilands, *J. Biol. Chem., 199,* 383 (1952).
9. O. Warburg and W. Christian, *Biochem. Z., 303,* 40 (1939).
10. G. T. Cori, W. M. Slein, and C. F. Cori, *J. Biol. Chem., 173,* 605 (1948).
11. M. Kunitz and M. R. McDonald, *J. Gen. Physiol., 29,* 393 (1946).
12. G. W. Rafter and E. G. Krebs, *Arch. Biochem., 29,* 233 (1950).
13. H. L. Segal and P. D. Boyer, *J. Biol. Chem., 204,* 265 (1953).
14. J. Harting and B. Chance, *Federation Proc., 12,* 3, 714 (1953).
15. E. Racker and I. Krimsky, *J. Biol. Chem., 198,* 731 (1952).
16. S. F. Velick, *J. Biol. Chem., 203,* 563 (1953).
17. C. F. Cori, S. F. Velick, and G. T. Cori, *Biochim. et Biophys. Acta, 4,* 160 (1950).
18. W. Langenbeck, in *Handbuch der Enzymologie,* by F. F. Nord and R. Weidenhagen, Academic Press, Leipzig, 1940.
19. M. Doudoroff, H. A. Barker, and W. Z. Hassid, *J. Biol. Chem., 170,* 147 (1947).
20. W. Z. Hassid and M. Doudoroff, *Advances in Carbohydrate Chemistry, 5,* 29 (1950).
21. M. J. Johnson and J. Berger, *Advances in Enzymology, 2,* 69 (1942).
22. E. L. Smith, *Advances in Enzymology, 12,* 191 (1951).
23. J. B. Neilands, *J. Biol. Chem., 208,* 225 (1954).
24. S. F. Velick, in *The Mechanism of Enzyme Action,* edited by W. D. McElroy and B. Glass, Johns Hopkins Press, Baltimore, Md., 1954.
25. K. J. Laidler, in *Introduction to the Chemistry of Enzymes,* McGraw-Hill Book Co., N. Y., 1954.
26. H. Neurath, J. A. Gladner, and E. W. Davie, in *The Mechanism of Enzyme Action,* edited by W. D. McElroy and B. Glass, Johns Hopkins Press, Baltimore, 1954.
27. P. George, *Biochem. J., 54,* 267 (1953).
28. B. Vennesland and F. H. Westheimer, in *The Mechanism of Enzyme Action,* edited by W. D. McElroy and B. Glass, Johns Hopkins Press, Baltimore, 1954.

29. B. Vennesland, T. T. Tchen, and F. A. Loewus, *J. Am. Chem. Soc., 76,* 3358 (1954).
30. H. Beinert, *J. Biol. Chem., 225,* 465, 479 (1957).
31. A. K. Balls and F. L. Aldrich, *Proc. Nat. Acad. Sc., 41,* 190 (1955).
32. G. H. Dixon and H. Neurath, *J. Biol. Chem., 225,* 1049 (1957).
33. C. E. McDonald and A. K. Balls, *J. Biol. Chem., 221,* 993 (1956).
34. B. J. Jandorf and H. O. Michel, *Ann. Rev. Biochem., 26,* 97 (1957).

15

Specificity of Enzymes

1. Introduction

Specificity is one of the most striking properties of the enzyme molecule. Although this phenomenon is exhibited by inorganic catalysts, the enzymes are far more selective and discriminating in their specificity requirements.

The last chapter dealt with enzyme-substrate compounds. A discussion of specificity is a logical transition from that subject, inasmuch as enzyme specificity *depends on the particular atomic structure and configuration of both the substrate and the enzyme.*

Studies on the specificity of enzymes will give a certain amount of detail about the structure of the active site. Thus the specificity study represents a type of chemical "impression" of the enzyme surface since it reveals which substrate atoms are concerned in the formation of the enzyme-substrate complex. As far as nature is concerned, the specificity of enzymes is one of the major factors in the coordination of a series of complicated reactions. The fermentation of glucose to alcohol by yeast requires more than a dozen different enzymes, and it is the selectivity of their reaction that "passes along" the partially degraded substrate.

Absolute group specificity implies that the enzyme is specific for a general type of substrate molecule such as the alcohols or aldehydes. The very rare instances in which only a single member of a substrate class is attacked should be classed under *absolute specificity*. Urease is said to decompose urea and nothing else (1), and the galactokinase of *Saccharomyces fragilis* (grown on whey) transfers phosphate from ATP only to D-galactose and not to the stereoisomers D-glucose and D-mannose (2). *Relative group specificity* describes those situations in which an enzyme acts preferentially on one class of compounds but will attack members of another class to a certain extent. The term may also be used to illustrate the different rates of reaction within a given class. *Optical specificity* is a common property of the vast number of enzymes which act on optically active substrates.

The above classification has subdivided enzymes according to their substrate specificities. However, it is apparent that specificity could also refer to the type of reaction catalyzed by the enzymes.

Excellent reviews are available on the subject of specificity. Articles by Helferich (3), Neurath and Schwert (4), Smith (5), and Gottschalk (2) are especially recommended. The excellent coverage of this subject in the literature necessitates only the barest outline here.

2. Absolute Group Specificity[1]

The proteolytic enzyme pepsin is usually regarded as specific for the hydrolysis of the peptide bond. Similarly, the dehydrogenases appear to show absolute specificity for certain classes of substrates. Alcohol and lactic dehydrogenases oxidize only alcohols and α-hydroxy acids, respectively.

3. Relative Group Specificity

Trypsin was originally considered to hydrolyze only amide bonds. However, more recent experiments demonstrate that this enzyme splits ester bonds as well (4). The variant rates found within a single class of substrate molecule have been studied most extensively with the proteolytic enzymes. The reason for this lies in the ease of preparing a large number of peptides of different constitution. Trypsin acts on peptide bonds the carbonyl group of which is contributed by either lysine or arginine.

$$RCONHCHCONHR'$$
Lysine — Trypsin
or
arginine

Crystalline chymotrypsin, on the other hand, prefers to split peptide bonds in which the carbonyl group is derived from an aromatic amino acid such as tyrosine or phenylalanine. Other enzymes such as carboxypeptidase or aminopeptidase require a free α-carboxy or α-amino group, respectively (4).

According to Meister (6), lactic dehydrogenase and DPNH will reduce a series of straight-chain α-keto acids. Pyruvate is reduced most rapidly, and the rate falls off with progressive chain length. A similar activity is shown by crystalline alcohol dehydrogenase of horse liver.

[1] Koshland and Stein (11) have found that for enzymes hydrolyzing compounds with an oxygen bridge, R—O—Q, the R—O cleavage occurs if the enzyme shows a high specificity for R and a low specificity for Q.

This enzyme, like so many of us, prefers ethanol, but it can apparently dehydrogenate straight-chain alcohols as high as vitamin A. Many of the dehydrogenases can use either DPN+ or TPN+, although one or the other coenzyme is generally greatly preferred.

4. Optical Specificity

Stereochemical specificity is strikingly exemplified by the action of the glycosidases. Maltase hydrolyzes maltose and several other α-glucosides but not β-glucosides. Emulsin contains a β-glucosidase which acts only on β-glucosides and not on α-glucosides. Carboxypeptidase hydrolyzes carbobenzoxyglycyl-L-phenylalanine but does not act on the D isomer. Other familiar examples are the D and L specific amino acid oxidases.

Optical specificity may be either absolute or relative.

The advent of deuterium has permitted a new approach to the problem of the mechanism of hydrogen transfer by the dehydrogenases. The Chicago group (7, 8) found that, with alcohol or lactic dehydrogenase, deuterium is transferred to and from one side of the plane of the nicotinamide ring. These dehydrogenases are therefore specific for one of the two diamers shown. Furthermore, the deuterium is

Diamers of deutero reduced DPN+(DPND)

transferred to only one position on the carbonyl compounds, acetaldehyde or pyruvate. The complete reaction may therefore be pictured as shown.

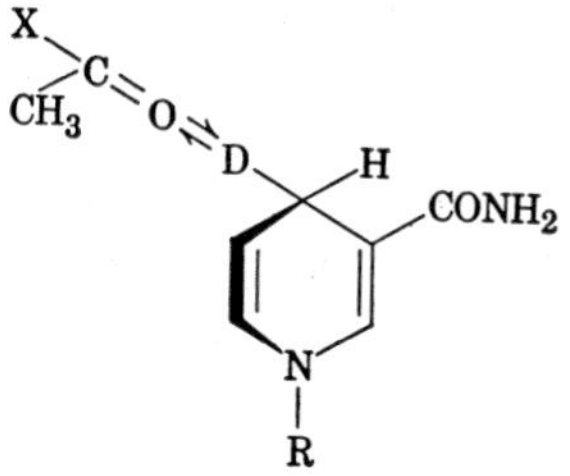

In 1941 Bergmann and Fruton (see reference 9) developed a "polyaffinity" theory to explain the mechanism of stereochemically specific enzymatic reactions. According to this theory there must be at least three specific points of attachment of the substrate to the enzyme.

The theory has also been used to explain the asymmetric degradation of citrate, a symmetrical compound (10).

For example, the symmetrical compound R—C—R′ might be at-

$$
\begin{array}{c}
H \\
| \\
R-C-R' \\
| \\
R'
\end{array}
$$

tached to an enzyme surface in a stereochemically specific fashion such that only one of the two R′ groups is placed in juxtaposition with a catalytic site. In the figure, the catalytic site might be either b or c. In either event, the symmetrical compound

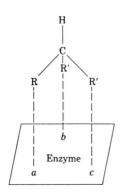

R—C—R′ would suffer asymmetric degrada-

$$
\begin{array}{c}
H \\
| \\
R-C-R' \\
| \\
R'
\end{array}
$$

tion.

The conditions necessary for this type of reaction are: (1) Site b or c may be catalytically active. The catalytic activities of the two sites, however, must be different. (2) There is a three-point attachment ("three-point landing") of the substrate to the enzyme. The fact that an asymmetric degradation is found in metabolic experiments cannot, therefore, rule out the existence of symmetrical intermediates.

References

1. J. B. Sumner and G. F. Somers, *Chemistry and Methods of Enzymes,* Academic Press, N. Y., third edition, 1953.

2. A. Gottschalk, *Advances in Carbohydrate Chemistry, 5,* 49 (1950).

3. B. Helferich, in *The Enzymes,* edited by J. B. Sumner and K. Myrbäck, Academic Press, N. Y., 1950.

4. H. Neurath and G. W. Schwert, *Chem. Revs., 46,* 69 (1950).

5. E. L. Smith, *Advances in Enzymology, 12,* 191 (1951).

6. A. Meister, *J. Biol. Chem., 184,* 117 (1950).

7. H. F. Fischer, E. E. Conn, B. Vennesland, and F. H. Westheimer, *J. Biol. Chem., 202,* 687 (1953).

8. F. A. Loewus, P. Ofner, H. F. Fischer, F. H. Westheimer, and B. Vennesland, *J. Biol. Chem., 202,* 699 (1953).

9. M. Bergmann and J. S. Fruton, *Advances in Enzymology, 1,* 63 (1941).

10. A. G. Ogston, *Nature, 162,* 963 (1948).

11. D. E. Koshland and S. S. Stein, *J. Biol. Chem., 208,* 139 (1954).

16

Mechanism of Enzyme Action

1. Introduction (References 1–3)

Enzymatic catalysis can be distinguished from non-enzymatic catalysis in at least three different ways. Enzymes in general (a) exhibit a higher turnover number, (b) catalyze specific, including stereochemically specific, reactions, and (c) promote reactions under very mild circumstances of external environment. In view of these facts it is little wonder that the problem of the chemical nature and mechanism of action of enzymes has excited the curiosity of generations of biochemists. But in spite of the hundreds, even thousands, of papers and monographs (1) dealing more or less exclusively with this subject, the intimate mechanism of action of enzymes has remained a closely guarded secret of nature.

In this chapter we shall attempt to sketch the degree of progress that has been made in this field. The treatment must, for obvious reasons, be severely limited in scope.

2. Some Characteristics of Enzyme-Catalyzed Reactions

In Chapter 8 we presented data that were not at variance with the proposed formation of an intermediate enzyme-substrate complex and in Chapter 14 we gave the requisite physical and chemical proof for the existence of such complexes.[1] As a result of these developments it has become customary to write the enzyme into the reaction as a stoichiometric, full-fledged reactant.

Another important development is the realization that more and more enzymes act as "group" transferases. This type of reaction is almost the general rule with enzymes and involves the transfer of a group (G) from a donor (DG) to an acceptor (A) molecule. Thus

---

[1] Two of the more significant discoveries in this field were: (a) the glucosylsucrose phosphorylase of Doudoroff, Barker and Hassid (20) and (b) the spectrophotometric identification of hemoprotein-substrate complexes by Chance (21).

even hydrolytic enzymes such as the phosphatases and esterases will

$$DG + En \rightleftharpoons D + EnG$$
$$EnG + A \rightleftharpoons En + AG$$
Sum: $$DG + A \rightleftharpoons D + AG$$

fit this definition if water is taken as the acceptor molecule. Indeed, several substances will compete with water for the group transferred by the so-called "hydrolytic" enzymes. (See Chapter 18.)

According to Koshland (19) three main mechanisms can account for the action of the hydrolytic and transfer enzymes. These mechanisms can also be applied to the transferase activities of the synthestase and oxidative enzymes. The three mechanisms are as follows (see Fig. 16.1):   z

$$DG + A \rightleftharpoons GA + D$$

I. *Single Displacement.* The acceptor substrate A makes a direct nucleophilic attack on the donor substrate DG.

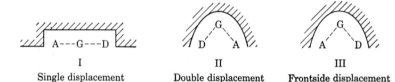

| I | II | III |
| Single displacement | Double displacement | Frontside displacement |

Fig. 16.1.   Mechanism of enzymatic hydrolytic and transfer reactions according to Koshland (19) (see text for further explanation).

II. *Double Displacement.* The enzyme makes a nucleophilic attack on the donor with the formation of a G-enzyme bond and concomitant liberation of D. The acceptor substrate A then displaces G from the active site with the formation of GA.

III. *Frontside Displacement.* This mechanism involves a displacement at an acute angle for D-G-A rather than at approximately 180° as in the single displacement mechanism.

3. Non-Enzymatic Catalysis

A solution to the riddle of the mechanism of enzyme action would be most welcome. Essentially, the problem can be attacked in one of two ways. The first of these is through a study of the behavior of small molecules which possess enzyme-like activity. This approach has in fact been the subject of very extensive researches by Langenbeck (4) and others. The second line of attack involves the isolation and characterization of the enzyme site (see Section 4, Chapter 16).

In the case of the enzyme catalase we know the nature of both the metal ion and the structure of the prosthetic group. It is therefore of interest to compare the catalase activity of ionic iron, hematin and the crystalline hemoprotein itself. Figure 16.2 shows the results of such a survey and includes for comparison an additional compound, triethylenetetraamine (5). Data such as these serve to emphasize the enormous contribution of the protein in enzymatic catalysis.

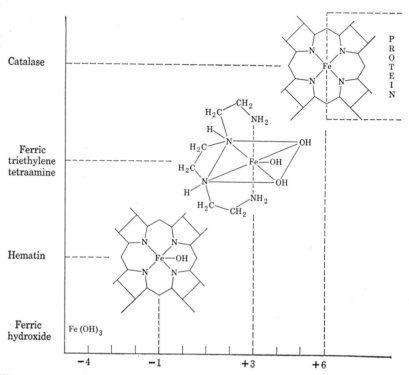

Fig. 16.2. Log$_{10}$ relative catalase activity of certain ferric complexes per mole of iron.

Special mention will be made here of the contributions of Metzler, Ikawa and Snell (6) on the mechanism of reactions catalyzed by pyridoxal. The phosphate of this compound is known to serve as the coenzyme for various amino acid transformations such as transamination, racemization and decarboxylation. Snell and his group found that pyridoxal plus a metal ion (Al^{+++}, Fe^{+++}, Cu^{++}) would, with mild heating, catalyze many of these reactions. The structural requirements for activity included a formyl group, an acidic phenolic hydroxyl ortho to the formyl and an electronegative, i.e., electron attracting group ortho or para to the formyl. Thus the common intermediate in these reactions is thought to be the metal chelate compound in Fig. 16.3 (7).

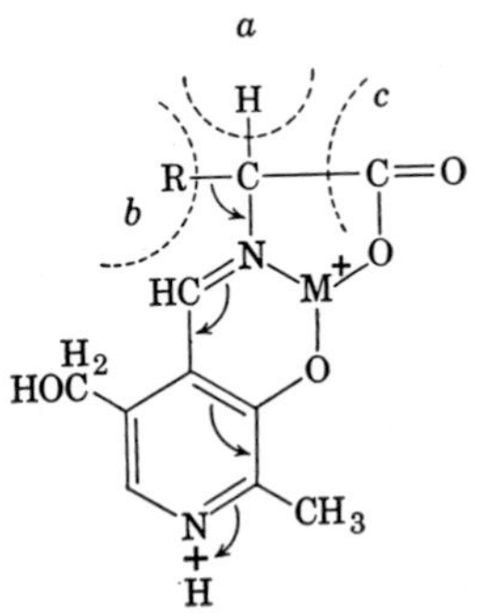

Electron displacement to the positively charged heterocyclic nitrogen atom in the direction indicated by the arrows weakens the bonds around the alpha carbon so that a variety of reactions, designated *a*, *b*, and *c*, may proceed. The metal ion probably assists in the removal of electrons and maintains the planar structure needed for the transfer of electrons through a conjugated system. The actual type of reaction which occurs will depend on the structure of the amino acid, the *pH* and similar influences. It is still not certain that the pyridoxal phosphate-requiring enzymes operate with a metal ion at the active site, however, since the apoprotein may replace the metal ion. A matter of great interest is the discovery of pyridoxal phosphate as a component of phosphorylase (8, 9); here, however, instead of participating in the catalytic reaction, the coenzyme appears to be required for maintenance of the overall structure of the enzyme.

Fig. 16.3. A common intermediate in pyridoxal catalyzed reactions formed from pyridoxal, metal ions and an amino acid (7).

4. Enzyme Active Sites: General Case

Since in the usual case the enzyme molecule is some 500 times larger than the substrate, the latter can only occupy a limited area on the protein surface. There is an increasing body of evidence that at least some, perhaps even large, proportions of the protein can be removed without impairment of catalytic activity. Thus the seat of activity must reside in that portion of the protein which has become known as the *active center* or *active site*. The number of these per mole is a characteristic of the enzyme and may range from 1 to 4. Although the active site represents a relatively restricted area on the enzyme, it must still be large enough to provide the multipoint attachment required of steriochemical specificity (see Chapter 15).

Now we have already noted that enzymatic activity can be abolished by various means, including denaturation reactions and treatment with various types of inhibitors. All of these facts, plus the failure to thus far (see above) obtain a small molecule with catalytic properties approaching that of an enzyme, leads to a picture of the enzyme active site as shown in Figure 16.4. Here the active site is shown as the minimum number of three loci on the coils of a Pauling helix. Denaturation would break the hydrogen bonds responsible for the structural integrity of the helix and hence the juxtaposition of the reactive group A, B and C would be destroyed. It is a known fact that mild denaturation is reversible; trypsin for example is inactive at 100° but regains activity on cooling. The heat stability of enzymes is often greatly magnified in the presence of the substrate and, in fact, this principle can be used in the purification of enzyme proteins.

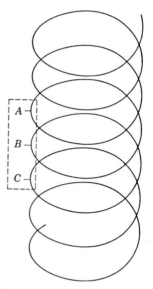

Figure 16.5 illustrates two methods that have been employed with some degree of success for characterization of the active site of enzymes. DFP^{32} (e.g., XG* in Fig. 16.5) has been used to label chymotrypsin (10) and a mixture of glucose-1-P^{32}:glucose-6-P^{32} (e.g., AG* in Fig. 16.5) was used for the labeling of phosphoglucomutase (11, 12). In spite of the dissimilarity in substrates for these enzymes, the phosphate residue was in each case found attached to a serine molecule. The active site peptide for chymotrypsin was identified as Asp. Ser. Gly. Glu. Ala. Val.; that for phosphoglucomutase appears to be a similar if not identical peptide. The sequence Asp. Ser. Gly also occurs in trypsin (24) and in thrombin (25). Koshland (11) interprets

Fig. 16.4. Schematic illustration of an enzyme active site as a constellation of reactive loci *A*, *B*, and *C* on the coils of a protein helix. (Note: the structure shown does not represent any specific protein; in the case of the α helix there are 3.7 amino acid residues per turn.)

this somewhat surprising result to mean that there may be a relatively small number of bond-breaking mechanisms among enzymes. If this is actually the case then the specificity of the reaction would be determined more by the adjacent structure of the protein rather than by the active site *per se*.

The work of Moore and Stein and of Anfinsen on the total structure of ribonuclease was mentioned briefly in Chapter 6. If not all of the protein is required for activity, as seems to be the case for several enzymes, it may prove experimentally expeditious to make a direct attack on the structure of the active site.

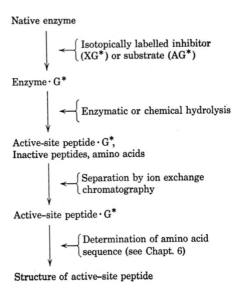

Fig. 16.5. Scheme for isolation and determination of the structure of the active site of an enzyme. G* refers to the isotopically labelled group.

5. Enzyme Active Sites: Specific Cases

Not many investigators have dared to set down on paper a map or picture of the particular enzyme with which they are most familiar, although the result of such an endeavor often bears a striking resemblance to an excavation for a new Empire State building, if not more grotesque than this. Nevertheless it will not be long before very accurate and detailed structures can be established, and hence we feel that a brief discussion of this field is in order. In the outline that follows we shall consider only those schemes that provide information on the nature of the protein molecule around the active center. And as our motto we shall adopt a quotation from Edmond Fischer (3): "I hope that in speaking of what is known today of the active sites of enzymes, I have succeeded in creating in your minds the utmost confusion. If so, I will be satisfied to believe that I have given you a rather truthful, though incomplete, account of our present knowledge of the structure of enzyme loci."

Fumarase:

$$\begin{array}{ccc}
COO^- & & COO^- \\
| & \text{Fumarase} & | \\
CHOH & \rightleftharpoons & CH \\
| & & \| \quad\quad + H_2O \\
CH_2 & & CH \\
| & & | \\
COO^- & & COO^-
\end{array}$$

The work of Alberty (13) and his associates with fumarase represents a deliberate and calculated approach to the solution of the mechanism of action of a specific enzyme. The work began with a careful selection of the proper enzyme. Such factors prominent in the choice of fumarase were (a) simplicity and reversibility of the catalyzed reaction, (b) availability of the reaction components, and (c) ease of assay. The reaction catalyzed by fumarase is surely as simple as can be encountered among enzymes. The reaction is easily reversible. The enzyme was crystallized in the early phases of the study and special spectrophotometric recording equipment was set up in order to follow the appearance or disappearance of fumarate. The latter substance owes its ultraviolet absorption to a carbonyl group conjugated with a double bond.

Figure 16.6 records the simplest mechanism that Alberty believes to

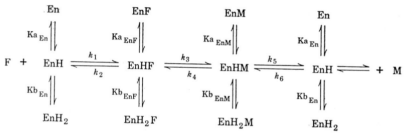

Fig. 16.6. Mechanism of action of fumarase according to Alberty (13).

account for the kinetics and pH effects for the forward and back reactions.

This study with fumarase represents the ultimate in the kinetic approach; unfortunately, not so much is known about the chemistry of the active site. Present evidence favors the hypothesis that the substrate is bound at the active site by two imidazole groups, each of which can alternately accept and release a proton.

When the fumarase reaction was carried out in a medium of pure D_2O it was found that the reaction was absolutely stereospecific with respect to the hydrogen atom which reversibly combines with the double bond of fumarate (22).

Cytochrome c. The characterization of a large peptide in the area of the heme moity of cytochrome c ranks as the best example of the purely chemical approach to the nature and mode of action of enzymes (Fig. 16.7). Tuppy and Paléus (14) obtained the peptide from cytochrome c by peptic digestion. The fact that the hemopeptide has

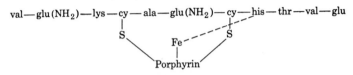

Fig. 16.7. Structure of a hemopeptide isolated from cytochrome c by Tuppy
and Paléus (14).

some of the properties of native cytochrome c is not surprising in
view of the ability of the histidyl residue to bind to the iron atom
(15).

Triose Phosphate Dehydrogenase. According to Krimsky and
Racker (16) the active thiol group of triose phosphate dehydrogenase
is derived from a glutathione molecule (Fig. 16.8).

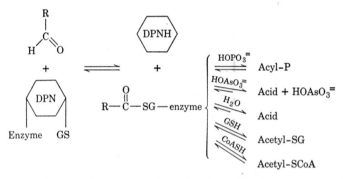

Fig. 16.8. Mechanism of action of triose phosphate dehydrogenase according to
Krimsky and Racker (16).

Acetylcholine Esterase. The case of acetylcholine esterase is interesting because it provides a good example of the type of work that
can be carried out even without a crystalline enzyme. The active site
of this enzyme has been described by Wilson (17). An anionic center
adjacent to the active site functions in binding-substituted ammonium
structures to the enzyme protein. The esteratic site H-G is made up
of a basic group . . and an acid group H. The basic group forms a
covalent bond with the carbonyl carbon atom of the ester moiety.
Meanwhile a hydrogen bond has been established between the acidic
group in the enzyme and the alkyl oxygen. A shift of electrons ensues
with the ejection of an alcohol. Water then reacts with the acyl
enzyme to reverse the process (Fig. 16.9).

Papain. Smith and his collaborators (18) have evolved the scheme
shown in Fig. 16.10 in order to account for the mechanism of action

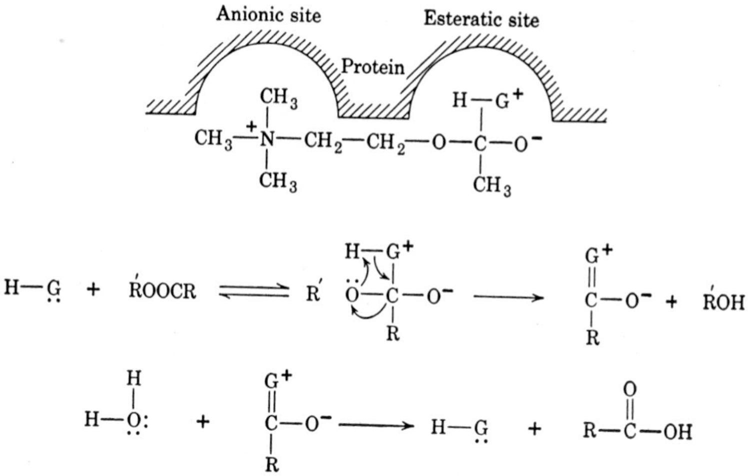

Anionic site   Esteratic site

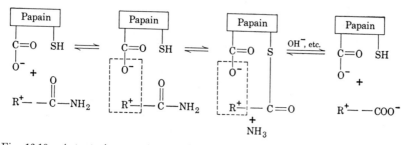

Fig. 16.9. Interaction between the active groups of acetylcholine esterase and the substrate and the mechanism of action of the enzyme. (Wilson 17).

of papain. The scheme is based on the observation that the most sensitive substrates are those with arginyl or lysyl side chains, i.e. cationic groups, on the fact that the enzyme can hydrolyze ester and thiol ester bonds as well as peptide bonds, on the requirement for a thiol group and, finally, on the demonstration that the enzyme can perform synthetic and transfer reactions.

Fig. 16.10. A tentative reaction mechanism for the hydrolytic action of papain on α-benzoyl-L-argininamide (Stockell and Smith 18).

Chymotrypsin. Chemical and kinetic evidence respectively suggest that serine and histidine are situated at the active site of this enzyme. The active center peptide, however, does not show histidine to be adjacent to serine and hence

gly-asp-ser-gly

Active center peptide from chymotrypsin

several authors have suggested that an imidazole group is somehow brought near the seryl residue by virtue of the helical configuration of the peptide strands. In the scheme shown in Fig. 16.11 (Westheimer 23) the unshared pair of electrons on an imidazole nitrogen attacks the carbonyl carbon of an amide or ester with the formation

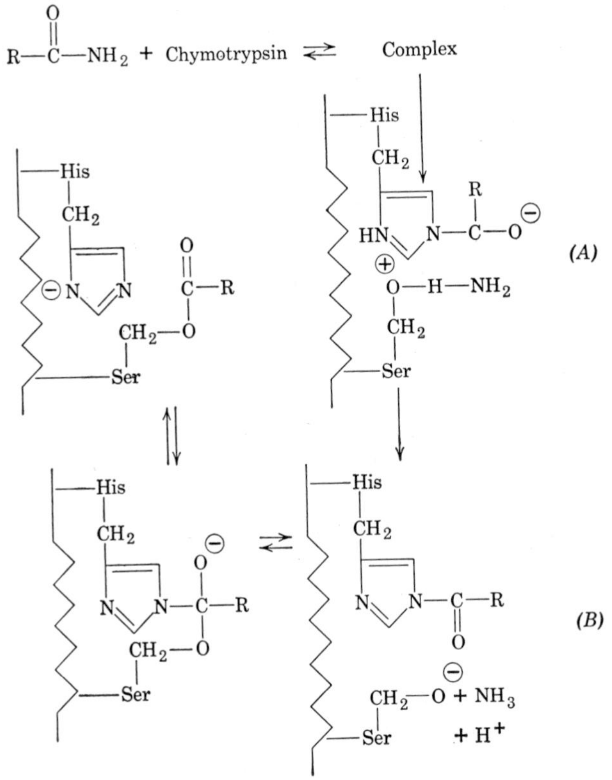

Fig. 16.11. Hypothesis for the mechanism of action of chymotrypsin according to Westheimer (23).

of the intermediate *A*. The latter then loses either ROH or NH_3 with the concomitant formation of the acyl imidazole-enzyme (*B*). From intermediate *B* the acyl group may be either hydrolyszed (as in the enzymatic reaction) or transferred to the neighboring hydroxyl group of serine. An alternative mechanism, which involves direct ester exchange to serine, catalyzed by imidazole, has been put forth by Cunningham (26).

References

General

1. W. D. McElroy and Bentley Glass, editors, *The Mechanism of Enzyme Action*, Johns Hopkins Press, Baltimore, 1954.

2. *Discussions Faraday Soc.*, No. 20, Aberdeen University Press, 1955.
3. T. E. King, editor *Proteins*, Biology Colloquium No. 17, Commercial Hall 107, Oregon State College, Corvallis, Oregon, 1956. Lib. Congress No. 52-19235.

Bibliography

4. W. Langenbeck, *Ergeb. Enzymforsch.*, *2*, 314 (1933).
5. J. H. Wang, *J. Am. Chem. Soc.*, *77*, 4715 (1955).
6. D. E. Metzler, M. Ikawa and E. E. Snell, *J. Am. Chem. Soc.*, *76*, 648 (1954).
7. E. E. Snell, in *Special Lectures in Biochemistry*, University College, H. K. Lewis and Co., 1954–1955.
8. T. Baranowski, B. Illingworth, D. H. Brown and C. F. Cori, *Biochem. Biophys. Acta*, *25*, 16 (1957).
9. E. H. Fischer, D. J. Graves and E. G. Krebs, *Federation Proc.*, *16*, 180 (1957).
10. J. A. Cohen et al., in *Discussions Faraday Soc.*, No. 20, Aberdeen University Press, 1955.
11. D. E. Koshland and M. J. Erwin, *J. Am. Chem. Soc.*, *79*, 2657 (1957).
12. L. Anderson, and G. R. Jollès, *Arch. Biochem. Biophys.*, *70*, 121 (1957).
13. R. A. Alberty and W. H. Peirce, *J. Am. Chem. Soc.* *79*, 1526 (1957).
14. H. Tuppy and S. Paléus, *Acta Chem. Scand.*, *9*, 353, 365 (1955).
15. A. Ehrenberg and H. Theorell, *Acta Chem. Scand.*, *9*, 1193 (1955).
16. I. Krimsky and E. Racker, *Science*, *122*, 319 (1955).
17. I. B. Wilson, in *Discussions Faraday Soc.*, No. 20, Aberdeen University Press, 1955.
18. A. Stockell and E. L. Smith, *J. Biol. Chem.*, *227*, 1 (1957).
19. D. E. Koshland, in *Discussions Faraday Soc.*, No. 20, Aberdeen University Press, 1955.
20. M. Doudoroff, H. A. Barker and W. Z. Hassid, *J. Biol. Chem.*, *168*, 725 (1947).
21. B. Chance, *Advances in Enzymology*, *12*, 153 (1951).
22. H. F. Fisher, et al., *J. Am. Chem. Soc.*, *77*, 4436 (1955).
23. F. H. Westheimer, *Proc. Natl. Acad. Sc.*, *43*, 969 (1957).
24. N. K. Shaffer et al., *Fed. Proc.*, *15*, 347 (1956).
26. L. W. Cunningham, *Science*, *125*, 1145 (1957).

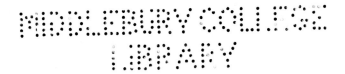

Part 3
TYPES OF COENZYMES
AND ENZYMES

17

Classification of Coenzymes

1. Introduction (References 1-3)

It is often difficult to distinguish between what is meant by the terms "coenzymes," "prosthetic groups," and "activators." Perhaps it is best to reserve the term "coenzyme" for the organic fragments that are normally not isolated with the apoenzyme. A "prosthetic group" would then represent a firmly attached coenzyme such as iron protoporphyrin, and "activator" might be reserved for metals, non-specific reducing agents, and so forth. At any rate, all these substances are generally of low molecular weight and are dialyzable and heat stable.

After 1930 a striking parallelism began to emerge between the vitamins and coenzymes. In short, as the new vitamins were isolated, they were often found to be coenzymes. The conclusion can only be that several coenzymes (or vitamins) cannot be synthesized by living cells at a rate sufficient to satisfy the demand made upon them by the metabolic machinery of life. This association is so general that today we routinely assay a new coenzyme for vitamin activity, and vice versa.

Vitamin deficiency can be rather accurately recorded as one or more specific syndrome, such as blacktongue, pellagra, or beriberi. However, we have yet to learn the connection between these syndromes and the known coenzymatic role of the vitamin.

Adequate discussion of the chemistry and function of the pyridine nucleotide and flavin coenzymes may be found in the writings of Horecker and Kornberg (1) and Lepage (2). A symposium on the metabolic functions of the classical coenzymes appeared in *Physiological Reviews* for October, 1953. A publication entitled *Symposium on Vitamin Metabolism* (3) contains an excellent series of articles dealing with the coenzymatic and other functions of the vitamins.

In this chapter we shall segregate the coenzymes into two groups, namely the *hydrogen-* and the *group-carrying* species. Those vitamins

which have not yet been promoted to the status of coenzymes will be
listed as the *cofactor group*. This type of classification is of course
quite superficial and has been made here for purely pedagogic reasons. The list as shown in Table 17.1 does not include substances of
unknown chemical structure. In the discussion which follows, more
space will be devoted to those coenzymes which are better established
as biochemical entities.

Table 17.1. Classification of the Coenzymes According to Function

Hydrogen-Carrying Coenzymes	Cofactor Group
Pyridine nucleotides	Biotin
Flavin nucleotides	Vitamin B_{12}
Lipoic acid	Ascorbic acid
	Choline
	Inositol
	Glutathione
	Vitamin K

Group-Carrying Coenzymes
Adenosine phosphates
Uridine phosphates
Cytidine phosphates
Guanosine phosphates
Sugar phosphates
Thiamine pyrophosphate
Coenzyme A
Pyridoxal phosphate
Folic acid family

2. Hydrogen-Carrying Coenzymes

A. *Pyridine Nucleotides.* We noted earlier that shortly after the
turn of the century Harden and Young found that phosphate stimulated the fermentation capacity of cell-free extracts of yeast. They
observed another heat-stable factor, with a similar effect, which could
be removed from the yeast juice by dialysis. The unknown factor,
which received the name coenzyme, was subjected to intensive research
by Myrbäck and Schlenk in von Euler's laboratory in Stockholm.

Meanwhile, in Berlin, Warburg and his group were at work on a
similar factor which was required for the oxidation of glucose-6-
phosphate to gluconic acid-6-phosphate. Warburg's factor was designated coenzyme II. The German workers isolated the compound in
a very short time and found it to contain nicotinamide. Within a
few years the major structural features of both coenzymes were elucidated.

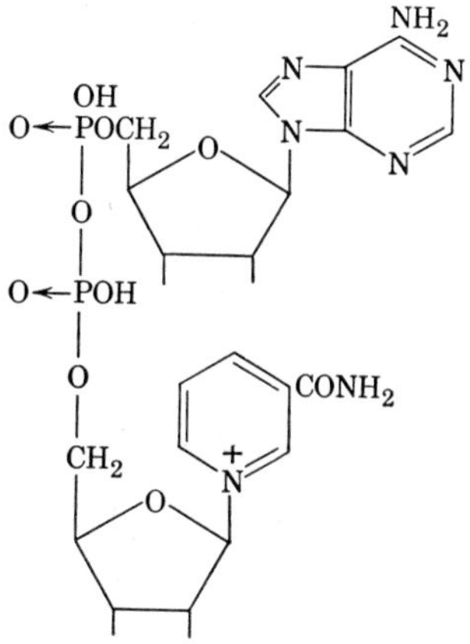

Diphosphopyridine nucleotide (DPN $^+$)
Coenzyme I (Co I)
Codehydrogenase I
Cozymase

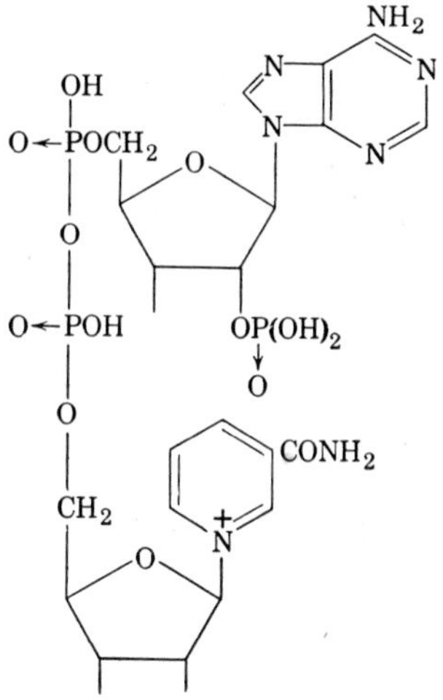

Triphosphopyridine nucleotide (TPN $^+$)
Coenzyme II (Co II)
Codehydrogenase II

The history of the isolation and chemical work is given in a very fine review by Schlenk (104). Singer and Kearney (4, 5) have reviewed the more recent literature on the pyridine nucleotides and their apoenzymes.

Elvehjem and co-workers (6) discovered nicotinic acid to be a vitamin. The free acid, the amide, and the coenzymes containing nicotinamide are all widely distributed in nature. Both DPN+ and TPN+ occur in liver in fairly high concentration; yeast, however, contains mainly DPN+. The main function of these coenzymes is to transport hydrogen from metabolites to the carrier of next highest oxidation-reduction potential, usually the flavoproteins. They are also involved at least indirectly in oxidative phosphorylation (see Chapter 24) and in many other reactions such as the oxidation of testosterone to androstenedione.

The original methods for isolating the pyridine nucleotide coenzymes were very tedious. Methods have now been developed in which essentially only two purification steps are used: adsorption on charcoal, and chromatography on synthetic ion-exchange resins (7, 8). The reduced pyridine nucleotides are much stronger acids than the oxidized forms and are very difficult to chromatograph on anion-exchange resins. One preparation procedure (9) calls for the reduction of chromatographically isolated DPN+ with ethanol and alcohol dehydrogenase. The reaction is carried out in unbuffered solution, and the pH is maintained at 10 to 11 by addition of sodium hydroxide

D. E. Green   Van R. Potter   A. L. Lehninger
1946   1947   1948

H. A. Lardy   B. Chance   A. Kornberg
1949   1950   1951

B. L. Horecker   E. R. Stadtman   A. Meister
1952   1953   1954

Recipients of the Paul-Lewis Laboratories Award in Enzyme Chemistry.

P. D. Boyer

M. Utter

1955

1956

G. R. Greenberg

E. P. Kennedy

1957

1958

Recipients of the Paul-Lewis Laboratories Award in Enzyme Chemistry.

solution. After complete reduction the enzyme is denatured with heat and the solution evaporated in order to remove the solvents. Reduction by chemical methods, as with sodium borohydride, may not give completely active products (10).

The chemistry of the pyridine nucleotides was thoroughly covered up to 1942 by Schlenk (11). The position of the third phosphate in TPN+, in doubt for some time, has now been established to be on the 2′ position of the adenylic acid moiety (12). The pyridine nucleotides and their barium salts are very soluble in water. DPN+ has two primary phosphoryl dissociations and no secondary phosphoryl dissociation. TPN+ has three primary and one secondary phosphoryl group. The pyridinium ion is a very strong base in the oxidized coenzymes. However, in the reduced coenzymes the tertiary N atom is a very weak base. The pKa of the heterocyclic ring N atom is probably below 4. The reduced coenzymes are relatively stable to alkali but are very labile in acid solution. The oxidized forms have just the reverse stability, being labile in alkali but quite stable in acid solution.

The mechanism of action of these coenzymes may be pictured as a reversible reduction of the pyridine ring. This reaction is catalyzed by a series of dehydrogenase enzymes which show mainly a class specific-

ity for their substrates. The reaction as written is a stoichiometric transfer of hydrogen from the metabolite to the coenzyme. One full equivalent of acid is generated in this reaction, inasmuch as a strongly basic quaternary nitrogen is converted to a weakly basic tertiary nitrogen atom. Under physiological conditions the reduced nucleotide is reoxidized by the flavoprotein systems.

For many years it was considered that the pyridine ring is reduced at either the second or sixth ring position (11). It happens that the reduced coenzyme has an additional absorption band in the ultraviolet, the maximum of the broad peak lying near 340 mμ. By reference to model compounds, Karrer (13) favored reduction at either of the two possible *ortho* positions. However, more recent experiments with deuterium indicate that the reduction most probably occurs at the *para* position (14). The absorption spectra of DPN⁺ and DPNH are given in Fig. 17.1. These spectra are typical of the pyridine nucleotides in the oxidized and reduced states. The band at 340 mμ is widely used in enzyme work for following the appearance or disappearance of DPNH by spectrophotometry.

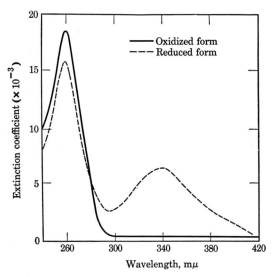

Fig. 17.1. Absorption spectra of oxidized and reduced diphosphopyridine nucleotide.

Many substances, in addition to the hydrogen atom, may complex with the pyridine nucleotides in the para position of the pyridine ring. A general reaction can be written for this event in which X⁻ may be cyanide or any one of a number of other reactants.

The first definitive evidence for a tryptophan-niacin nutritional relationship was established by Krehl et al. (105). Henderson (106) pictures the precursor role of tryptophan as follows:

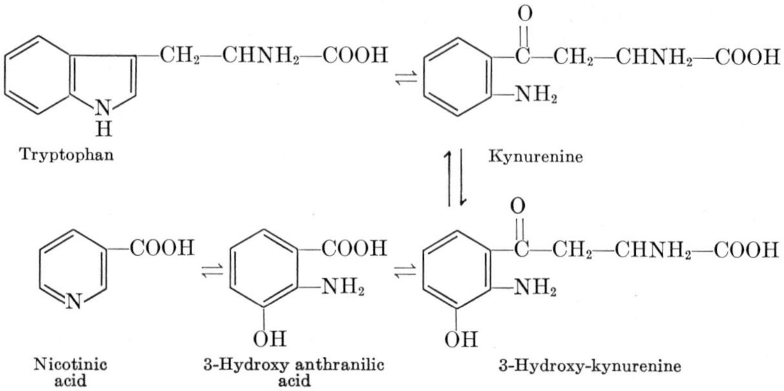

$$\text{Tryptophan} \rightleftharpoons \text{Kynurenine}$$

Tryptophan

Kynurenine

Nicotinic acid   3-Hydroxy anthranilic acid   3-Hydroxy-kynurenine

Many details of this biosynthetic route have yet to be clarified. The last reaction, in which a nitrogen atom somehow gets inside the ring, is particularly intriguing. Kaplan (107) finds that nicotinamide and other closely related compounds, such as β-picoline, give rise to pyridine nucleotides.

Kornberg (15) has described enzymes from yeast and liver which synthesize DPN$^+$ according to the equation

$$\text{Nicotinamide mononucleotide} + \text{ATP} \underset{}{\overset{Mg^{++}}{\rightleftharpoons}} \text{DPN}^+ + \text{Pyrophosphate}$$

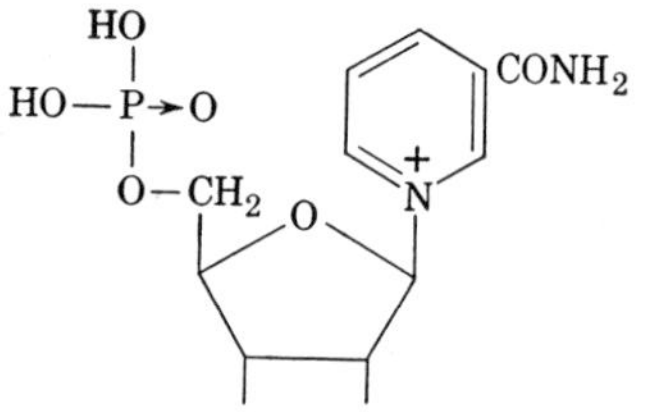

Nicotinamide mononucleotide (NMN$^+$)

He has also found an enzyme in yeast which phosphorylates DPN$^+$ to give TPN$^+$ (16).

$$\text{DPN}^+ + \text{ATP} \overset{Mg^{++}}{\rightleftharpoons} \text{TPN}^+ + \text{ADP}$$

Nicotinamide mononucleotide is derived from the following series of reactions:

$$\text{Nicotinamide} + \text{Ribose-1-phosphate} \rightleftharpoons \text{Nicotinamide riboside} + \text{H}_3\text{PO}_4$$
$$\downarrow \text{ATP}$$
$$\text{Nicotinamide mononucleotide}$$

Zatman et al. (101) have found that nicotinamide inhibits the hydrolytic removal of the nicotinamide from diphosphopyridine nucleotide by a spleen enzyme through competition with water for an ade-nine-ribose-phosphate-phosphate-ribose-enzyme complex.

B. *Flavin Nucleotides.* Szent-Györgyi and Banga (17) found a yellow substance in heart muscle which they called "cytoflav." They observed that it changed color on oxidation and reduction. Warburg and Christian, about the same time, discovered a yeast "yellow en-zyme" or flavoprotein which carried hydrogen in the following system:

$$\text{Glucose-6-phosphate} + \text{TPN}^+ \rightleftharpoons$$
$$\text{Gluconic acid-6-phosphate} + \text{TPNH} + \text{H}^+$$
$$\text{TPNH} + \text{H}^+ + \text{Flavoprotein}_{ox} \rightleftharpoons \text{TPN}^+ + \text{Flavoprotein}_{Red}$$
$$\text{Flavoprotein}_{Red} + \text{O}_2 \rightleftharpoons \text{Flavoprotein}_{ox} + \text{H}_2\text{O}_2$$

Work in the institutes of Warburg, Kuhn, and Karrer showed the yel-low component to be an isoalloxazine compound. This substance, ribo-flavin (Rb) or 6,7-dimethyl-9-D-*ribityl* isoalloxazine, proved to be identical with vitamin B$_2$. Theorell, in a classical investigation, crys-tallized the calcium salt of the prosthetic group of Warburg's yellow enzyme and found it to be flavin monophosphate, which, somewhat erroneously termed flavin mononucleotide (FMN), was synthesized by Kuhn and the phosphate determined to be on the 5′ position of the ribityl moiety.

OH OH OH O

CH$_2$C—C—CCH$_2$OPOH

H H H OH

H$_3$C ... N N ... O

H$_3$C ... NH

O

Flavin mononucleotide (FMN)

In succeeding years several yellow oxidation-reduction enzymes were discovered: D-amino acid oxidase, xanthine oxidase, nitrate reductase, and cytochrome *c* reductase, to mention only a few. The prosthetic group of D-amino acid oxidase, which Warburg and Chris-tian isolated in 1938, contained adenylic acid in pyrophosphate linkage with FMN. The structure of flavin adenine dinucleotide is shown.

Theorell, who has himself contributed greatly to our knowledge of the flavin compounds, has prepared an excellent review on the back-ground and development of knowledge in this field (18).

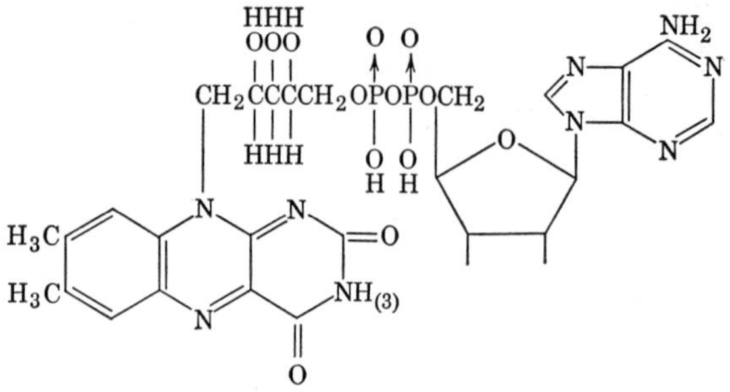

Flavin adenine dinucleotide (FAD)

Flavin mononucleotide, FAD, and riboflavin all occur in tissues, although the concentration of the latter is quite low. The suggestion of Warburg and Christian (21) that FMN might be an artifact formed by the degradation of FAD is probably not correct.

Riboflavin is produced commercially from *Eremothecium ashbyii*, a fungus which produces so much of the vitamin that it crystallizes out in the mycelium. The organism also contains FAD (108) and Yagi et al. (109) have worked out a simplified procedure for preparation of the dinucleotide from this source. FMN, the first coenzyme to be chemically synthesized, is obtained from riboflavin by direct phosphorylation. The dinucleotide is more difficult to obtain. Methods based on chromatographic techniques have been described by Dimant et al. (19) and Whitby (97). Todd and his school (22) have had some success in synthesizing FAD by chemical means.

It should be noted that these substances are not strictly members of the nucleotide class. The bond between the isoalloxazine nucleus and the pentose is not glycosidic, because the sugar residue is the corresponding alcohol of ribose, ribitol. All flavin compounds show three main absorption bands in the neighborhood of 260, 375, and 450 mμ. The complete absorption curve for flavine adenine dinucleotide is given in Fig. 17.2. As a consequence of coupling to the apoenzyme, the bands of FMN are displaced to longer wavelengths. The dinucleotide is reddish yellow; riboflavin and FMN are greenish yellow. Irradiation of the flavin compounds with light leads to their destruction. In alkaline solution a portion of the carbohydrate side chain of FMN is split off in the light to give lumiflavin. The chemical assay of the flavin compounds takes advantage of the much greater fluorescence of FMN than FAD as well as the difference in solubility of FMN and riboflavin in benzyl alcohol (20). The adenine portion of FAD is thought to quench the fluorescence of the flavin nucleus. Riboflavin

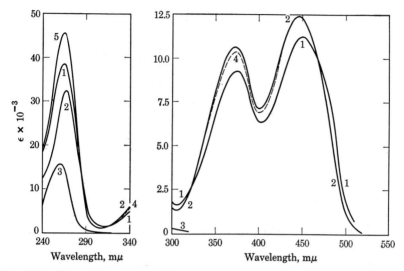

Fig. 17.2. Absorption spectra of flavins and of adenosine-5′-phosphate (97). Reproduced from *Biochemical Journal*, Cambridge University Press, London and New York.

1. Flavin adenine dinucleotide.
2. Riboflavin.
3. Adenosine-5′-phosphate.
4. Flavin mononucleotide.
5. Theoretical spectrum of 3 + 4.

was the first vitamin for which a suitable bacterial assay could be worked out (23).

The reversible oxidation-reduction of the isoalloxazine nucleus is shown in the accompanying formulas. Hydrogen adds in a familiar 1–4 pattern to give the leuco compound. This reduction can be performed with hydrosulfite, and the reoxidation may be achieved by shaking in air.

On the basis of evidence such as titration data, magnetic properties, and spectral changes, several investigators have concluded that riboflavin is oxidized and reduced via single electron steps. The semi-quinoid intermediates were found to have appreciable stability under some conditions. In an elegant series of experiments, Beinert (110) has provided evidence that such intermediates play a significant role in flavoprotein catalysis.

The biosynthesis of riboflavin has been investigated by a number of workers and a rather complete picture of the origin of the isoalloxazine ring has been established (25, 103, 111). The ring system of riboflavin contains a purine moiety and indeed McNutt (112) has found that adenine is incorporated *in toto* into the vitamin. The accompanying formulae are taken from the article by Plaut (111) and show the biosynthetic relationship between riboflavin, purine and leucopterin.

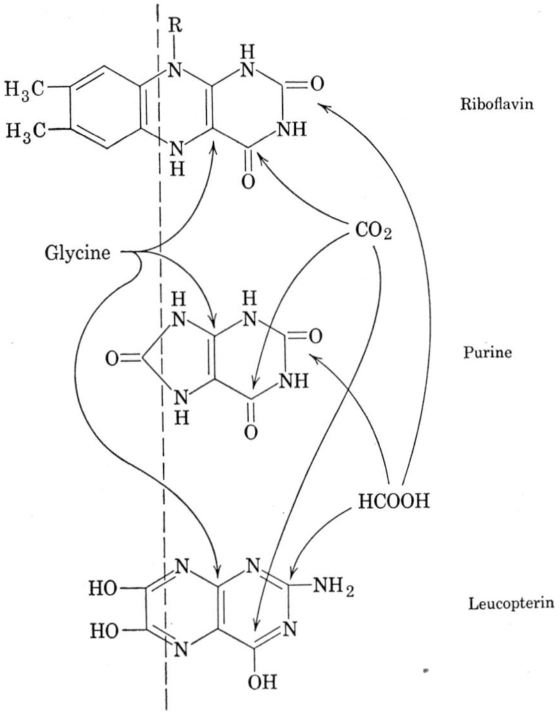

Schrecker and Kornberg (24) have prepared an enzyme from yeast which catalyzes the following reaction:

$$FMN + ATP \rightleftharpoons FAD + Pyrophosphate$$

The metabolism of flavin compounds by yeast is shown in the diagram (26).

$$\text{Riboflavin} \underset{\text{Phosphatase}}{\overset{\text{Flavokinase (ATP)}}{\rightleftharpoons}} \text{FMN} \underset{\text{Pyrophosphatase}}{\overset{\text{FAD synthetase (ATP)}}{\rightleftharpoons}} \text{FAD}$$

C. Lipoic Acid. W. H. Peterson at the University of Wisconsin many years ago began a study of the nutrition of the lactic acid bacteria. This work has led either directly or indirectly to the discovery of several new and interesting compounds with vitamin activity. Thioctic acid is the most recent addition to the list.

Intensive research on the nutrition of the lactic acid bacteria resulted in the discovery of a factor which could replace acetate for the growth of *Lactobacillus casei.* The substance was named "acetate replacement factor." Studies on the nutrition of the protozoan *Tetrahymena geleii* also implicated an unknown compound termed "Protogen" (27). A compound essential for oxidative decarboxylation of pyruvate by resting cells of *Streptococcus faecalis* was also uncovered a little later (28); it was called "pyruvate oxidation factor" (POF). These substances were shown to be very probably identical with a crystalline compound, α-lipoic acid, from liver. The structure of the substance suggests that the designation thioctic acid is probably the most descriptive of its chemistry; however, the term *lipoic acid* enjoys priority.

6,8–Dithio–*n*–octanoic acid
Thioctic acid
Acetate replacement factor
Pyruvate oxidation factor
Protogen
α–Lipoic acid

Lipoic acid is widely distributed in plant, animal, and microbial cells. It occurs as the disulfide, dimercapto, or mono-S-acyl-mono-mercapto form. In natural materials it exists in a firmly bound state, from which it can only be isolated by acidic, alkaline, or enzymatic hydrolysis. The last procedure yields a complex form which is active for a mutant of *Escherichia coli.* This complex form is believed to be the amide of thiamine pyrophosphate and thioctic acid, lipothiamide (LTPP) (29).

Lipoic acid is made available by routine organic-chemical synthetic methods (30).

The new vitamin is chemically a rather simple compound. The carbon skeleton is related to *n*-octanoic acid. The isolated substance is the 6,8-dithio acid, a yellow crystalline solid. Several isomers such as the 4,8 and 5,8 dithioacids have been tested, but they are less active.

The molecule contains one asymmetric carbon atom, and only the (+) α-lipoic is active in the pyruvic oxidase system.

The mechanism of action of lipoic acid is no doubt in some way concerned with the opening and closing of the cyclic disulfide ring. Several theories have been advanced concerning its role in the oxidative decarboxylation of pyruvate but the exact mechanism is still obscure.

$$
\underset{\substack{\text{Thioctic acid}\\\text{(oxidized)}}}{H_2C\text{---}CH_2\text{---}(CH_2)_4COOH} \underset{-2H}{\overset{+2H}{\rightleftharpoons}} \underset{\substack{\text{Thioctic acid}\\\text{(reduced)}}}{H_2C\text{---}CH_2\text{---}(CH_2)_4COOH}
$$

From studies with *E. coli*, Hager and Gunsalus (31) have concluded that the oxidized form of lipoic acid is reduced during the oxidation of pyruvate. An enzyme, thioctic acid dehydrogenase, then transfers the hydrogen to DPN⁺ (also cf. Chapter 24). Gunsalus (113) considers lipoic acid and thiaminepyrophosphate, DPT, to play the following role in the oxidation of pyruvate:

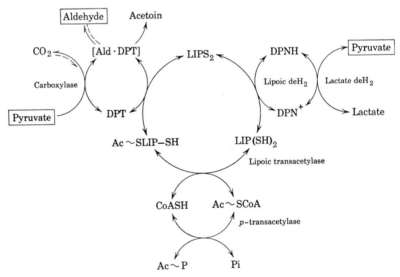

The biosynthesis of lipoic acid has not been explored.

3. Group-Carrying Coenzymes (See Chapter 25)

A. *Adenosine Phosphates.* The mono- and polyphosphates of adenosine may be regarded as coenzymes for the transport of the phosphate group. This system of phosphate transport has been found in all living cells that have been thoroughly examined for its presence. It occurs even in bacteria which oxidize substrates other than carbon compounds such as the sulfur bacteria, and in higher plants.

Adenosine triphosphate was isolated from muscle by Lohmann in 1928 (32). In later years he demonstrated its stepwise dephosphorylation to adenosine di- and monophosphates. ATP is now isolated from yeast on a commercial scale, and ADP is obtained from the triphosphate by gentle hydrolysis. The two nucleotides can be easily separated by chromatography on synthetic ion-exchange resin (Dowex-1) since ATP has a higher negative charge than ADP.

See Chapter 12 for the structure of the adenosine phosphates.

The two terminal phosphates of ATP are in pyrophosphate linkage, and therefore each liberates of the order of 7 to 8 kilocalories of free energy on hydrolysis. The adenosine nucleotides are white solids which are stable in the dry state but relatively unstable in solution (33). In dilute alkali at 100° both the pyrophosphate bonds are hydrolyzed, but the ester phosphate bond is stable. After 7 minutes in 1 N HCl at 100°, both pyrophosphate bonds are broken, and the adenine-ribose linkage is partially decomposed. Isomers in which the phosphate is attached at carbon 2 or 3 of the ribose also occur in nature, e.g., in triphosphopyridine nucleotide and coenzyme A.

The mechanism of action of the adenosine phosphates may be illustrated by the following reactions:

$$AMP + R{\sim}\overset{\overset{\displaystyle O}{\|}}{\underset{\underset{\displaystyle OH}{|}}{P}}{-}OH \rightleftharpoons ADP + RH$$

$$ADP + R{\sim}\overset{\overset{\displaystyle O}{\|}}{\underset{\underset{\displaystyle OH}{|}}{P}}{-}OH \rightleftharpoons ATP + RH$$

These nucleotides exist in dynamic equilibrium with other high-energy phosphate compounds derived from the oxidation of metabolites, e.g., acyl, enol, guanidino, or pyrophosphate compounds. The above reactions are catalyzed by a class of enzymes known as the transphosphorylases.

Once the high-energy bond has been synthesized, it may be "spent" in some other reaction, for example, the phosphorylation of glucose. These reactions are catalyzed by the kinases; in the following example it is hexokinase.

$$Glucose + ATP \rightleftharpoons Glucose\text{-}6\text{-}phosphate + ADP$$

Chapters 22–23 describes further biological functions of these compounds. Methods using specific enzymes to degrade the nucleotides are available for their quantitative assay (34).

B. *Uridine Phosphates.* (See Chapter 26.) Park and Johnson (35) found that *Staphylococcus aureus* cells accumulated a new form of acid-labile phosphate when the bacterium was grown in the presence of penicillin. Park (36) later identified these compounds as phosphates of uridine. Meanwhile Caputto et al. (37) reported the structure for the coenzyme for the reaction galactose-1-phosphate ⇌ glucose-1-phosphate to be uridine diphosphate glucose. The group in Lipton's laboratory (38) have succeeded in isolating uridine-5′-triphosphate from yeast. Leloir (39) and his group have also reported a urdine-5′-diphosphate acetyl glucosamine from yeast, and Dutton and Storey (40) have found in liver a compound of uridine diphosphate and glucuronic acid. A synthetic process for UTP has been reported by Khorana (99).

See Chapter 12 for the structure of the uridine phosphates.

In their chemical properties this new class of compounds resemble the adenosine phosphates and adenylic acid-containing coenzymes. Of great interest is the discovery by Leloir (41) of the following biosynthetic reaction for sucrose formation:

$$\text{UDPG} + \text{Fructose} \rightleftharpoons \text{Sucrose} + \text{UDP}$$

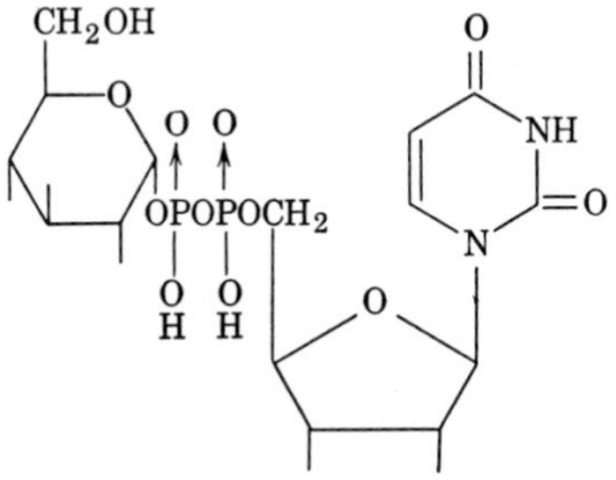

Uridine-5′-diphosphate glucose (UDPG)

The enzymatic synthesis of UDPG proceeds according to the following reaction (39):

$$\text{UTP} + \text{Glucose-1-phosphate} \rightleftharpoons \text{UDPG} + \text{Pyrophosphate}$$

C. *Cytidine Phosphates.* In 1952 Kornberg and Pricer (114) found that phosphorylcholine was converted to an unknown phospholipid. Later Kennedy and Weiss (115) discovered that the incorporation of phosphorylcholine into lecithin was activated by amorphous but not crystalline ATP. The impurity turned out to be cytidine triphosphate. (See Chapter 12 for the structure of the cytidine phosphates.) The actual coenzyme for this transformation is cytidine diphosphate choline. Analogous structures are known in which ethanolamine replaces choline.

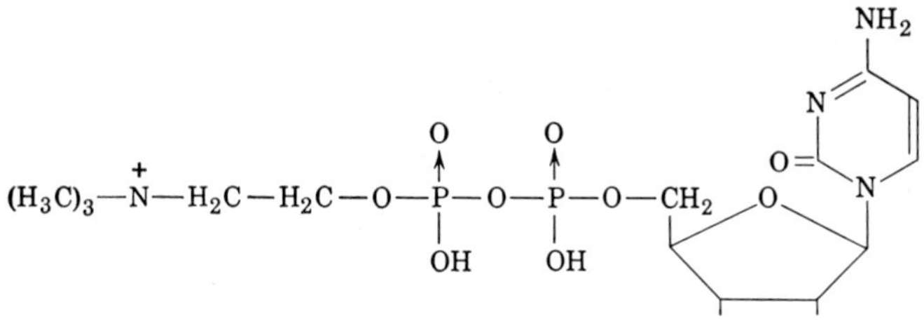

$$(H_3C)_3 - \overset{+}{N} - H_2C - H_2C - O - \overset{O}{\underset{OH}{\overset{\uparrow}{P}}} - O - \overset{O}{\underset{OH}{\overset{\uparrow}{P}}} - O - CH_2$$

Cytidine diphosphate choline

CTP + phosphoryl choline ⇌

Pyrophosphate + Cytidine diphosphate choline

$$CH_2OOCR$$

Cytidine diphosphate choline + $\overset{|}{C}HOOCR$ ⇌ Lecithin + CMP

$$\overset{|}{C}H_2OH$$
(Diglyceride)

D. *Guanosine Phosphates.* Sanadi and co-workers (94, 116) have shown that the phosphorylation of ADP coupled to the breakdown of succinylCoA in animal tissues proceeds via a two-step reaction with GDP. In the first step the GDP is phosphorylated to give GTP. The next step is catalyzed by nucleoside diphosphate kinase and is a transfer of phosphate from GTP to ADP. The enzyme for

Step 1   Succinyl-S-CoA + GDP + P$_i$ ⇌ Succinate + CoASH + GTP

Step 2   GTP + ADP ⇌ GDP + ATP

Step 1 has been named *phosphorylation* enzyme.

See Chapter 12 for the structure of the guanosine phosphates.

E. *Sugar Phosphates.* An enzyme which converts glucose-1-phosphate to glucose-6-phosphate has been known for several years. The Leloir school found this transformation to be accelerated by glucose-1,6-diphosphate (39), which is regarded as the coenzyme for phosphoglucomutase. The solubility properties of glucose-1,6-diphosphate are very similar to these of fructose-1,6-diphosphate, a fact that explains why it remained undiscovered for so long. Heating in alkaline solution, however, destroys fructose-1,6-diphosphate, and the glucose diphos-

$$O$$
$$\uparrow$$
$$CH_2OPOH$$
$$|$$
$$OH$$

$$OPOH$$
$$|$$
$$OH$$

Glucose-1,6-diphosphate

phate can then be isolated. The compound has been synthesized from glucose-6-phosphate. The phosphate groups were blocked with phenyl groups, and the hydroxyls of the sugar were acetylated. Treatment with HBr gave the bromohydrin, which was reacted with silver diphenyl phosphate. Removal of acetyl and phenyl groups by standard procedures gave α-glucose-1,6-diphosphate. The substance is relatively stable in alkali, labile in acid. The phosphate on carbon 1 is more stable than that of glucose-1-phosphate.

The mechanism of action of glucose-1,6-diphosphate is interesting in that it provides a new type of coenzymatic function in which the coenzyme is continually being formed from the substrate. The process is a continual "head-to-tail" transfer of phosphate in which glucose-6-phosphate accumulates. Apparently the function of the coenzyme is that of phosphorylation of the enzyme protein; once the latter has been phosphorylated the coenzyme is no longer required. The work of Jagannathan and Luck (117) and others (95, 118) shows that the

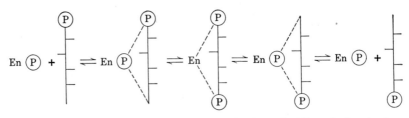

Fig. 17.3. Schematic presentation of the mechanism of action of phosphogluco-mutase.

enzyme alternately phosphorylates a sugar monophosphate and accepts phosphate from the resulting diphosphate. (Fig. 17.3.)

Klenow (119, 120) and Tarr (121) have found that comparable reactions occur with the five-carbon sugars.

Ribose-1-P (Deoxyribose-1-P) + Ribose-1:5-P$_2$ (Deoxyribose-1:5-P$_2$) $\rightleftharpoons$

Ribose-1:5-P$_2$ (Deoxyribose-1:5-P$_2$) + Ribose-5-P (Deoxyribose-5-P)

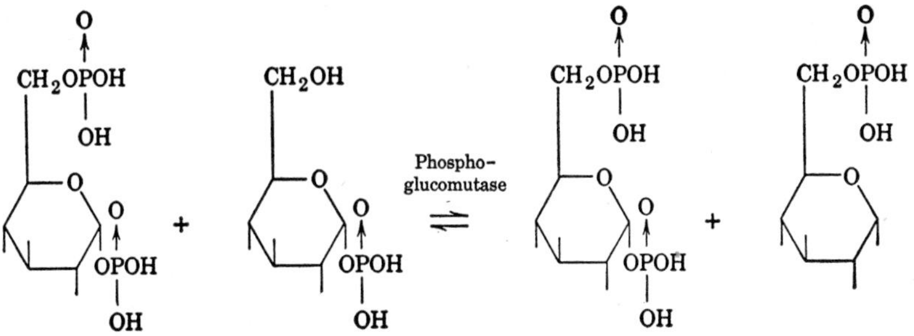

The biological synthesis of glucose-1,6-diphosphate proceeds according to either of the two reactions (42):

$$\text{ATP} + \text{Glucose-1-phosphate} \rightleftharpoons \text{ADP} + \text{Glucose-1,6-diphosphate}$$

or

$$2 \text{ Glucose-1-phosphate} \rightleftharpoons \text{Glucose-1,6-diphosphate} + \text{Glucose}$$

The mechanism of action of phosphoglyceric acid mutase was shown by Sutherland et al. (43) to be very similar to that of the phosphoglucomutase. Here, the "coenzyme" is the 2,3-diphosphoryl-D-glyceric acid.

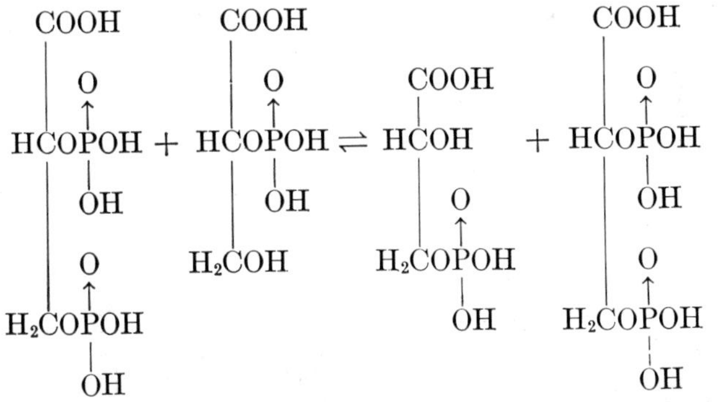

2,3-Diphosphoryl-   2-Phosphoryl-   3-Phosphoryl-   2,3-Diphosphoryl-
D-glyceric acid   D-glyceric acid D-glyceric acid D-glyceric acid

This substance is constantly generated while the 3-phosphoryl-D-glyceric acid is "left behind."

Rapoport and Luebering (44, 45) have obtained evidence for a biological synthesis of 2,3-diphosphoryl-D-glyceric acid.

3-Phosphoryl-D-glyceric acid + ATP $\rightleftharpoons$

2,3-Diphosphoryl-D-glyceric acid + ADP

A chemical synthesis has been reported by Baer (46). This particular ester occurs in red blood cells in rather high concentration.

Diphosphoglyceric acid mutase, the enzyme that forms 2,3-diphosphoglyceric acid from 1,3-diphosphoryl-D-glyceric acid, is activated by 3-phosphoryl-D-glyceric acid. Again the mechanism may be pictured as a coenzymatic function of 3-phosphoryl-D-glyceric acid. The reac-

$$
\begin{array}{cccc}
\underset{\substack{\text{1,3-Diphosphoryl-}\\ \text{D-glyceric acid}}}{
\begin{array}{c}
\text{O} \quad \text{O} \\
\parallel \quad \uparrow \\
\text{CO}\!\sim\!\text{POH} \\
\mid \quad \bullet \\
\text{OH} \\
\mid \\
\text{HCOH} \\
\mid \\
\text{O} \\
\mid \quad \uparrow \\
\text{H}_2\text{COPOH} \\
\mid \\
\text{OH}
\end{array}}
&
+ \;
\underset{\substack{\text{3-Phosphoryl-}\\ \text{D-glyceric acid}}}{
\begin{array}{c}
\text{O} \\
\parallel \\
\text{COH} \\
\mid \\
\text{HCOH} \\
\mid \\
\text{O} \\
\mid \quad \uparrow \\
\text{H}_2\text{COPOH} \\
\mid \\
\text{OH}
\end{array}}
& \rightleftharpoons \;
\underset{\substack{\text{3-Phosphoryl-}\\ \text{D-glyceric acid}}}{
\begin{array}{c}
\text{O} \\
\parallel \\
\text{COH} \\
\mid \\
\text{HCOH} \\
\mid \\
\text{O} \\
\mid \quad \uparrow \\
\text{H}_2\text{COPOH} \\
\mid \\
\text{OH}
\end{array}}
& + \;
\underset{\substack{\text{2,3-Diphosphoryl-}\\ \text{D-glyceric acid}}}{
\begin{array}{c}
\text{O} \\
\parallel \\
\text{COH} \\
\mid \\
\text{O} \\
\mid \quad \uparrow \\
\text{HCOPOH} \\
\mid \\
\text{OH} \\
\mid \\
\text{O} \\
\mid \quad \uparrow \\
\text{H}_2\text{COPOH} \\
\mid \\
\text{OH}
\end{array}}
\end{array}
$$

tion proceeds very far to the right because the high free energy of 1,3-diphosphoryl-D-glyceric acid is dissipated.

F. *Thiamine Pyrophosphate.* The earlier work on this important coenzyme has been recorded by Lepage (2). In 1911, Neuberg and Karczag (47) described a yeast enzyme that converted pyruvic acid to acetaldehyde and carbon dioxide. Some 26 years later Lohmann and Schuster (48) isolated the coenzyme for this reaction and showed it to be thiamine pyrophosphate. This substance acts as a coenzyme for important decarboxylation reactions such as those catalyzed by pyruvic acid oxidase, α-ketoglutaric acid oxidase, and transketolase.

$$
\underset{\substack{\text{CH}_3}}{\overset{\text{N}}{\diagup}}\!\!\!\diagdown
$$

Thiamine pyrophosphate (cocarboxylase)

Cocarboxylase is ubiquitous in nature. In animal tissues the highest concentrations are in the liver and kidney. In thiamine deficiency the ability of animal tissues to decarboxylate pyruvate is decreased, and the keto acid consequently accumulates.

Cocarboxylase is never prepared by isolation since the compound is available by chemical synthesis. One molecule of phosphate is easily hydrolyzed, as would be anticipated from its pyrophosphate linkage. An enzyme in carp and several species of seafish, thiaminease, cleaves the molecule into the pyrimidine and the thiazole portions.

It is discouraging that cocarboxylase, although one of the first co-enzymes to be discovered, has generally resisted attempts to unravel its fundamental mechanism of action. Lipmann (49) showed that the thiazole part of the molecule could be reduced with hydrosulfite, but the physiological significance of this reaction is questionable. One other property of the thiazole ring is of interest. In alkaline solution

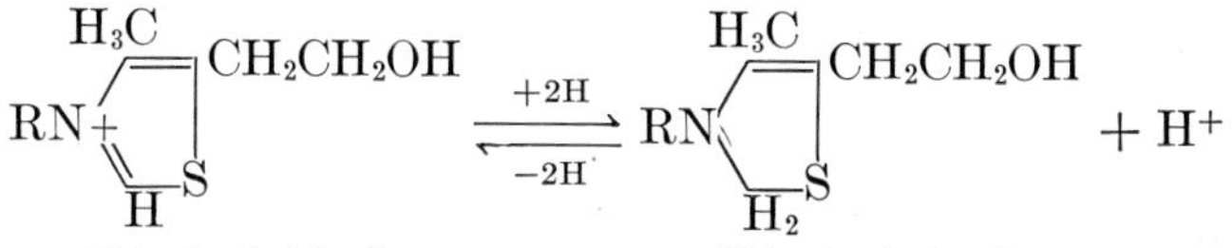

Thiamine (oxidized)   Thiamine (reduced)

the ring opens, probably in the sequence shown. Examination of thia-

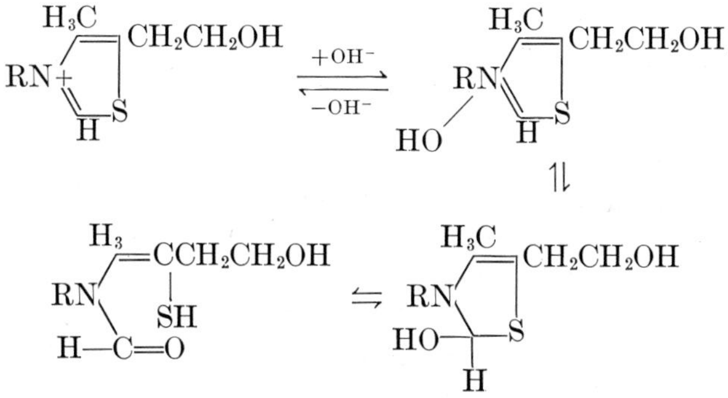

mine in the automatic titration apparatus (50) shows that it decomposes in the range pH 10–11. On back titration with acid nothing is titrated until the pH falls below 8. Then 2 equivalents of acid are rapidly taken up as if the proton were being placed on the sulfhydryl group and the charge on the nitrogen atom generated simultaneously. That is, the thiazole ring snaps shut again at neutral pH. The mechanism of action of cocarboxylase was at one time thought to be associated with this opening and closing of the thiazole ring (51), inasmuch as a sulfhydryl group appears during the process.

The C-2 anion of thiazolium salts is formally analogous to a cyanide ion (i.e., anions on a carbon atom multiply bonded to nitrogen) and according to Breslow (131) this fact may account for the capacity of both of these anions to catalyze the benzoin condensation. The biological reactions of thiamine, as a thiazolium salt, are also formally analogous to the benzoin condensation.

$$C_6H_5-\overset{\downarrow}{\underset{\overset{\|}{O}\longleftarrow}{C}}-H + O=\underset{|}{\overset{\cdot}{C}}-C_6H_5 \xrightarrow[\text{salts}]{\text{NaCN} \atop \text{Thiazolium}} C_6H_5-\underset{\underset{OH}{|}}{CH}-\underset{\overset{\|}{O}}{C}-C_6H_5$$

Benzaldehyde   Benzoin

Breslow has shown that the hydrogen at C-2 of thiazolium salts exchanges in D_2O more rapidly than almost any other "active" carbon-bound hydrogen. This experiment provides proof for the following structure in thiazolium salts:

$$\underset{\underset{S}{\overset{\ominus}{\|}}}{\overset{+}{R_3-N}}\underset{}{\overset{}{=\!=\!=}}\underset{R_5}{\overset{R_4}{}}$$

As a consequence of this work, and particularly that of Downes and Sykes (132), it seems probable that the C-2 acts as a region of high electron density. The adjacent N and S atoms enhance this effect.

The inductive form of the α-keto acid, $RCH_2-\overset{+}{\underset{\underset{O^-}{|}}{C}}-COO^-$ is attacked in its electrophilic area by the electron-rich C-2 to form a complex which immediately rearranges to yield CO_2 and a carbonyl-thiazole product. The latter may then dissociate to give RCHO and thiamine.

G. *Coenzyme A.* Pantothenic acid was the first vitamin to be discovered, isolated, and characterized solely by work with microorganisms. This achievement can be attributed almost exclusively to one man, R. J. Williams. The chemistry and physiology of the vitamin have been outlined in an article by its discoverer (52).

The chemistry and function of coenzyme A (acetylation) have also been reviewed by its discoverer, Fritz Lipmann (53). Novelli (54) has recorded the known metabolic functions of the coenzyme.

Lipmann, during his studies of the acetylation of aromatic amines, found that a heat-stable cofactor was required for full activity. He used the acetylation of sulfanilamide as a test system since there exists a very precise colorimetric assay for this drug.

$$CH_3COOH + H_2N\langle\underset{\downarrow}{\overset{O}{\uparrow}}\rangle\underset{O}{\overset{}{S}}NH_2 \rightleftharpoons CH_3CONH\langle\underset{\downarrow}{\overset{O}{\uparrow}}\rangle\underset{O}{\overset{}{S}}NH_2$$

Acetic acid   Sulfanilamide   Acetylsulfanilamide

The first concentrates of coenzyme A, CoA, contained no detectable amounts of any of the known vitamins, including pantothenic acid. However, on acid hydrolysis, large amounts of β-alanine appeared (55). Finally, Lipmann and his group were able to liberate pantothenic acid from the coenzyme by hydrolysis with two enzymes, a liver enzyme and alkaline phosphatase (see ref. 56).

Pure pantothenic acid itself has never been isolated from natural materials, and the coenzyme form proved to be almost as difficult to purify. Interest in the coenzyme increased when it became apparent that it functions generally as a carrier of the acetyl group. Thus various workers showed that it participated in the acetylation of choline and in the condensation of acetate with oxalacetic acid to form citrate. Lynen's brilliant research cleared up the chemical picture when he isolated the acetyl coenzyme from yeast.

The occurrence of CoA in nature parallels that of pantothenic acid. Yeast and heart are two excellent sources of the coenzyme.

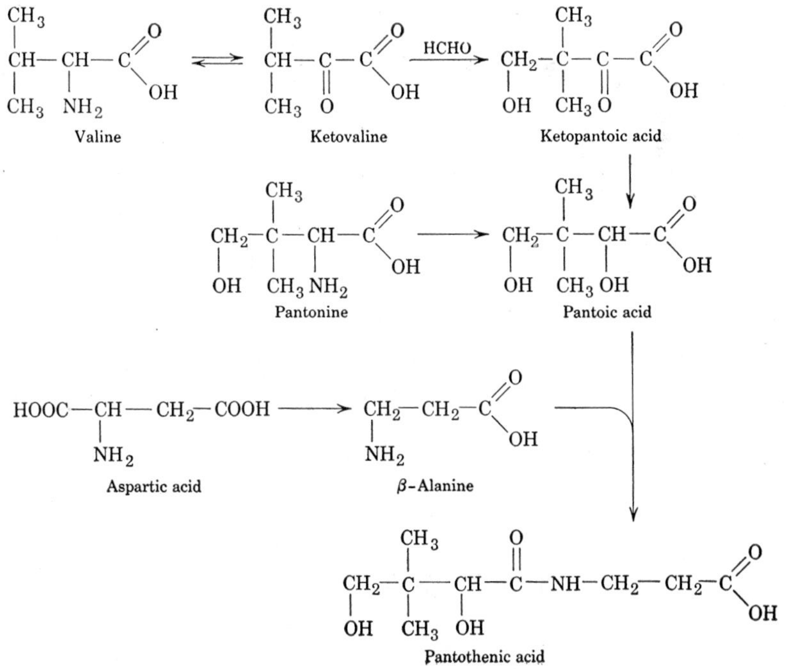

Isolation procedures for coenzyme A were greatly improved when it became known that the molecule contained sulfur. The Wisconsin group use disulfide coprecipitation with glutathione as a major purification step (57). Stadtman and Kornberg (58) have employed chromatography on ion-exchange resins for the isolation of CoA from yeast.

The fact that CoA had to be hydrolyzed with a phosphatase in order to liberate pantothenic acid activity for the test bacteria proved the

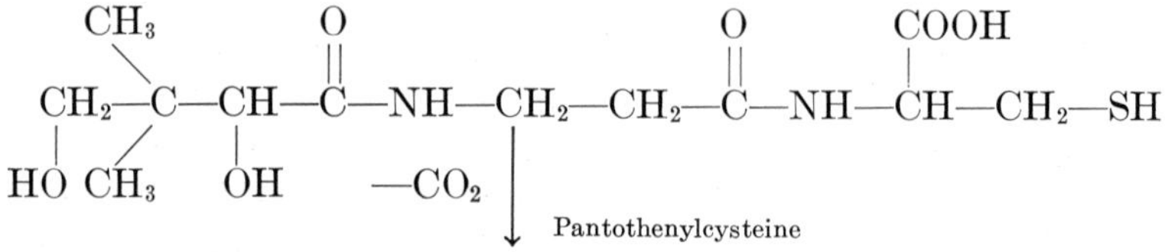

$$CH_2-C-CH-C-NH-CH_2-CH_2-C-NH-CH-CH_2-SH$$

Pantothenylcysteine

coenzyme to contain phosphate. In line with other coenzymes, the

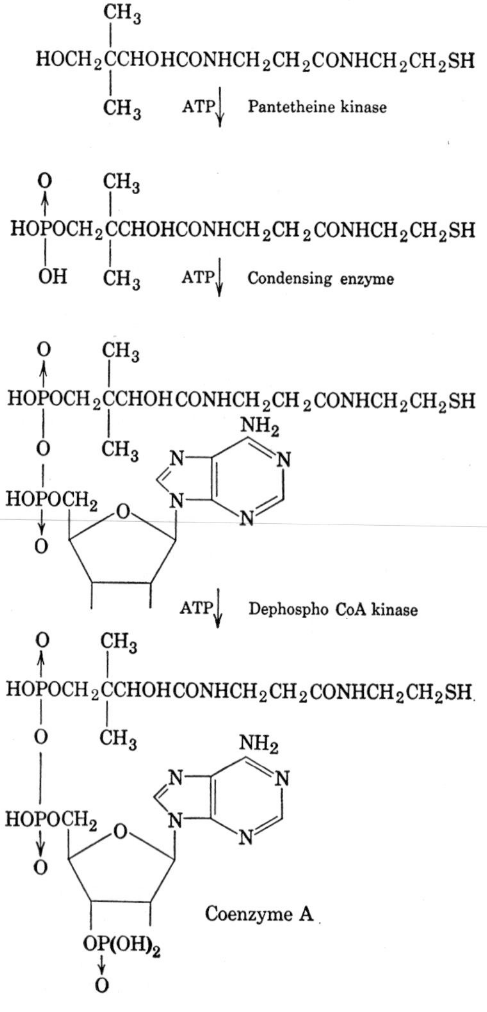

$$\overset{CH_3}{\underset{CH_3}{HOCH_2CCHOHCONHCH_2CH_2CONHCH_2CH_2SH}}$$

ATP | Pantetheine kinase

$$\overset{O\quad CH_3}{\underset{OH\quad CH_3}{HOPOCH_2CCHOHCONHCH_2CH_2CONHCH_2CH_2SH}}$$

ATP | Condensing enzyme

$$HOPOCH_2CCHOH CONHCH_2CH_2CONHCH_2CH_2SH$$

ATP | Dephospho CoA kinase

$$HOPOCH_2CCHOHCONHCH_2CH_2CONHCH_2CH_2SH$$

Coenzyme A

presence of adenine and ribose was therefore suspected.. Now Williams et al. (59) found CoA to be a good source of a *Lactobacillicus bulgaricus* factor, LBF. This factor, named "pantetheine," was later proved to be pantothenic acid attached via the carboxyl group of its β-alanine moiety in amide linkage to thioethylamine. The third phosphate is on carbon atom 3 of the ribose, and hence CoA belongs to the so-called *b* series of nucleotides.

The mechanism of action of CoA centers around its terminal sulfhydryl group. This group can be alternately acetylated and deacetylated just as the pyridine ring of the pyridine nucleotides can be alternately oxidized and reduced. More precisely, it appears from the work on fatty acid oxidation (60) that CoA can transfer acetyl compounds in general.

$$R\overset{\overset{\displaystyle O}{\|}}{-}C-OH + HS-CoA \rightleftharpoons R\overset{\overset{\displaystyle O}{\|}}{-}C\sim S-CoA + H_2O$$

Acyl compound   CoA   Acyl coenzyme A

Evidence for the above biosynthetic route for CoA has been brought forth (61, 122).

H. *Pyridoxal and Pyridoxamine Phosphate.* Knowledge of the chemistry and function of these vitamins and coenzymes has been brought up to date by Snell (62). Historically, the parent substance is the vitamin pyridoxine. Snell later showed that the aldehyde and amine analogs, pyridoxal and pyridoxamine, occur in nature in probably considerably greater concentration than pyridoxine. The phosphorylated form of pyridoxal takes part in the decarboxylation of amino acids, transamination between amino and keto acids, racemization of amino acids, dehydration (deamination) of hydroxy amino

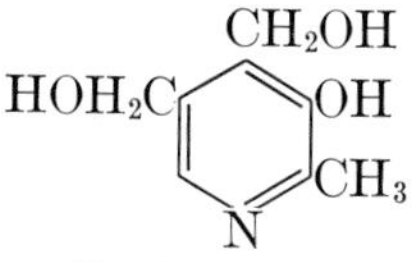

Pyridoxine (PINE)

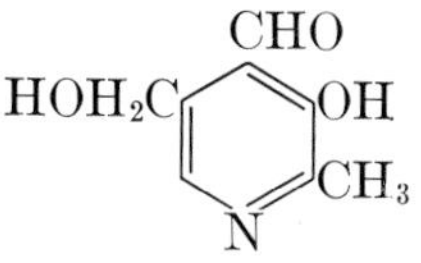

Pyridoxal (PAL)

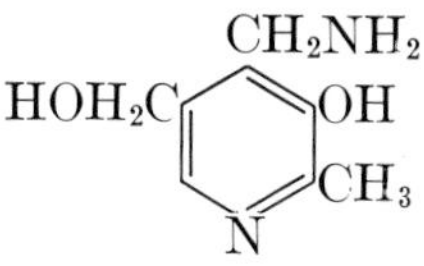

Pyridoxamine (PAM)

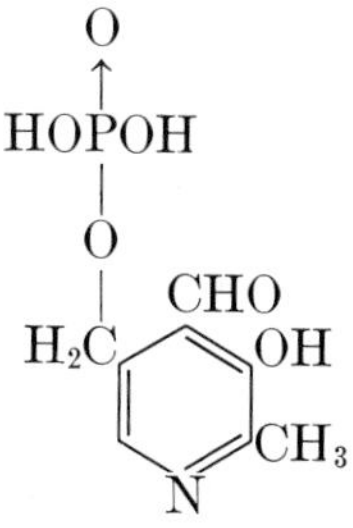

Pyridoxal-5-phosphate (PALPO)

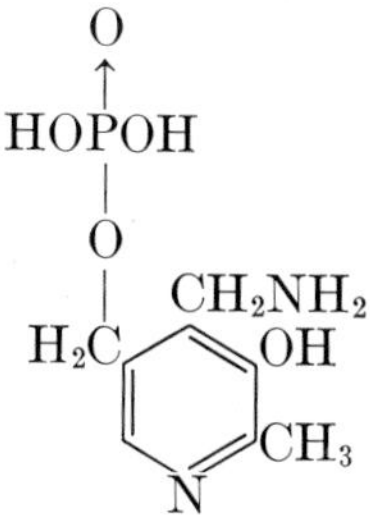

Pyridoxamine-5-phosphate (PAMPO)

acids, and desulfhydration of sulfur-containing amino acids as well as miscellaneous transformations of the amino acids.

The coenzymes, the pyridoxal and pyridoxamine phosphates, are available by synthetic methods from the simpler compounds. Pyridoxamine phosphate is obtained by direct phosphorylation of pyridoxamine (63), and pyridoxal phosphate is synthesized from a pyridoxal derivative in which the aldehyde group is later generated (64).

The phosphate in pyridoxal phosphate has been definitely established to be on the 5 position. The substitution on the ring makes the phenolic hydroxyl and ring nitrogen more acidic and basic, respectively, than in phenol and pyridine (65). The aldehyde compounds have enough light absorption around 400 mμ to be yellow. However, all the members of this class have intense and characteristic spectra in the ultraviolet (66).

The mechanism of action of these coenzymes is not definitely established, and a pure transaminase has not yet been isolated. The best preparation is probably that of Cammarata and Cohen (67). However, there is good evidence that an intermediate Schiff base may be formed with the amino acid. This intermediate would then decompose into the corresponding keto acid and the amine form of the coenzyme. Meister, Sober, and Peterson (68) have found that both the pyridoxal and pyridoxamine phosphates act as coenzymes for heart apotransaminase.

Snell (62) and his associates have found that certain metals activate non-enzymatic transamination with pyridoxal. The reaction requires, in addition to the metal, the presence of the free aldehyde, phenolic hydroxyl, and ring nitrogen in the pyridoxal. They, and other workers (69), suggest that the metal (Cu^{++}, Fe^{+++}, Al^{+++}) forms a chelate with the phenolic hydroxyl of the pyridoxal and the nitrogen atom from the Schiff base formed by interaction of the vitamin and amino acid. Schiff base formation with amino acids and pyridoxal is shown herewith.

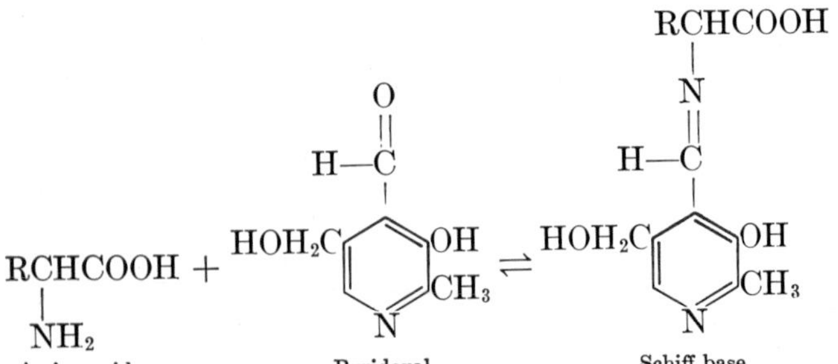

Williams and Neilands (66) made an extensive study of the ionization constants, spectral properties, and metal chelation of these compounds. At pH 7.0 the copper chelate of pyridoxamine has the structure shown. The precise role of metals in this reaction will have to

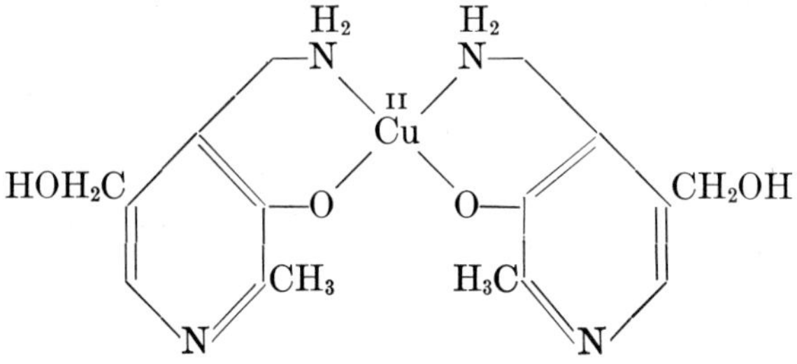

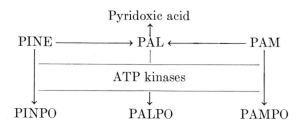

Copper chelate of pyridoxamine

await isolation of pure apotransaminase. The preparation of Cammarata and Cohen (67) contained several metals, as judged by emission spectrography.

It will be recalled that in Fig. 16.3 we presented a structure which Snell and his group (96, 100) consider to be the common intermediate in pyridoxal catalyzed reactions of the non-enzymatic variety. An exciting and totally unexpected development in this field was the identification of the yellow color of crystalline phosphorylase as pyridoxal phosphate (123, 124). (See Chapter 22.)

The following scheme illustrates the metabolic interconversions in the vitamin B_6 family.

<pre>
                  Pyridoxic acid
                       ↑
   PINE ──────────→ PAL ←────────── PAM
    │   ─────────────────────────   │
    │   ATP kinases   │
    │   ─────────────────────────   │
    ↓   ↓   ↓
  PINPO   PALPO   PAMPO
</pre>

I Folic acid:

The folic acid family is made up of a group of compounds containing pteroic acid, p-aminobenzoic acid and a variable number of glutamic acid residues. As with lipoic acid, a great profusion of names have been applied to the same compounds. The most common alternate name for folic acid is pteroylglutamic acid. Organisms can be found which require only the p-aminobenzoic acid, the p-aminobenzoic acid-glutamate complex, or other derivates such as a N-formyltetrahydrofolic acid (71).

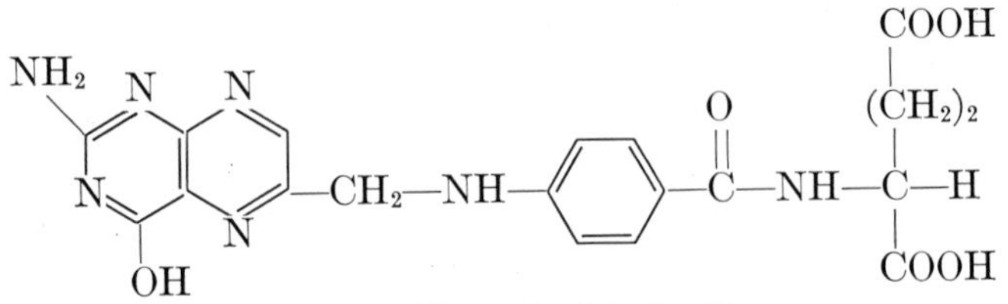

$$NH_2 \quad N \quad N \qquad\qquad O \qquad (CH_2)_2 \qquad COOH$$

-CH_2-NH- (benzene ring) -C-NH-C-H

OH   COOH

Folic acid (N-pteroyl-L-glutamic acid)

A well-authenticated role of tetrahydrofolic acid activity is that of formimino group transfer (125, 126). Rabinowitz and Pricer (127) formulate this reaction as follows:

Formimino glycine + Tetrahydrofolic acid

$\rightleftharpoons$ Glycine + NH_3 + N^{10}-formyltetrahydrofolic acid

N^{10}-formyltetrahydrofolic acid + ADP + Pi

$\rightleftharpoons$ HCOOH + ATP + Tetrahydrofolic acid

4. Cofactor Group

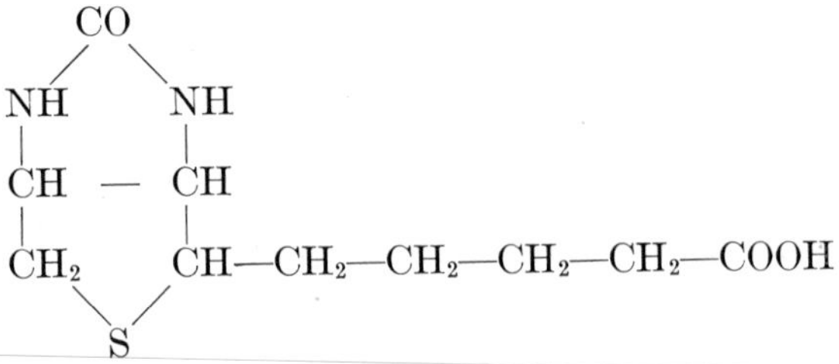

CO

NH   NH

CH   —   CH

$CH_2 \qquad CH-CH_2-CH_2-CH_2-CH_2-COOH$

S

Biotin

COOH CH_2SH

$NH_2CHCH_2CH_2CO-NHCHCO-NHCH_2COOH$

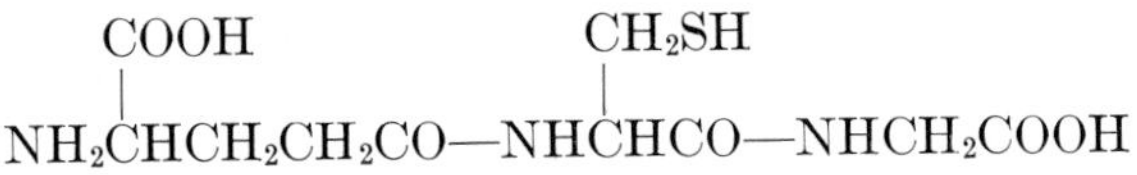

Glutathione

The above four cofactors have been selected more-or-less at random from the literature as examples of compounds which will one day be identified as coenzymes. Since biotin is required in very minute amounts it may turn out that this substance is indirectly involved in the synthesis of enzymes (70, 128). There is some evidence that it may be involved in the synthesis of C_2 to C_{16} fatty acids (133). Ascorbic acid is needed in fairly large doses nutritionally (in man, monkey, and the guinea pig) and may serve as an intracellular reducing agent. The biosynthetic route of ascorbic acid from glucose is now fairly well understood (129). Apart from a general stimulation

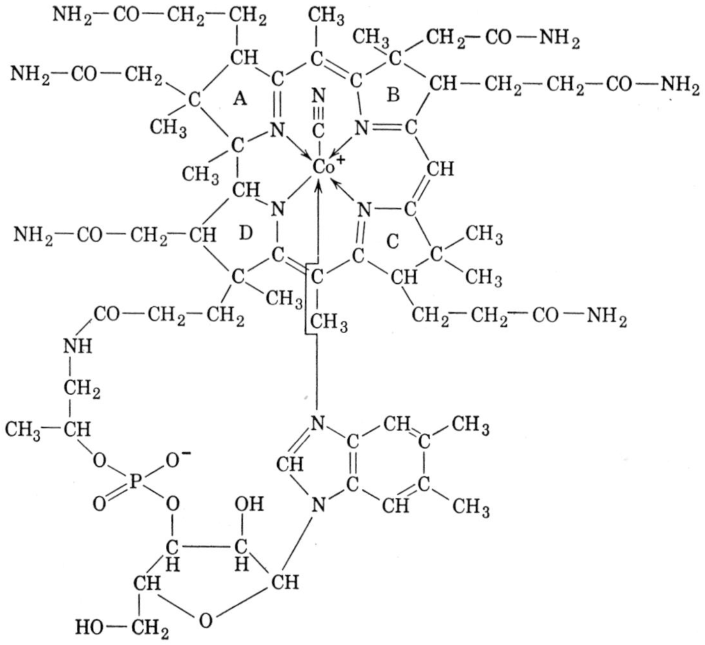

Formula of Vitamin B$_{12}$. [Reproduced from Hodgkin *et al.*, Formula I, *Nature*, 178, 65 (1950).]

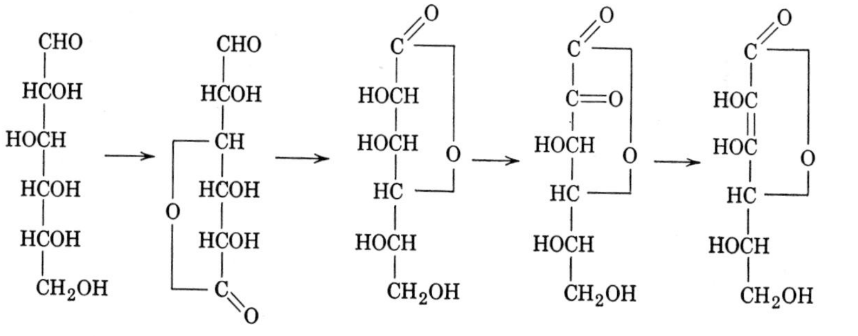

| D-Glucose | D-Glucurono-lactone | L-Gulono-lactone | 2-Keto-L-gulono-lactone | L-Ascorbic acid |

Pathway for conversion of D-glucose to L-ascorbic acid in rats (129).

of the glyoxalase enzymes, a similar role has been supposed for gluta-thione. Thus:

$$\text{Substrate H}_2 + \text{TPN or DPN} \rightleftharpoons \text{Substrate} + \text{TPNH or}$$
$$\text{DPNH} + \text{H}^+$$
$$\text{TPNH or DPNH} + \text{GSSG} + \text{H}^+ \rightleftharpoons 2\text{GSH} + \text{TPN or DPN}$$
$$2\text{GSH} + \text{RSSR} \rightleftharpoons \text{GSSG} + 2\text{RSH}$$

Table 17.2. Properties of Coenzymes

Coenzyme	Function	Source	Molecular Weight (free acid)	Structural Units	Ionization* Constants	Absorption* Maxima and Molar Extinction Coefficients	Stability
Adenosine phosphates							
AMP	Phosphate transport	Yeast	347	Adenine; ribose; phosphate	3.7(NH₂); 6.1(P₂)	Max. at 260 mµ; see ref. 91 for extinction coefficients	Labile in both acid, and alkali, especially pyrophosphate bonds
ADP			427	Adenine; ribose; 2 phosphates	4.0(NH₂); 6.3(P₂)		
ATP			507	Adenine; ribose; 3 phosphates	4.0(NH₂); 6.5(P₂) All ref. (89)		
Pyridine nucleotides							
DPN⁺	Hydrogen transport	Yeast	664	Adenylic acid; NMN	3.7(NH₂) (90)	Reduced form ε at 340 mµ, 6.22 × 10³ (92)	Oxidized form labile in alkali, more stable in acid; reverse stability for reduced form
TPN⁺		Liver	744	Adenosine-2'-phosphate; phosphate; NMN		Same (92)	
Flavin nucleotides							
FMN	Hydrogen transport	Synthetic	456	Dimethyl isoalloxazine; ribitol phosphate	6.1(P₂); 9.9(N-3) (90)	Max. at 375 and 450 mµ	Labile to light, acid, and alkali
FAD		Yeast	785	Dimethyl isoalloxazine; ribitol phosphate; adenylic acid		Max. at 260, 375, and 450 mµ; ε at 450 mµ, 1.13 × 10⁴ (19, 97)	
Coenzyme A	Acyl group transport	Yeast	767	Adenosine-3'-phosphate; 2 phosphates; pantetheine	4.0(NH₂); 6.4(P₂); 9.6(SH) (102)	Max. at 260 mµ; acyl ester has band at 238 mµ	Labile to acid and alkali
Pyridoxal phosphate	Various amino acid transformations	Synthetic	247	Pyridoxal; phosphate	4.1(OH); 6.2(P₂); 8.7(N) (66)	ε at 388 mµ, 4.9 × 10³ (pH 7.0) (93); see ref. 66 for ultraviolet spectra	Relatively stable

Pyridoxamine phosphate		Synthetic	248	Pyridoxamine; phosphate	3.7(OH); 5.8(P$_2$); 8.6(N); 10.9(NH$_2$) (66)	Labile to acid and alkali
Thiamine pyrophosphate	Decarboxylation of keto acids	Synthetic	425	2-Methyl, 4-amino pyrimidine; methylene bridge; 1 methyl, 2 hydroxyl ethyl thiazole; pyrophosphate	5.0(NH$_2$) (90)	
Lipoic acid	Hydrogen transport	Synthetic	206	6,8-Dithiooctanoic acid	334 mμ (90)	Stable
Uridine diphosphate glucose	Isomerization of carbohydrate	Synthetic	566	Uracil; ribose; 2 phosphates; glucose		Labile to acid and alkali
Glucose-1,6-diphosphate	Mutation of glucose phosphate	Synthetic	340	Glucose; 2 phosphates		Labile to acid and alkali

* The original references must be consulted for conditions such as pH and temperature. P$_2$ = secondary phosphate.

Racker (72, 130) however, has found this peptide to be present in preparations of triose phosphate dehydrogenase.

It is obviously very difficult to make rigid rules about what substances should and should not be regarded as cofactors. Thus even such mundane metabolites as glutamine and fumaric acid can be considered as cofactors in the biosynthesis of N bases and urea, respectively.

5. Metals

All the trace metals essential for living cells must be somehow concerned with catalytic processes.

Some of the metal-containing or metal-activated enzymes are listed in Table 17.1. The list, by no means complete, is intended only to

Table 17.1. Some Representative Metal-Containing or
Metal-Activated Enzymes *

Metal	Enzymes	Reference
Iron	Cytochromes	77
	Hydroperoxidases	78
	Cytochrome c reductase	79
	Histidine decarboxylase	80
Copper	Tyrosinase	81
	Ascorbic acid oxidase	81
Zinc	Carbonic anhydrase	83
	Peptidases	84
Magnesium	Phosphatases	85
	ATP-enzymes	85
	Peptidases	84
Manganese	Peptidases	84
Molybdenum	Xanthine oxidase	86
	Nitrate reductase	87
	Hydrogenase	98
Cobalt	Peptidases	84
Potassium	ATP-phosphopyruvate transphosphorylase	88
Calcium	Actomyosin	85

* As a general reference, see the review by Williams (76). Butyryl CoA dehydrogenase, originally reported to contain copper (82), is apparently not a metalloenzyme.

illustrate which metals have thus far been implicated in enzyme action. Detailed information on the iron porphyrins may be found in the comprehensive book by Lemberg and Legge (73); others are briefly referred to in the book by Sumner and Somers (74). The book by Martell and Calvin (75) provides information on the mechanism of chelation by various metals. A most useful review on the metal enzymes is that of Williams (76).

6. Table of Properties of Coenzymes

Table 17.2 summarizes the general properties of some coenzymes which have been well characterized.

References

General

1. B. L. Horecker and A. Kornberg, in *Biochem. and Physiol. of Nutrition*, II, edited by G. H. Bourne and G. W. Kidder, Academic Press, N. Y., Chapter 18, 1953.
2. G. A. Lepage, in *Respiratory Enzymes*, edited by H. A. Lardy, Burgess Publishing Co., Minneapolis, Minn., 1949. See also *Physiol. Rev., 33* (October, 1953).
3. *Symposium on Vitamin Metabolism*, National Vitamin Foundation, N. Y. 22, N. Y., 1956.

Bibliography

4. T. P. Singer and E. B. Kearney, *Advances in Enzymology, 15,* 79 (1954).
5. T. P. Singer and E. B. Kearney, in *The Proteins,* edited by H. Neurath and K. Bailey, Academic Press, N. Y., 1954.
6. C. A. Elvehjem et al., *J. Am. Chem. Soc., 59,* 1767 (1937).
7. J. B. Neilands and Å. Åkeson, *J. Biol. Chem., 188,* 307 (1951).
8. A. Kornberg and B. L. Horecker, *Biochem. Preps., 3,* 24 (1953).
9. R. K. Bonnichsen, *Acta Chem. Scand., 4,* 714 (1950).
10. M. B. Mathews and E. E. Conn, *J. Am. Chem. Soc., 75,* 5428 (1953).
11. F. Schlenk, in a *Symposium on Respiratory Enzymes,* University of Wisconsin Press, Madison, 1942.
12. A. Kornberg and W. E. Pricer, *J. Biol. Chem., 186,* 557 (1950).
13. P. Karrer et al., *Helv. Chim. Acta, 20,* 720 (1937).
14. M. E. Pullman, *Federation Proc., 12,* 255 (1953). See also *J. Biol. Chem., 206,* 121, 129 (1954).
15. A. Kornberg, *J. Biol. Chem., 182,* 779 (1950).
16. A. Kornberg, *J. Biol. Chem., 182,* 805 (1950).
17. A. Szent-Györgyi and I. Banga, *Biochem. Z., 246,* 203 (1932).
18. H. Theorell, in *The Enzymes,* edited by J. B. Sumner and K. Myrbäck, Academic Press, N. Y., 1951.
19. E. Dimant, D. R. Sanadi, and F. M. Huennekens, *J. Am. Chem. Soc., 74,* 5440 (1952).
20. O. A. Bessey, O. H. Lowry, and R. H. Love, *J. Biol. Chem., 180,* 755 (1949).
21. O. Warburg and W. Christian, *Biochem. Z., 298,* 150 (1938).
22. S. M. H. Christie, G. W. Kenner, and A. R. Todd, *J. Chem. Soc., 1954,* 46.
23. E. E. Snell and F. M. Strong, *Ind. Eng. Chem., Anal. Ed., 11,* 346 (1939).
24. A. W. Schrecker and A. Kornberg, *J. Biol. Chem., 182,* 795 (1950).

25. G. W. E. Plaut, Abstr., 124 Meeting Am. Chem. Soc., Chicago, September, 1953.

26. E. B. Kearney and S. Englard, *J. Biol. Chem., 193,* 821 (1951).

27. G. W. Kidder and V. C. Dewey, *Arch. Biochem., 20,* 433 (1949).

28. D. J. O'Kane and I. C. Gunsalus, *J. Bact., 56,* 499 (1948).

29. L. J. Reed and B. G. DeBusk, *J. Biol. Chem., 199,* 881 (1952).

30. M. W. Bullock, J. A. Brockman, E. L. Patterson, J. V. Pierce, and E. L. R. Stokstad, *J. Am. Chem. Soc., 74,* 3455 (1952). See also *J. Am. Chem. Soc., 76,* 4109 (1954).

31. L. P. Hager and I. C. Gunsalus, *J. Am. Chem. Soc., 75,* 5767 (1953).

32. K. Lohmann, *Biochem. Z., 203,* 164 (1928).

33. S. A. Morell, S. H. Lipton, and A. Frieden, *Science, 114,* 333 (1951).

34. H. M. Kalckar, in *The Enzymes,* edited by J. B. Sumner and K. Myrbäck, Academic Press, N. Y., 1951.

35. J. T. Park and M. J. Johnson, *J. Biol. Chem., 179,* 585 (1949).

36. J. T. Park, *J. Biol. Chem., 194,* 877, 885, 897 (1952).

37. R. Caputto, L. F. Leloir, C. E. Cardini, and A. C. Paladini, *J. Biol. Chem., 184,* 333 (1950).

38. S. H. Lipton, S. A. Morell, A. Frieden, and R. M. Bock, *J. Am. Chem. Soc., 75,* 5449 (1953).

39. L. F. Leloir, *Advances in Enzymology, 14,* 193 (1953). See also *Progress in the Chemistry of Organic Natural Products, 8,* 48 (1951).

40. G. J. Dutton and I. D. E. Storey, *Biochem. J., 53,* xxxvii (1953).

41. L. F. Leloir and C. E. Cardini, *J. Am. Chem. Soc., 75,* 6084 (1953).

42. A. C. Paladini, R. Caputto, L. F. Leloir, R. E. Trucco, and C. E. Cardini, *Arch. Biochem., 23,* 55 (1949).

43. E. W. Sutherland, T. Posternak, and C. F. Cori, *J. Biol. Chem., 181,* 153 (1949).

44. S. Rapoport and J. Luebering, *J. Biol. Chem., 183,* 507 (1950).

45. S. Rapoport and J. Luebering, *J. Biol. Chem., 196,* 583 (1952).

46. E. Baer, *J. Biol. Chem., 185,* 763 (1950).

47. C. Neuberg and L. Karczag, *Biochem. Z., 36,* 68, 76 (1911).

48. K. Lohmann and P. Schuster, *Biochem. Z., 294,* 188 (1937).

49. F. Lipmann and G. Perlmann, *J. Am. Chem. Soc., 60,* 2574 (1938).

50. J. B. Neilands, unpublished observations.

51. T. Matsukawa and S. Yurugi, *Science, 118,* 109 (1953).

52. R. J. Williams, *Advances in Enzymology, 3,* 253 (1943).

53. F. Lipmann, *Bact. Revs., 17,* 1 (1953).

54. G. D. Novelli, *Physiol. Rev., 33,* 509 (1953).

55. F. Lipmann et al., *J. Biol. Chem., 186,* 235 (1950).

56. G. D. Novelli, N. O. Kaplan, and F. Lipmann, *J. Biol. Chem., 177,* 97 (1949).

57. H. Beinert et al., *J. Am. Chem. Soc., 74,* 854 (1952).

58. E. R. Stadtman and A. Kornberg, *J. Biol. Chem., 203,* 47 (1953).

59. W. L. Williams, E. Hoff-Jorgensen, and E. E. Snell, *J. Biol. Chem., 177,* 933 (1949).

60. F. Lynen, *Federation Proc., 12,* 3, 683 (1953).

61. G. D. Novelli, *Federation Proc., 12,* No. 3, 675 (1953); *J. Biol. Chem., 207,* 767 (1954).

62. E. E. Snell, *Physiol. Rev., 33,* 509 (1953).

63. E. A. Peterson, H. A. Sober, and A. Meister, *Biochem. Preps., 3,* 29 (1953).

64. J. Baddiley and A. P. Mathias, *J. Chem. Soc., 1952,* 2538.

65. S. A. Harris, T. J. Webb, and K. Folkers, *J. Am. Chem. Soc., 62,* 3198 (1940).

66. V. R. Williams and J. B. Neilands, *Arch. Biochem. and Biophys.,* in press.

67. P. S. Cammarata and P. P. Cohen, *J. Biol. Chem., 193,* 45, 53 (1951).

68. A. Meister, H. A. Sober, and E. A. Peterson, *J. Am. Chem. Soc., 74,* 2385 (1952).

69. J. Baddiley, *Nature, 711,* 710 (1952).

70. H. A. Lardy, *Physiol. Rev., 33,* 509 (1953).

71. C. A. Nichol, in *Symposium on Vitamin Metabolism,* National Vitamin Foundation, N. Y., N. Y., 1956.

72. E. Racker, in *The Mechanism of Enzyme Action,* edited by W. D. McElroy and B. Glass. Johns Hopkins Press, Baltimore, 1954.

73. R. Lemberg and J. W. Legge, *Hematin Compounds and Bile Pigments,* Interscience Publishers, N. Y., 1949.

74. J. B. Sumner and G. F. Somers, *Chemistry and Methods of Enzymes,* Academic Press, N. Y., 1953.

75. A. E. Martell and M. Calvin, *Chemistry of the Metal Chelate Compounds,* Prentice-Hall, N. Y., 1952.

76. R. J. P. Williams, *Biolog. Revs., 28,* 381 (1953).

77. K. G. Paul, in *The Enzymes,* edited by J. B. Sumner and K. Myrbäck, Academic Press, N. Y., 1951.

78. H. Theorell, in *The Enzymes,* edited by J. B. Sumner and K. Myrbäck, Academic Press, N. Y., 1951.

79. H. R. Mahler and D. G. Elowe, *J. Am. Chem. Soc., 75,* 5679 (1953).

80. B. M. Guirard and E. E. Snell, *J. Am. Chem. Soc., 76,* 4745 (1954).

81. C. R. Dawson and W. B. Tarpley, in *The Enzymes,* edited by J. B. Sumner and K. Myrbäck, Academic Press, N. Y., 1951.

82. H. R. Mahler, *J. Am. Chem. Soc., 75,* 3288 (1953).

83. D. Keilin and T. Mann, *Biochem. J., 34,* 1163 (1940).

84. E. L. Smith, in *The Enzymes,* edited by J. B. Sumner and K. Myrbäck, Academic Press, N. Y., 1951.

85. A. L. Lehninger, *Physiol. Revs., 30,* 393 (1950).

86. D. E. Green and H. Beinert, *Biochim. et Biophys. Acta, 11,* 599 (1953).

87. D. J. D. Nicholas, A. Nason, and W. D. McElroy, *Nature, 172,* 34 (1953).

88. H. A. Lardy and J. A. Ziegler, *J. Biol. Chem., 159,* 343 (1945).

89. R. A. Alberty, R. M. Smith, and R. M. Bock, *J. Biol. Chem., 193,* 425 (1951).

90. J. B. Neilands, unpublished.

91. *Bulletin on Properties of Nucleic Acid Derivatives,* California Foundation for Biochemical Research, 3408 Fowler St., Los Angeles 63, California.

92. B. L. Horecker and A. Kornberg, *J. Biol. Chem., 175,* 385 (1948).

93. E. A. Peterson, H. A. Sober, and A. Meister, *Biochem. Preps., 3,* 34 (1953).

94. D. R. Sanadi and P. Ayengar, *Federation Proc., 13,* 287 (1954).

95. M. E. Pullman and V. A. Najjar, *Federation Proc., 13,* 277 (1954).

96. D. E. Metzler, M. Ikawa, and E. E. Snell, *J. Am. Chem. Soc., 76,* 648 (1954).

97. L. G. Whitby, *Biochem. J.*, *54*, 437 (1953).

98. A. L. Shug, P. W. Wilson, D. E. Green, and H. R. Mahler, *J. Am. Chem. Soc.*, *76*, 3355 (1954).

99. R. H. Hall and H. G. Khorana, *Abstracts, Am. Chem. Soc. Meeting*, Kansas City, March-April, 1954.

100. E. E. Snell in *Special Lectures in Biochemistry*, University of London, (1954–1955).

101. L. J. Zatman, N. O. Kaplan, and S. P. Colowick, *J. Biol. Chem.*, *200*, 197 (1953).

102. H. Beinert, R. W. Von Korff, D. E. Green, D. A. Buyske, R. E. Handschumacher, H. Higgins and F. M. Strong, *J. Biol. Chem.*, *200*, 385 (1953).

103. T. W. Goodwin and S. Pendlington, *Biochem. J.*, *57*, 631 (1954).

104. F. Schlenk, in *The Enzymes*, edited by J. B. Sumner and K. Myrbäck, Academic Press, N. Y., 1951.

105. W. A. Krehl et al., *Science*, *101*, 489 (1945).

106. L. M. Henderson, *Symposium on Vitamin Metabolism*, National Vitamin Foundation, N. Y., 1956.

107. N. O. Kaplan, *Symposium on Vitamin Metabolism*, National Vitamin Foundation, N. Y., 1956.

108. T. Masuda et al., *J. Pharm. Soc. Japan*, *75*, 358 (1955).

109. K. Yagi et al., *J. Biochem.*, *43*, 93 (1956).

110. H. Beinert, *J. Am. Chem. Soc.*, *78*, 5323 (1956).

111. G. W. E. Plaut, in *Symposium on Vitamin Metabolism*, National Vitamin Foundation, N. Y., 1956.

112. W. S. McNutt, *J. Biol. Chem.*, *219*, 365 (1956).

113. I. C. Gunsalus, *Symposium on Vitamin Metabolism*, National Vitamin Foundation, N. Y., 1956.

114. A. Kornberg and W. E. Pricer, *Fed. Proc.*, *11*, 242 (1952).

115. E. P. Kennedy and S. B. Weiss, *J. Biol. Chem.*, *222*, 193 (1956).

116. D. R. Sanadi et al., *J. Biol. Chem.*, *218*, 505 (1956).

117. V. Jagannathan and J. M. Luck, *J. Biol. Chem.*, *179*, 569 (1949).

118. L. Anderson and G. Jolles, *Arch. Biochem. Biophys.*, *70*, 121 (1957).

119. H. Klenow, *Arch. Biochem. Biophys.*, *46*, 186 (1953).

120. H. Klenow and E. Emberland, *Arch. Biochem. Biophys.*, *58*, 276 (1955).

121. H. L. A. Tarr, *Chem. & Industry*, 562 (1957).

122. G. M. Brown, in *Symposium on Vitamin Metabolism*, National Vitamin Foundation, N. Y., 1956.

123. T. Baranowski et al., *Biochem. Biophys. Acta*, *25*, 16 (1956).

124. E. Fischer, personal communication.

125. R. D. Sagers et al., *J. Am. Chem. Soc.*, *78*, 694 (1956).

126. A. Miller and H. Waelsch, *Arch. Biochem. Biophys.*, *63*, 263 (1956).

127. J. C. Rabinowitz and W. E. Pricer, *J. Am. Chem. Soc.*, *78*, 4176 (1956).

128. L. D. Wright, in *Symposium on Vitamin Metabolism*, National Vitamin Foundation, N. Y., 1956.

129. J. J. Burns, in *Symposium on Vitamin Metabolism*, National Vitamin Foundation, N. Y., 1956.

130. I. Krimsky and E. Racker, *Science*, *122*, 319 (1955).

131. R. Breslow, *J. Am. Chem. Soc.*, *79*, 1762 (1957).

132. J. E. Downes and P. Sykes, *Chemistry & Industry*, 1095 (1957).

133. E. B. Titchener, D. M. Gibson and S. J. Wakil, *Fed. Proc.* 17, 322 (1958).

18

Classification of Enzymes

1. Introduction

In general, enzymes may be assigned to large groups based on the type of biochemical reaction they catalyze. Thus lipases and phosphatases, being hydrolytic enzymes, logically fall into the group of hydrolases. Subdivision within these large groups is in turn based on the substrate specificity associated with these enzymes. Lipases are included with those hydrolytic enzymes which cleave organic acid-alcohol ester linkages, whereas the phosphatases are correctly associated with those hydrolytic enzymes which split phosphate bonds. A stimulating discussion of the many problems of enzyme classification is presented in a review by Hoffman-Ostenhof (7).

Since the number of biochemical reactions is too great, only the more important types will form the basis of classification to be presented in this chapter. These include hydrolysis, transference, addition, isomerization, carboxylation, and respiration.

2. Hydrolysis

Historically, enzymes collected in this group had been known and studied many decades before the science of enzymology had acquired a firm footing. Thus the proteolytic enzymes of the digestive system were described in general terms by Réaumur in 1752, and such hydrolytic enzymes as the amylases were noted in 1814. Only since the 1940's, however, has the nature of the hydrolytic process been described in terms of modern concepts. Thus it appears as if the hydrolytic system is a special case of the general system:

$$R\text{—}X + HEn \rightleftharpoons R\text{—}En + XH$$

$$H_2O \diagup \quad \Big\Vert \, YH$$

$$R\text{—}OH + HEn \qquad R\text{—}Y + HEn$$

(Hydrolysis)   (Transference)

where R—X is the substrate or the donor system.

R is transferable group.

Y is the general acceptor system.

H_2O is a special acceptor system.

Typical hydrolases are:

A. *Phosphatases.*

$$R—O—PO_3H_2 + H_2O \rightleftharpoons ROH + H_3PO_4$$

B. *Proteolytic Enzymes.*

$$\overset{O}{\overset{\|}{RC}}—NHR^1 + H_2O \rightleftharpoons \overset{O}{\overset{\|}{RC}}—OH + NH_2R^1$$

C. *Glycosidases.*

$$Sugar^1—O—Sugar^2 + H_2O \rightleftharpoons Sugar^1 + Sugar^2$$

D. *Lipases and Esterases.*

$$\overset{O}{\overset{\|}{R^1C}}—OR^2 + H_2O \rightleftharpoons \overset{O}{\overset{\|}{R^1C}}—OH + R^2OH$$

In all these general examples H_2O is the final acceptor of the transferable group of the donor. However, in some systems, a suitable acceptor, if present in adequate concentrations, may compete successfully with water to capture the donor moiety. In such cases a transfer reaction is said to have taken place (see section 3 for further details).

3. Transference (4)

The concept of the transfer of reactive groups from one compound to another with a simultaneous preservation of the bond energy associated with these groups has become an integral part of biological energetics in metabolism.

The transfer reaction, in essence, involves a donor substrate (D-X), an acceptor (A), an enzyme responsible for the catalysis of the system (En), and the moiety that is being transferred (X):

$$A + D\text{-}X \overset{En}{\rightleftharpoons} D + A\text{-}X \qquad (1)$$

Although equation 1 represents the gross aspects of the transfer reaction, the following points must be stressed:

(*a*) When X is being transferred from D → A, the bond energy in D-X is not dissipated but often is transferred with little if any loss in energy; the system is reversible with a small change of ΔF. In some transfers a considerable part of the energy is lost as heat; the transfer system is then thought to be largely irreversible with a large decrease in ΔF.

(b) In the actual mechanism of transfer the enzyme undoubtedly participates as the mediator by forming an En-X complex:

$$D\text{-}X + En \rightleftharpoons D\text{-}X - En \rightleftharpoons D + En\text{-}X \qquad (2)$$

$$En\text{-}X + A \rightleftharpoons A\text{-}En - X \rightleftharpoons A\text{-}X + En \qquad (3)$$

The various transferase systems may be classified by the groups which they transfer. Table 18.1 lists some important transferase systems.

4. Addition

The generalized equation for an addition reaction is:

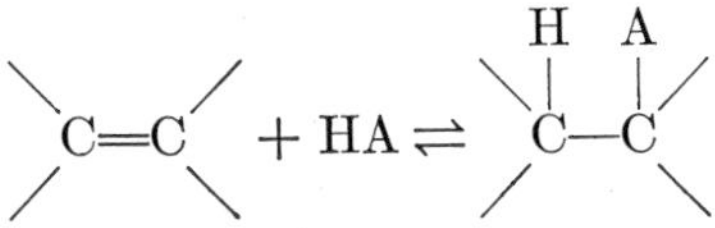

$$\begin{matrix} \diagdown \\ \diagup \end{matrix} C{=}C \begin{matrix} \diagup \\ \diagdown \end{matrix} + HA \rightleftharpoons \begin{matrix} & H & A \\ & | & | \\ \diagdown & | & | & \diagup \\ \diagup & C{-}C & \diagdown \end{matrix}$$

Addition of HA to a double bond system is undoubtedly influenced by the inductive effects exerted by groups adjacent to the bond and by polarization effects of the enzyme protein on the double bond system in the substrate. Thus the addition of NH_3 to acrylyl CoA to form β-alanyl CoA may be depicted in the following manner:

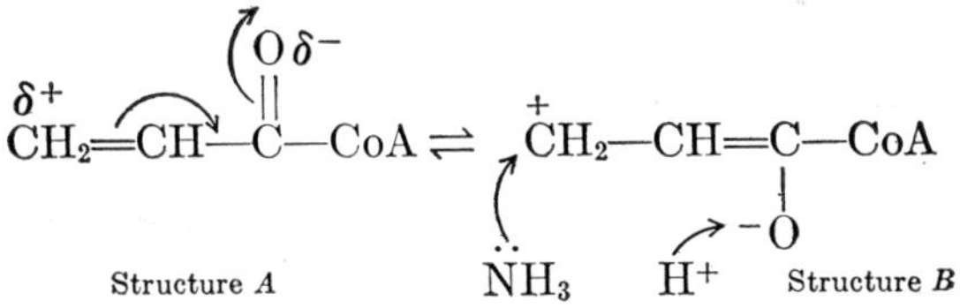

$$\overset{\delta+}{CH_2}{=}CH\overset{\overset{\displaystyle O\,\delta-}{\|}}{C}{-}CoA \rightleftharpoons \overset{+}{CH_2}{-}CH{=}\overset{|}{C}{-}CoA$$

| Structure A | NH_3 | H^+ | Structure B |

The electronegativity of oxygen tends to pull electrons from the carbon atoms with a simultaneous shift of electrons from the double bond to structure B, the resonanting form. Structure B presumably attaches to the enzyme protein at its polar areas. NH_3 with its pair of unshared electrons will make a nucleophilic attack at the β-carbon of the substrate which has an electrophilic center. By this attack, the ammonia molecule displaces the enzyme-substrate bond at the β-carbon; simultaneously a proton displaces the enzyme–oxygen bond at the carbonyl group and the reaction product rearranges to yield β-alanyl CoA.

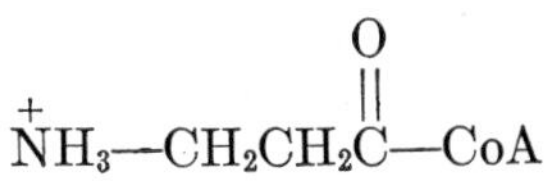

$$\overset{+}{NH_3}{-}CH_2CH_2\overset{\overset{\displaystyle O}{\|}}{C}{-}CoA$$

Table 18.1. Transferase Systems

Group	Reaction	Enzyme
A. Transphosphorylases		
1. High-energy systems with small $-\Delta F$	$ATP + Creatine \rightleftharpoons ADP + Creatine\ phosphate$	Creatine transphosphorylase
	$ATP + AMP \rightleftharpoons 2ADP$	Adenylic kinase (myokinase)
2. High-energy systems with large $-\Delta F$	$ATP + Glucose \rightleftharpoons ADP + Glucose\text{-}6\text{-}PO_4$	Glucokinase
	$ATP + Fructose \rightleftharpoons ADP + Fructose\text{-}1\text{-}PO_4$	Fructokinase
	$ATP + Fructose\text{-}6\text{-}PO_4 \rightleftharpoons ADP + Fructose\text{-}1,6\text{-}DiPO_4$	Phosphofructokinase
3. Low-energy systems	$Nitrophenyl\text{-}PO_4 + Methanol \rightleftharpoons Nitrophenol + Methyl\text{-}PO_4$	Citrus phosphatase
	$Glucose\text{-}1\text{-}PO_4 + Glycerol \rightleftharpoons Glycerol\text{-}PO_4 + Glucose$	Acid or alkaline phosphatase
B. Transglycosidases		
1. Polysaccharide transglycosidases	$Glucose\text{-}1\text{-}PO_4 + (Glucose)_n \rightleftharpoons (Glucose)_{n+1} + PO_4$	Phosphorylase
	$Amylose + Q\ enzyme \rightleftharpoons (Glucose)_{20}\text{-}Q\ enzyme$	Q enzyme
	$(Glucose)_{20}\text{-}Q\ enzyme + Amylose \rightleftharpoons Amylopectin + Q\ enzyme$	Q enzyme
	$n(Glucose\text{-}glucose) \rightleftharpoons (Glucose)_n + n\text{-}Glucose$	Amylomaltase
2. Transfructosidases	$n(Glucose\text{-}fructose) \rightleftharpoons (Fructose)_{n(2,6)} + n\text{-}Glucose$	Levansucrase
3. Oligosaccharide transglucosidases	$Glucose\text{-}1\text{-}PO_4 + Fructose \rightleftharpoons Glucose\text{-}fructose + PO_4$	Sucrose phosphorylase
	$Glucose + \beta\text{-}Glucose\text{-}1\text{-}PO_4 \rightleftharpoons Maltose + PO_4$	Maltose phosphorylase
	$UDPG + Glucose\text{-}6\text{-}PO_4 \rightleftharpoons Trehalose\text{-}PO_4 + UDP$	UDPG – G-6-P Transglycosylase
	$UDPG + Fructose \rightleftharpoons Sucrose + UDP$	UDPG – fructose Transglycosylase
4. Trans-N-glycosidases	$Purine\text{-}N\text{-}9\text{-}riboside + PO_4 \rightleftharpoons Purine + Ribose\text{-}1\text{-}PO_4$	
	$Pyrimidine\text{-}N\text{-}3\text{-}riboside + PO_4 \rightleftharpoons Pyrimidine + Ribose\text{-}1\text{-}PO_4$	
C. Transaminases	$Glutamate + Oxalacetate \rightleftharpoons \alpha\text{-}Ketoglutarate + Aspartate$	Glutamate-aspartate transaminase
	$Glutamate + Pyruvate \rightleftharpoons \alpha\text{-}Ketoglutarate + Alanine$	Glutamate-alanate transaminase
	$Glutamate + X\text{-}\alpha\text{-}Ketoacid \rightleftharpoons \alpha\text{-}Ketoglutarate + X\text{-}\alpha\text{-}Amino\ acids$	General series of transaminases
D. Transacylases		
1. CoA-transferases	$Acetyl\ CoA + Propionate \rightleftharpoons Propionyl\ CoA + acetate$	CoA transferase (*Cl. kluyveri*)
	$Succinyl\ CoA + Acetoacetate \rightleftharpoons Acetoacetyl\ CoA + Succinate$	CoA transferase (animal)

Similar patterns of reaction can be visualized for other addition reactions; typical examples are presented in Table 18.2.

5. Isomerization (5)

Isomerization occurs at different points of metabolism. Most of the reactions catalyzed by isomerases are not important as energy-yielding reactions but they play critical roles in preparing and modifying substrates for subsequent reactions. This group reaction is rather heterogeneous in character but the majority of the known reactions occur in the area of carbohydrate metabolism. Table 18.5 summarizes some of these.

6. Carboxylation (6)

This group of enzymes is responsible both for the formation of carbon dioxide from organic substrates, and for the incorporation of carbon dioxide into an organic molecule. No general mechanism can be presented since the cofactor requirements of each enzyme catalyzed system varies with the type of substrate attacked. α-keto acid carboxylases require a divalent cation and thiamin pyrophosphate; l-amino acid carboxylases pyridoxal phosphate; malic enzyme a divalent cation and TPN^+; oxaloacetic carboxylase a divalent cation; and the carboxylating enzyme (ribulose diphosphate), a divalent cation. In Table 18-6 are gathered together a list of typical carboxylating enzymes.

Table 18.2. Addition Systems

Reaction	Enzyme
Citrate $\xrightleftharpoons{\pm H_2O}$ *cis*-Aconitate $\xrightleftharpoons{\pm H_2O}$ Isocitrate	Aconitase
Phosphoenolpyruvate $\xrightleftharpoons{\pm H_2O}$ 2-Phosphoryl D-Glycerate	Enolase
Fumarate $\xrightleftharpoons{\pm H_2O}$ Malate	Fumarase
Crotonyl-CoA $+ H_2O \rightleftharpoons \beta$ Hydroxyl butyryl CoA	Enoyl hydrase

Table 18.3. Isomerization

Structural Isomerization:	Enzyme

Transfer of PO_4 group

$$\text{Glucose 1-PO}_4 \underset{\longleftarrow}{\overset{\text{gl-1,6-diPO}_4}{\longrightarrow}} \text{Glucose 6-PO}_4 \qquad\qquad \text{Phosphogluco-mutase}$$

Shift of H in $C_1 \rightleftharpoons C_2$ of sugar series

$$\text{Glucose 6-PO}_4 \rightleftharpoons \text{Fructose 6-PO}_4 \qquad\qquad \text{Phosphohexo-isomerase}$$

Shift of CH_3 group

Methyl malonyl CoA $\rightleftharpoons$ Succinyl CoA — Methyl malonyl CoA isomerase

Stereoisomerization:
Sugar series
C_1 shift

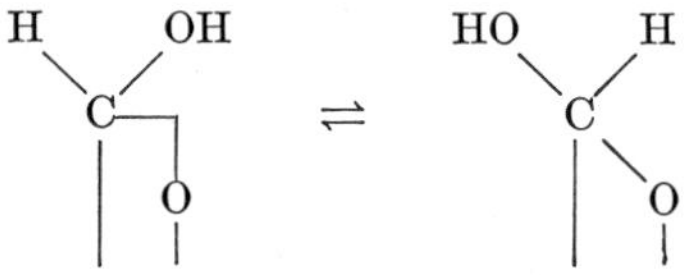

Mutarotase

C_2 shift

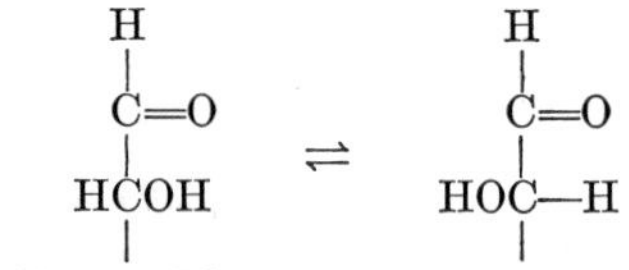

Glucose 6-PO₄   Mannose 6-PO₄   Mannose 6-PO₄ isomerase

C_3 shift

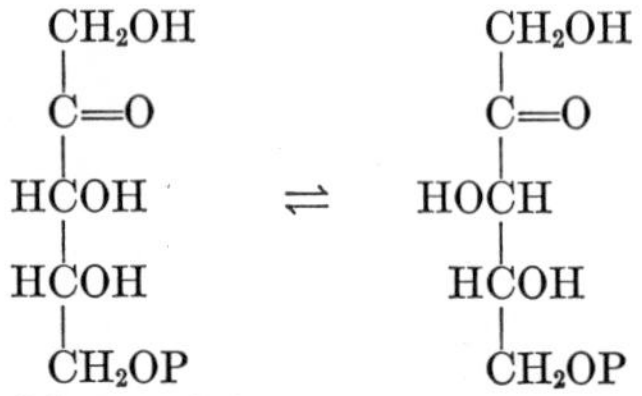

D-Ribulose 5-PO₄   D-Xylulose 5-PO₄   Phosphoketo pento-epimerase

C_4 shift

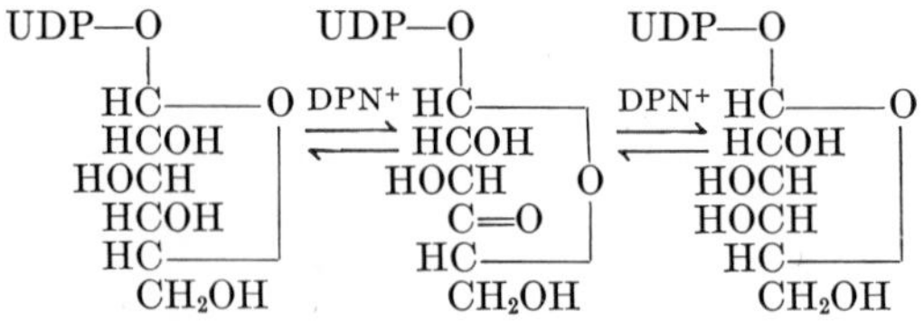

4-Ketohexose-epimerase

Racemases:

D-Glutamic $\rightleftharpoons$ L-Glutamic — Glutamic racemase

$$\text{D-Lactic} \underset{\longleftarrow}{\overset{\text{DPN}^+}{\longrightarrow}} \text{L-Lactic} \qquad\qquad \text{Lactic racemase}$$

Table 18.4. Carboxylation Systems

Reaction	Enzyme
Pyruvate $\rightleftharpoons$ Acetaldehyde $+ CO_2$	Pyruvate carboxylase
α-Ketoglutarate $\rightleftharpoons$ Succinate semialdehyde $+ CO_2$	α-Ketoglutarate carboxylase
Oxalacetate $\rightleftharpoons$ Pyruvate $+ CO_2$	Oxalacetate carboxylase
Oxalosuccinate $\rightleftharpoons$ α-Ketoglutarate $+ CO_2$	Oxalosuccinate carboxylase
Malate $+ TPN^+ \rightleftharpoons$ Pyruvate $+ TPNH + CO_2$	Malic enzyme *
Oxalacetate $+ ITP \rightleftharpoons$ Phosphorylenolpyruvate $+ IDP + CO_2$	Phosphorylenolpyruvate carboxylase (animal)
Oxalacetate $+ PO_4 \rightleftharpoons$ Phosphorylenolpyruvate $+ CO_2$	Phosphorylenolpyruvate carboxylase (plant)
6-Phosphogluconate $\underset{}{\overset{TPN^+}{\rightleftharpoons}}$ 5-Phosphoribulose	6-Phosphogluconate dehydrogenase
$RCHCOOH \rightleftharpoons RCH_2NH_2 + CO_2$ $\|$ NH_2	A large series of amino acid carboxylases, many being highly specific and requiring pyridoxal phosphate
Ribulose diphosphate $+ CO_2 \rightarrow$ 2, 3-Phosphoryl glyceric acid	Carboxylating enzyme

* Complex rather than simple carboxylases

7. Respiration

Cf. Chapter 17.

References

1. Phosphatases: J. Roche, in *The Enzymes*, edited by J. B. Sumner and K. Myrbäck, Academic Press, N. Y., 1950, p. 473; G. Schmidt, *Phosphorus Symposium*, edited by McElroy and Glass, 1951, p. 443.

2. Proteolytic Enzymes: A. K. Balls and E. F. Jansen, *Advances in Enzymology*, *13*, 321 (1952); E. L. Smith, *ibid.*, *12*, 191 (1951); H. Neurath and G. W. Schwert, *Chem. Revs.*, *46*, 69 (1950).

3. Glycosidases: S. Peat, *Advances in Enzymology*, *11*, 339 (1951); E. J. Hehre, *ibid.*, *11*, 297 (1951); A. Lineweaver and E. F. Jansen, *ibid.*, *11*, 267 (1951); K. Meyer and M. M. Rappoport, *ibid.*, *13*, 199.

4. Transferance Reactions: I. C. Gunsalus, *Mechanism of Enzyme Action*, p. 545, 1954; D. E. Koshland, Jr., *ibid.*, p. 608; H. M. Kalckar, *ibid.*, p. 675.

5. Isomerization: L. F. Leloir, *Advances in Enzymology*, *14*, 193 (1953).

6. Carboxylations: S. Ochoa, *Physiol. Revs.*, *31*, 56 (1951); *The Enzymes*, II, Part 2, p. 929, 1952.

7. O. Hoffman-Ostenhof, *Advances in Enzymology*, *14*, 219 (1953).

19

Respiratory Enzymes

1. General Concepts

We now know that the site of oxidations is the tissue cells and not the blood or lungs, as was once supposed. Cells are able to oxidize, with remarkable ease, a wide variety of metabolites many of which are completely stable in air. The enzymes that take part in these energy-yielding reactions are grouped under the term "respiratory." The reaction sequence from substrate to oxygen may be crudely illustrated as follows, the arrows showing the direction of transfer of hydrogen or electrons:

Substrate → Pyridine nucleotide dehydrogenases →

Flavoproteins → Cytochromes → O_2

It should not be assumed that all the electron-transporting agents at the substrate level can be fitted into one of these groups. For example, the dehydrogenation of succinic acid is catalyzed by an enzyme the coenzymatic structure of which is still unknown (1). This enzyme, succinic dehydrogenase, is generally studied in homogenates or in extracts which still contain particulate matter. For example, Green and his associates (85) have obtained a preparation which is free from cytochrome oxidase, DPNH dehydrogenase, cytochrome c, and all the known enzymes of the citric acid cycle. Certain other dehydrogenases, for example the α-glycerophosphate dehydrogenase of muscle particles, also do not seem to be phosphopyridine-nucleotide-linked (2). Flavoproteins such as notatin (glucose oxidase) may also dehydrogenate substrates directly. The distinction between certain oxidases and dehydrogenases is that dehydrogenases transfer hydrogen to an acceptor, whereas oxidases transfer hydrogen directly to oxygen.

2. Pyridine Nucleotide Dehydrogenases (76, 87)

A. *Introduction.* The pyridine-nucleotide-requiring enzymes compete with the proteolytic enzymes as to the number of them which have been crystallized. The stability and ease of isolation of these enzymes have made possible a vast amount of research on their mechanism of action. The glyceraldehyde-3-phosphate dehydrogenase of muscle and yeast has been studied most extensively (cf. Chapter 14); however, since alcohol dehydrogenase of horse liver has also been examined in detail, it will be of interest to discuss the mechanism of action of that enzyme here. At least part of this rapid progress may be attributed to the value of oxidation-reduction dyes, such as methylene blue, in activity measurements on respiratory enzymes. Spectrophotometric techniques, once developed, were quickly applied to the pyridine nucleotides, since these substances when reduced have a molar absorption coefficient of greater than 6×10^3 at 340 mμ.

Several excellent reviews are available on the pyridine nucleotide dehydrogenases: Singer and Kearney (3), Schlenk (1, 4), and Snell (5).

B. *General Properties of the Pyridine Nucleotide Dehydrogenases.* Glyceraldehyde-3-phosphate dehydrogenase of muscle and yeast, alcohol dehydrogenase of yeast and liver, lactic dehydrogenase of heart

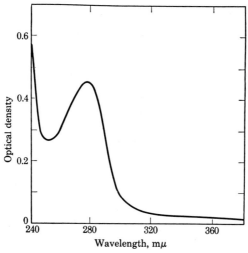

Fig. 19.1. Absorption spectrum of a typical pyridine nucleotide apodehydrogenase.

and liver, and glutamic dehydrogenase of liver are examples of DPN-linked enzymes which have been crystallized. Standard methods such as ammonium sulfate and solvent fractionation were used in their isolation. Their absorption spectra are characterized only by the "protein" band near 280 mμ; there is negligible absorption in the visi-

ble region of the spectrum. The spectrum of a typical pyridine nucleotide apodehydrogenase is shown in Fig. 19.1.

Yeast alcohol dehydrogenase (6) is soluble in distilled water,
whereas heart lactic dehydrogenase precipitates from a salt-free solution. The molecular weights range from 73,000 for liver alcohol dehydrogenase to about 1,000,000 for liver glutamic dehydrogenase. The
molecular weight of yeast alcohol dehydrogenase is about twice as high
as that of the liver enzyme (7, 8). The molecular weights of heart
and liver lactic dehydrogenase are similar although the isoelectric
points are dissimilar (9, 10). To summarize, it may be concluded that
the physical properties of the apoenzymes give no clue as to the reason
for their substrate specificity or their type of catalytic activity.

C. *Mechanism of Action of the Pyridine Nucleotide Dehydrogenases.* Chemically, the common denominator for activity appears
to be the presence of intact sulfhydryl groups. A very great range of
sensitivity to thiol reagents, however, is observed. Muscle glyceralde-
hyde-3-phosphate dehydrogenase is inhibited by a variety of sulfhydryl reagents, while heart lactic dehydrogenase is inhibited only, and
very slowly, by *p*-chloromercuribenzoate. Malic dehydrogenase, although not yet crystallized, is also inhibited by sulfhydryl reagents.

Theorell and Bonnichsen (8) and Theorell and Chance (11) found
that reduced diphosphopyridine nucleotide is rather firmly bound to
the apoenzyme. They were led to this discovery when they noticed a
change in the spectrum of the reduced coenzyme in the presence of
stoichiometric quantities of the crystalline apoenzyme. They were
able to calculate that $\frac{1}{2}$ mole of apoenzyme gave the maximum spectral shift at pH 7, indicating that 2 moles of DPNH are bound. At
pH 10, a 1:1 complex was favored. The holoenzyme is decomposed
with *p*-chloromercuribenzoate, a reagent which strongly inhibits the
enzyme, to liberate the spectrum of the free reduced coenzyme. These
data were interpreted to mean that a sulfhydryl group of the enzyme is
in one way or another linked to the dihydropyridine ring. It is of interest to note that Meyerhof (12) and more recently Colowick et al.
(13) have been able to find similar spectral shifts by the action of
cyanide or bisulfite on DPN$^+$.

It has been shown that lactic dehydrogenase also binds DPNH
(10). The apparent dissociation constant of the complex is some 70
times larger than that of the alcohol dehydrogenase-DPNH compound. Generally speaking, the affinity of these cofactors for their
proteins is not very great. Thus glyceraldehyde-3-phosphate dehydrogenase is the sole known example where the coenzyme is attached
to the isolated protein. According to the spectrum published by Tay-

Table 19.1. Reactions Catalyzed by Pyridine Nucleotide Enzymes (1)

Enzyme	Substrate	Product	Coenzyme
Type: $R(R')CHOH + Coenzyme_{ox} \rightleftharpoons R(R')C{=}O + Coenzyme_{Red}$			
Alcohol dehydrogenase	Ethanol	Acetaldehyde	DPN+
	Vitamin A	Retinine	
Isocitric dehydrogenase	Isocitrate	Oxalosuccinate or α-Keto-glutarate + CO_2	TPN+
Isocitric dehydrogenase	Isocitrate	α-Ketoglutarate + CO_2	DPN+
α-Glycerophosphate dehydrogenase	α-Glycerophosphate	Dihydroxyacetone phosphate	DPN+
β-hydroxybutyric dehydrogenase	β-Hydroxybutyrate	Acetoacetate	DPN+
β-hydroxyacyl coenzyme A dehydrogenase	β-Hydroxyacyl coenzyme A	β-ketoacyl coenzyme A	DPN+
Lactic dehydrogenase	L(+) Lactate	Pyruvate	DPN+
Malic dehydrogenase	L-Malate	Oxalacetate	DPN+
Malic enzyme	L-Malate	Pyruvate + CO_2	TPN+
Choline dehydrogenase	Choline	Betaine aldehyde	DPN+
Lysine α-keto analogue reductase	Lysine α-keto analogue	Pipecolate	DPNH TPNH
Tartrate dehydrogenase	D- or meso-tartrate	Oxaloglycolate Diketosuccinate	DPN+
Galactowaldenase	UDP glucose	UDP glucuronic acid	DPN+
Type: $H_2O + RCHO + Coenzyme_{ox} \rightleftharpoons RCOOH + Coenzyme_{Red}$			
Formic dehydrogenase	Formate	CO_2	DPN+
Glyceraldehyde-3-phosphate dehydrogenase	D-Glyceraldehyde-3-phosphate + acyl acceptor, e.g., H_3PO_4	1,3-Diphosphoglycerate	DPN+
Glucose dehydrogenase	D-Glucose	D-Gluconate	DPN+
Glucose-6-phosphate dehydrogenase	D-Glucose-6-phosphate	6-Phospho-D-gluconate	TPN+
Betaine aldehyde dehydrogenase	Betaine aldehyde	Betaine	DPN+
H_2O Type: $RCHNH_2COOH + Coenzyme_{ox} \overset{}{\underset{}{\rightleftharpoons}} RCOCOOH + NH_3 + Coenzyme_{Red}$			
Glutamic dehydrogenase	Glutamate	α-Ketoglutarate + NH_3	DPN+ TPN+
Type: $RSSR + Coenzyme_{Red} \rightleftharpoons 2RSH + Coenzyme_{ox}$			
Glutathione reductase	Glutathione$_{ox}$	Glutathione$_{Red}$	TPNH
Cystine reductase	Cystine	Cysteine	DPNH
Type: Miscellaneous reactions			
Ketoglutaric dehydrogenase	Ketoglutarate	Succinyl coenzyme A + CO_2	DPN+
Pyruvic dehydrogenase	Pyruvate	Acetyl coenzyme A + CO_2	DPN+
Quinone reductase	p-Benzoquinone	Hydroquinone	DPNH TPNH
Nitrate reductase	Nitrate	Nitrite	TPNH
Cysteine sulfinate dehydrogenase	L-Cysteine sulfinate	L-Cysteic acid	———
Steroid dehydrogenase	HO-steroids	Keto-steroids	DPN+ TPN+

lor and co-workers (14), DPNH is not bound to this enzyme in a manner analogous to either the alcohol or lactic dehydrogenases.

A remarkable development in the field of the pyridine nucleotide enzymes was the discovery by Vallee that several contain the metal zinc (88). This metal ion has been found in crystalline alcohol, lactic and glutamic dehydrogenases, and is suspected to be present in other dehydrogenases as well. The precise role of zinc in these enzymes is still obscure although Vallee has produced some evidence to show that they are concerned in the binding of the coenzyme (or substrate) to the protein.

Theorell and co-workers (89) have shown that ion effects may be very important in the study of the kinetics of pyridine nucleotide dehydrogenases. Apparently the ions exert their influence through specific binding, through altering the charge on the protein or through changing the ionic strength of the medium. In the case of alcohol dehydrogenase, a critical concentration of reactants and anions were needed for maximal effect.

Studies on the mechanism of action of alcohol dehydrogenase reveal that substrate, coenzyme, and protein form a ternary complex. This reaction is relatively rapid compared to the reversible oxido-reduction which occurs on the protein surface. Sizer and Gierer (90), in an interesting communication, have shown that the protons at the active site, which have a pKa of about 7, exchange only slowly with the medium.

From their studies of the peculiar reactivity of the free pyridine nucleotides (see Chapter 17), Kaplan et al. have concluded that one of the first steps in reactions involving these compounds is a combination of substrate and coenzyme (91).

D. *Specificity of the Pyridine Nucleotide Dehydrogenases.* The pyridine nucleotide dehydrogenases are generally highly specific for one class of compounds. Although glutamic dehydrogenase reacts only with glutamic acid and not with a series of closely related compounds, liver alcohol dehydrogenase oxidizes ethanol, higher alcohols, and even vitamin A; it does not attack methanol or tertiary butanol. Lactic dehydrogenase (with DPNH) shows a similar type of specificity for α-keto acids. The specificity requirement as regards the coenzyme is a striking illustration of the economy of nature. By introducing a third phosphate into DPN$^+$, the hydrogen-transferring property is retained but the new coenzyme now forms holoenzymes with new proteins which are specific for a new series of substrates. Instances in which either DPN$^+$ or TPN$^+$ shows high activity are uncommon, although they are known (for example, glutamic dehydrogenase). Usually, either complete specificity or vast preference for one form is shown (15).

The stereospecific reaction between various dehydrogenases and the pyridine ring of the required coenzyme has already been mentioned in connection with the general specificity of enzymes (see Chapter 15). Further work by Vennesland et al. (92) has shown that it is possible to relegate these enzymes into two groups depending upon which side of the pyridine ring they utilize for the addition and abstraction of hydrogen. The two types have been named α and β.

α-Type Dehydrogenase	β-Type Dehydrogenase
Alcohol	Hydroxy-steroid
Malate	Transhydrogenase
Lactate	Triose phosphate
Acetaldehyde	Glucose
Glycerate	Glycerophosphate
Dihydroorotate	Glutamate
	DPNH-cytochrome *c*

E. *Reactions Catalyzed by Pyridine Nucleotide Dehydrogenase.* Table 19.1 summarizes the various reactions catalyzed by the pyridine nucleotide dehydrogenases (5). Some of the substrates listed may be oxidized by dehydrogenases which do not require these coenzymes; examples are α-glycerophosphate and glucose. The direct oxidation (TPN⁺) of substrates such as glucose-6-phosphate may constitute a main route of carbohydrate oxidation in animal tissues (16).

Diphosphopyridine nucleotide occurs in high concentration in the cells of the stomach wall, and its reduction may be a source of hydrochloric acid (17). These coenzymes are involved in many reactions not directly on the metabolic path of carbohydrate utilization, such as the oxidation-reduction of sterols (18).

3. Flavin Nucleotide Dehydrogenases

A. *Introduction.* An excellent review on the subject of flavoproteins is that of Theorell (19). The reader is also referred to the articles by Mahler and Green (82) and Nicholas (93) for recent developments in this field.

B. *General Properties of the Flavin Nucleotide Dehydrogenases.* The isolation of the "old yellow enzyme" from yeast was complicated by the presence of large amounts of polysaccharide material. Theorell was able to crystallize the enzyme by employing his newly constructed electrophoresis apparatus at the terminal stages of purification. The protein parts of the yellow enzymes have no outstanding properties, and the particular characteristics of the holoenzymes appear to be derived from the coenzymes. The coenzymes have been discussed at length in the preceding chapter.

C. *Mechanism of Action of the Flavin Nucleotide Dehydrogenases.* The flavoproteins are of great historical importance in enzymology. One of them, the "old yellow enzyme," was the first holoenzyme to be reversibly dissociated into coenzyme and apoenzyme. This brilliant experiment by Theorell (20) threw considerable light on our understanding of the chemistry and mechanism of action of enzymes in general. Figure 19.2 shows the activating effect of the coenzyme,

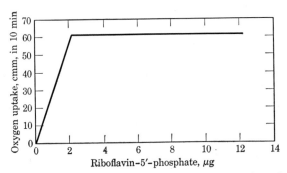

Fig. 19.2. Resynthesis of the "old yellow enzyme" by addition of riboflavin-5'-phosphate to the apoenzyme (20).

flavin-mononucleotide (FMN), on the velocity of oxidation of glucose-6-phosphate.

The general function of the flavoproteins is to bridge the electron transport gap between the pyridine nucleotides and the cytochromes. Some of them, however, react with *non-catalyst* substrates such as glucose or the D or L amino acids.

The old yellow enzyme catalyzes the oxidation of glucose-6-phosphate according to the following series of reactions:

$$\text{Glucose-6-phosphate} + \text{TPN}^+ \underset{\text{``Zwischenferment''}}{\overset{\longrightarrow}{\rightleftharpoons}}$$

$$6\text{-Phosphogluconate} + \text{TPNH} + \text{H}^+$$

$$\text{TPNH} + \text{H}^+ + \text{Old yellow enzyme}_{Ox} \rightleftharpoons$$

$$\text{TPN}^+ + \text{Old yellow enzyme}_{Red}$$

$$\text{Old yellow enzyme}_{Red} \xrightarrow{\text{O}_2} \text{Old yellow enzyme}_{Ox} + \text{H}_2\text{O}_2$$

$$\text{Old yellow enzyme}_{Ox} + 2\text{Fe}^{++} + 2\text{H}^+$$

The TPN^+ specific glucose-6-phosphate dehydrogenase (zwischenferment = "between-enzyme") has never been crystallized. The old yellow enzyme apparently occurs only in yeast.

Some years after the isolation of the old yellow enzyme by Theorell (21), Haas obtained from yeast what became known as the "new yellow enzyme" (22). The catalytic system for the old and new enzymes was similar except that methylene blue had to be added to the new in order to speed the O_2 uptake. The prosthetic group of the Haas enzyme, however, is flavin adenine dinucleotide (FAD). After they had obtained FAD, the Warburg school regarded FMN as an artifact formed from the dinucleotide by degradation. This is probably an oversimplification since both coenzymes occur in tissues. The protein of the old yellow enzyme with FAD, i.e., the "crossed" or "synthetic" yellow enzyme, is slightly less active than the old yellow enzyme.

It was stated above that, among the pyridine nucleotide dehydrogenases, only glyceraldehyde-3-phosphate dehydrogenase is isolated with the coenzyme attached to the protein. In contrast, the flavoproteins are routinely isolated in the intact state. The dissociation constants of the compound of DPNH with horse liver alcohol dehydrogenase or heart lactic dehydrogenase are 10^{-7} M and 7×10^{-6} M, respectively. The Michaelis constants for these enzymes are of the order of 10^{-5} M. Table 19.2 lists the constants for four flavin enzymes.

Table 19.2.   Dissociation Constants of Some Flavin Enzymes. Hogness (23)

Enzyme	Dissociation Constant
D-Amino acid oxidase	250×10^{-9}
Old yellow enzyme	60×10^{-9}
New yellow enzyme	27×10^{-9}
Cytochrome c reductase	1×10^{-9}

These figures are probably close to the Michaelis constants. It is apparent that the prosthetic group is very tightly bound indeed.

Coupling of FMN to the protein of the old yellow enzyme causes the spectral bands in the visible to be displaced to slightly longer wavelengths. In addition, the oxidation-reduction potential is raised and the fluorescence of FMN vanishes. Since riboflavin is enzymatically inactive, these data show that FMN is attached to the protein by at least one linkage in addition to the phosphate. There is evidence that

the $\overset{\displaystyle |}{-\text{N}}$—H group in position 3 of the isoalloxazine ring takes part in the attachment of FMN to the apoenzyme, since the fluorescence vanishes either on the titration of this group or the formation of the holoenzyme.

Working with acyl dehydrogenase, Beinert (94) has observed that a new flavin compound with absorption maximum at 565 mμ appeared as an intermediate. Later he discovered a similar phenomenon with free flavin compounds and thus established definite spectral proof for the semiquinoid or free-radical flavin intermediates observed by previous workers (95). The strong effect of the protein is evident from the fact that more free radical was formed with acyl dehydrogenase, L-amino acid oxidase or old yellow enzyme than with free

Table 19.3.   Reactions Catalyzed by Flavin Nucleotide Enzymes

Enzyme	Substrate	Product	Coenzyme

Type: RCHNHR'COOH + Flavoprotein$_{\text{ox}}$ $\overset{\text{H}_2\text{O}}{\rightleftharpoons}$ RCOCOOH + H$_2$NR' + Flavoprotein$_{\text{Red}}$

Enzyme	Substrate	Product	Coenzyme
D-Amino acid dehydrogenase	D-Amino acids	Keto acids + NH$_3$	FAD
L-Amino acid dehydrogenase	L-Amino acids	Keto acids + NH$_3$	FMN
Glycine dehydrogenase	Glycine	Glyoxylic acid	FAD
D-Aspartate dehydrogenase	D-Aspartate	Oxalacetate	FAD

Type: RCHOHCOOH + Flavoprotein$_{\text{ox}}$ $\rightleftharpoons$ RCOCOOH + Flavoprotein$_{\text{Red}}$

Enzyme	Substrate	Product	Coenzyme
L-Hydroxy acid dehydrogenase	L-Hydroxy acids	α-Keto acids	FMN
Glycollic acid dehydrogenase	Glycollate	Glyoxylate	FMN

Type: $\dfrac{\text{DPNH}}{\text{TPNH}}$ + H$^+$ + Flavoprotein$_{\text{ox}}$ $\rightleftharpoons$ $\dfrac{\text{DPN}^+}{\text{TPN}^+}$ + Flavoprotein$_{\text{Red}}$

Enzyme	Substrate	Product	Coenzyme
DPN$^+$-cytochrome c reductase	DPNH	DPN$^+$	FAD
TPN$^+$-cytochrome c reductase	TPNH	TPN$^+$	FMN
			FAD

Type:
$$\text{R}-\overset{\text{O}}{\underset{}{\overset{\|}{\text{C}}}}-\text{H} \left. \begin{array}{c} \\ -\text{N} \\ \diagdown \\ \text{C}-\text{H} \\ \diagup \\ -\text{N} \\ | \\ \text{H} \end{array} \right] + \text{Flavoprotein}_{\text{ox}} \overset{\text{H}_2\text{O}}{\rightleftharpoons} \left[\begin{array}{c} \text{R} \cdot \text{COOH} \\ \text{H} \\ | \\ -\text{N} \\ \diagdown \\ \quad\text{C}=\text{O} \\ \diagup \\ -\text{N} \\ | \\ \text{H} \end{array} \right. + \text{Flavoprotein}_{\text{Red}}$$

Enzyme	Substrate	Product	Coenzyme
Notatin (glucose dehydrogenase)	D-Glucose	D-Gluconate	FAD
Aldehyde dehydrogenase	Aldehydes	Carboxylic acids	FAD
Xanthine dehydrogenase	Xanthine	Uric acid	FAD
	Hypoxanthine	Xanthine	
	Aldehydes	Carboxylic acids	
	Xanthopterin	Leucopterin	
Quinone oxidase	Aldehydes	Carboxylic acids	FAD
	Quinoline	Carbostyril	
	Cinchona alkaloids	Carbostyril analogues	
	N'-Methyl nicotinamide	6-Pyridone of N'-methyl nicotinamide	

Type: —CH$_2 \cdot$ CH$_2$— + Flavoprotein$_{\text{ox}}$ $\rightleftharpoons$ —CH=CH— + Flavoprotein$_{\text{Red}}$

Enzyme	Substrate	Product	Coenzyme
Acyl coenzyme A dehydrogenase	Acyl coenzyme A derivatives	α,β-Unsaturated acyl coenzyme A derivatives	FAD
Fumaric reductase	Fumarate	Succinate	FAD

Type: Miscellaneous Reactions

Enzyme	Substrate	Product	Coenzyme
Hydrogenase	H$_2$	2H$^+$ + 2e	FAD
Nitrate reductase	Nitrate	Nitrite	FAD
Nitrite reductase	Nitrite	Hydroxylamine	FAD
Hydroxylamine reductase	Hydroxylamine	Ammonia	—

FMN or FAD. Thus the mechanism of action of acyl dehydrogenase is pictured as follows:

$$\text{En—flavin} + \text{RH}_2 \rightleftharpoons \left[\text{En—flavin—R} \underset{\diagup \text{H}}{\overset{\diagdown \text{H}}{}} \right] \rightleftharpoons \left[\text{En—flavin—R} \underset{\diagdown \text{H}}{\overset{\diagup \text{H}}{}} \right] \rightleftharpoons$$

$$\left[\text{En—flavin—R} \underset{\diagdown \text{H}}{\overset{\diagup \text{H}}{}} \right] \rightleftharpoons \text{En—flavin} + \text{R} \underset{\diagdown \text{H}}{\overset{\diagup \text{H}}{}}$$

Theorell and co-workers (98) at the Nobel Institute in Stockholm have used their sensitive fluorescence recorder for a study of the mechanism of action of the crystalline "old yellow enzyme." Amino and phenolic groups, but not sulfhydryl, are important for the functioning of the enzyme.

Unfortunately, there exist few good inhibitors for the flavin enzymes. However Yagi (96) has corrected this situation somewhat by his synthesis of the sulfate analogues of the flavin coenzymes. These inhibitors should be particularly suitable for the study of FAD linked reactions.

D. *Flavoproteins and Metals* (82, 93). An important development in the field of flavoproteins has been the implication of heavy metals as activators or constituents of the enzymes. Xanthine oxidase was highly purified in 1938 by Ball (24), working in Warburg's laboratory, and as a result of this study it has been assumed that the enzyme contains a type of flavin derivative. Westerfeld and Richert (25) made a sustained investigation of a dietary factor needed for the establishment and maintenance of normal levels of xanthine oxidase activity in the liver and intestine of the rat. They eventually found the factor to be molybdenum. This element is also present in nitrate reductase (27, 84) where it is suspected that electrons are transferred in the following sequence:

$$\text{TPNH} \rightarrow \text{FAD(FMN)} \rightarrow \text{Mo} \rightarrow \text{NO}_3$$

Hydrogenase (79) and several other enzymes (77) contain flavin and molybdenum (see Table 19.4). Although butyryl coenzyme A contains copper in the crude state, purified preparations of the enzyme contain only traces of this metal and there is no evidence that copper is required by the enzyme (28). Mahler (29) pictures the role of the iron in DPNH-cytochrome c reductase to be as follows:

$$\text{DPNH} \xrightarrow{2e} \text{Flavin} \xrightarrow{1e} \text{Fe}^{+++} \xrightarrow{1e} \text{Cytochrome } c \text{ (Fe}^{+++}\text{)}$$
$$\lfloor\!\!\!-\!\!\!- \text{Enzyme} -\!\!\!\rfloor$$

The low turnover number of the old yellow enzyme has rendered its physiological significance doubtful. It may be that the activity of these enzymes could be enhanced by the addition of specific metals.

E. *Reactions Catalyzed by Flavin Nucleotide Dehydrogenases.* Table 19.3 contains a list of some of the known flavin enzymes. Such tables will be constantly expanded as new flavin enzymes are discovered.

Table 19.4.   Metals in Flavoproteins. Nicholas (93)

Iron

DPNH, cyt. *c* reductase
Fumaric hydrogenase
Succinic dehydrogenase
Nitrate reductase (*E. coli*)
Hydrogenase (*A. vinelandii*)
Lactic oxidase (yeast)

Iron and Copper

DPNH oxidase complex
Nitrite reductase (*N. crassa*)
Hyponitrite reductase (*N. crassa*)
Nitrite reductase (*Pseudomonas stutzeri*)
Nitric oxide reductase (*Pseudomonas stutzeri*)

Iron and Molybdenum

Xanthine oxidase (milk)
Xanthine oxidase (bird liver)
Xanthine oxidase (mammalian liver)
Xanthine oxidase (bacterial)
Aldehyde oxidase

Molybdenum

Hydrogenase (*C. pasteurianum*)
Nitrate reductase (*N. crassa*)
Nitrate reductase (*E. coli*)
Nitrate reductase (green plants)

Manganese

Hydroxylamine reductase (*N. crassa*)
Hydrogenase (*H. ruhlandii*)

4. The Iron-Containing Enzymes and the Metal Oxidases

A. *Introduction.* The pioneer work of Warburg on the role of iron enzymes in tissue respiration served to focus attention on the metallic constituents of enzymes. Warburg has summarized this research in his interesting book: *Heavy Metals as the Prosthetic Group of Enzymes* (30). Lemberg and Legge (31) have prepared a useful book on the biochemistry of the porphyrins, their metal chelates, and the iron porphyrin enzymes.

B. *Catalytic Role of Heavy Metals.* Iron is quantitatively the most important metal concerned in enzymatic activity. All the iron in biological material probably participates directly or indirectly in enzymatic reactions of one type or another. Hemoglobin may be considered a "half-enzyme" in that it transports but does not modify the substrate oxygen. Ferritin (32) is a storehouse for the iron which is subsequently to be used for enzyme synthesis. Proteins such as siderophilin or transferrin (33) appear to have an iron-transport function. Ferrichrome (34–38) and coprogen (39) are further examples of non-porphyrin iron compounds which, as a consequence of their growth factor activity, are suspected to be connected with specific enzymes.

Iron is the catalytic center of two large classes of enzymes, the hydroperoxidases and the cytochromes. Much less is actually known of the enzymatic functions of copper, although tyrosinase and ascorbic acid oxidase are definitely known to contain this metal (73, 40).

C. *Chemistry of the Porphyrins and Their Metal Chelates.* Virtually all the isolated enzymes which contain iron have the metal chelated within a porphyrin or tetrapyrrole framework rather than attached directly to the protein. The only possible known exception to this rule is the DPNH-cytochrome *c* reductase of Mahler (29). In view of the fundamental nature of the reactions catalyzed by the iron porphyrin proteins or hemoproteins, a brief discussion of porphyrin chemistry is in order.

The basic chemical unit of the porphyrins is the pyrrole nucleus. Pyrrole itself is a distillable liquid (b.p. 130°). The open-chain tetrapyrroles, of which biliverdin is a common example, are termed the bile pigments. Before proceeding further with the chemistry of porphyrins, it may be helpful to define some of the terms used in this highly specialized field.

Bile pigment = open-chain tetrapyrrole.

Porphyrin = iron-free cyclic tetrapyrrole.

Protoporphyrin IX = the most common naturally occurring porphyrin, the four methyl, two vinyl, and two carboxyethyl groups being arranged in a particular manner (isomer IX).

Metalloporphyrin = porphyrin metal chelate.

Hematin = ferriprotoporphyrin IX hydroxide.

Heme = ferroprotoporphyrin IX.

Hemin = ferriprotoporphyrin IX chloride.

Hemochrome = coordination compound of nitrogenous bases with the reduced metalloporphyrin.

Porphyrinogen, i.e., tetrapyrrylmethane or reduced-bridge porphyrin.

The bile pigments are green, blue, or yellow. It is important to note that they have no characteristic spectral band near 400 mμ. They are not believed to be active constituents of enzymes. As might be de-

$$\text{HO}\underset{\underset{\text{Biliverdin}}{}}{\overset{\begin{array}{cccc}\text{COOH} & \text{COOH} \\ | & | \\ \text{CH}_2 & \text{CH}_2 & \text{CH}_2 & \text{CH}_2 \\ \| & | & | & \| \\ \text{CH}_3 \ \text{CH} & \text{CH}_3 \ \text{CH}_2 & \text{CH}_2 \ \text{CH}_3 & \text{CH}_3 \ \text{CH}\end{array}}{\big\langle\!\!\big\langle\text{N}\big\rangle\!\!\big\rangle\cdots\big\langle\!\!\big\langle\text{N}\big\rangle\!\!\big\rangle\cdots\big\langle\!\!\big\langle\text{N}\big\rangle\!\!\big\rangle\cdots\big\langle\!\!\big\langle\text{N}\big\rangle\!\!\big\rangle}}\text{OH}$$

duced from their structure, the bile pigments are derived from spent hemoproteins through oxidative removal of 1 carbon atom from the porphyrin methene bridge.

The complicated porphyrin molecule is synthesized by animal tissues, such as nucleated erythrocytes, from the simple units glycine and succinate. As a result of the work of David Shemin (41) and a number of other investigators we may formulate a possible reaction se-

$$
2\begin{array}{c}\text{COOH}\\|\\\text{CH}_2\\|\\\text{CH}_2\\|\\\text{COOH}\end{array}
\begin{array}{c}\\+\\\\2\begin{array}{c}\text{CH}_2\text{NH}_2\\|\\\text{COOH}\end{array}\end{array}
\xrightarrow{-\text{H}_2\text{O}}
2\begin{array}{c}\text{COOH}\\|\\\text{CH}_2\\|\\\text{CH}_2\\|\\\text{C}=\text{O}\\|\\\text{HCNH}_2\\|\\\text{COOH}\end{array}
\xrightarrow{-\text{CO}_2}
\longrightarrow \text{porphobilinogen (A monopyrrole)}
$$

Succinic acid and glycine   α-NH$_2$-β-keto adipic acid   δ-NH$_2$-levulinic acid (2 moles)

quence as shown (80, 78). It was stated earlier that coenzymatic activity and vitamin function often go hand-in-hand and it is therefore not unusual to find that heme shows growth factor activity for certain microbial species. The growth of both *Hemophilus influenzae* and *Pilobolus kleinii* is stimulated by heme. It is interesting that in animals, in contrast to the porphyrin part, the iron is salvaged from the spent hemoprotein and stored with almost miserly care.

Serratia marcesens, the bacterium responsible for "bloody bread," contains a tripyrrole pigment of prodigious red color. It is quite appropriately named *prodigiosin.* The simplest tetrapyrrole, porphin, has not been found in nature. In porphin, the β positions on the pyrrole nuclei are occupied simply by hydrogen atoms. Obviously, complica-

Prodigiosin

tions in nomenclature are introduced by the large possible number of β-substituted isomers. The list below shows the type of substituents carried on the β position of the various porphyrins. The total number of substituents is, of course, always **8**. The porphyrins of chlorophylls *a* and *b* are structurally similar to the compounds listed except for the following modifications. One of the carboxyethyl groups has

Nomenclature of Some Common Porphyrins

Porphyrin	Number and Type of Substituents
Etioporphyrin	4 Methyl, 4 ethyl
Mesoporphyrin	4 Methyl, 2 ethyl, 2 β-carboxyethyl
Protoporphyrin	4 Methyl, 2 vinyl, 2 β-carboxyethyl
Deuteroporphyrin	4 Methyl, 2 hydrogen, 2 β-carboxyethyl
Hematoporphyrin	4 Methyl, 2 hydroxyethyl, 2 β-carboxyethyl
Coproporphyrin	4 Methyl, 4 β-carboxyethyl
Uroporphyrin	4 Carboxymethyl, 4 β-carboxyethyl

been oxidized, esterified with methanol, and attached to a methene bridge of the porphyrin to form a new five-membered ring. The other carboxyethyl residue has been esterified with phytol, a long-chain alcohol ($C_{20}H_{39}OH$).

Protoporphyrin is by far the most important porphyrin in enzymology. All the isolated hemoprotein enzymes as well as hemoglobin and myoglobin contain this particular porphyrin, or some derivate thereof. The 4 methyl, 2 vinyl, and 2 β-carboxyethyl groups may be arranged about the β pyrrole positions in a large number of ways. Hans Fischer began to arrange these in all the possible ways; when he came to isomer **9** he had duplicated the structure of protoporphyrin. The natural isomer is therefore referred to as protoporphyrin IX. This compound, like all the porphyrins, has two outstanding physical properties. The porphyrins have an exceedingly intense and brilliant fluorescence when irradiated with ultraviolet light. This characteristic has been employed to measure the porphyrin content of single erythrocytes! Secondly, the porphyrin absorption spectrum is very intense and highly specific. The type of spectrum shown by protoporphyrin

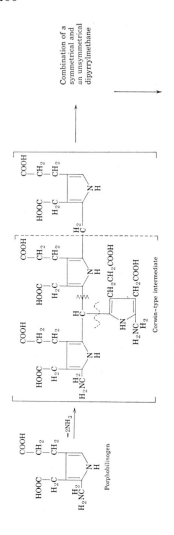

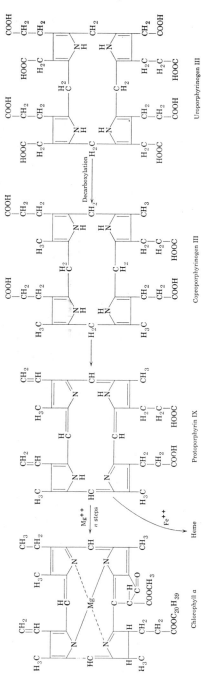

IX under neutral or alkaline and under acidic conditions is exemplified by the behavior of the closely related coproporphyrins (Fig. 19.3) (42).

The very high band in the region of 400 mμ is easily the best spectral landmark of the porphyrins. It is termed the Soret band, after its discoverer. The band is absent in the open-chain tetrapyrroles such as the bile pigments. The particular type of absorption in the

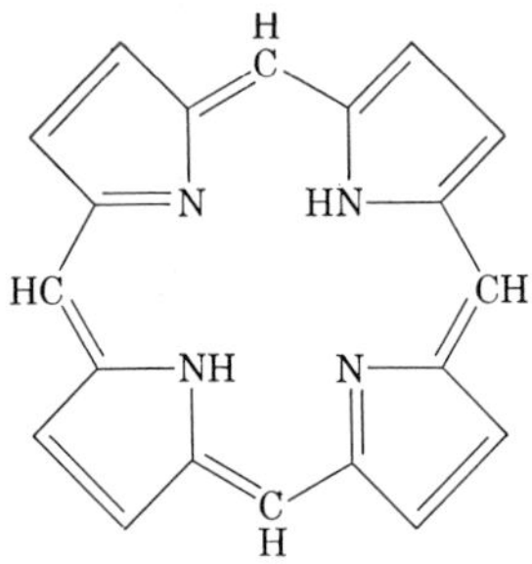

Porphin

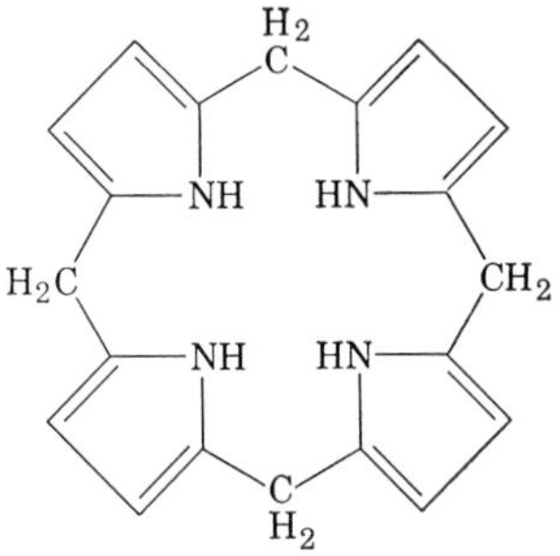

Porphyrinogen

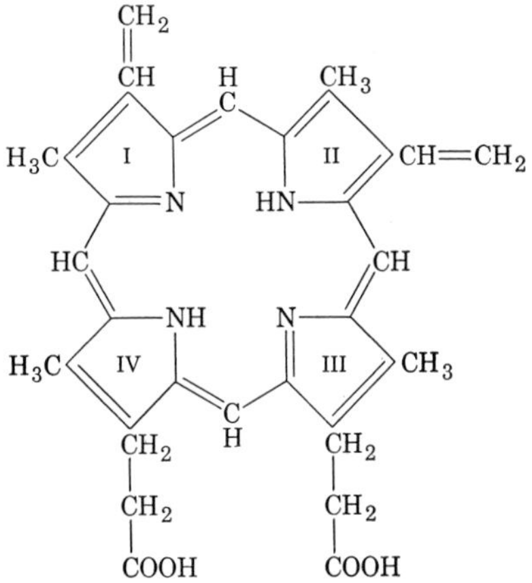

Protoporphyrin IX

visible imparts a beautiful wine-purple color to porphyrin solutions. The higher-wavelength bands are clearly visible in the hand spectroscope, and Hans Fischer made extensive use of this tool in his synthetic work.

Fischer synthesized iron protoporphyrin IX, identical in every respect with the natural material. The iron atom may be inserted by heating protoporphyrin IX with ferrous acetate and acetic acid. Very little change in the molar volume results from the fixation of the iron atom, and it may be concluded that the porphyrin molecule is a flat, planar structure. Hemin is routinely isolated by heating defibrinated blood with acetic acid. This process splits off heme from globin, and, in the presence of a little sodium chloride, the chelate is collected as hemin crystals. These, known as Teichman crystals, have such a characteristic shape that they are often sought in forensic medicine. The iron chelates of protoporphyrin IX are not fluorescent, and, furthermore, the striking spectrum in the visible is not present. Conse-

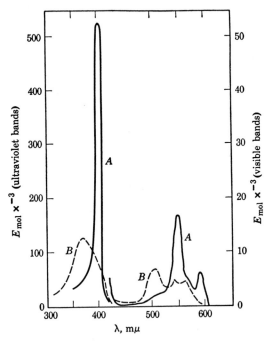

Fig. 19.3. Spectral absorption curves of coproporphyrins I and III in acidic (*A*) and basic (*B*) solution (42). Reproduced from *Biochemical Journal,* Cambridge University Press, London and New York.

quently, their solutions are a nondescript brown color. However, the Soret band is retained. A matter of considerable annoyance is the low solubility of heme compounds in both aqueous and non-aqueous solvents at physiological pH.

Methods for determination of the bond type, whether ionic or covalent, were outlined in Chapter 6. The magnetochemical data for heme show it to have 4 unpaired electrons, and hence the bonds involved in chelate formation are essentially ionic. The two positive

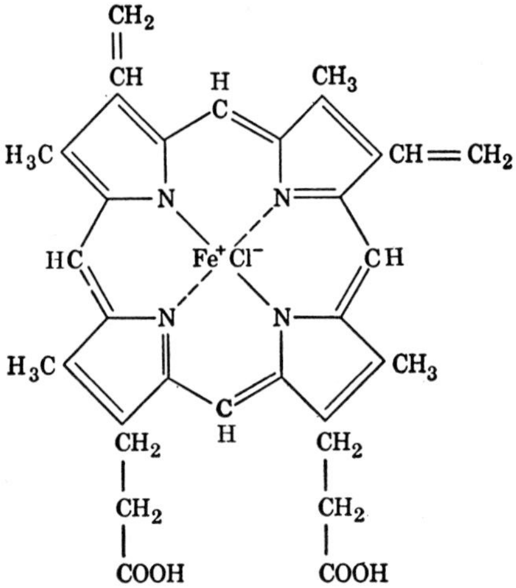

$$CH_2$$
$$\|$$
$$CH \quad H \quad CH_3$$

Ferriprotoporphyrin IX chloride (hemin)

charges on the ferrous ion are therefore balanced by the displacement of 2 protons from the nitrogen atoms of the pyrrole nuclei. The bonds in hematin are also essentially ionic, although here the extra positive charges on the iron atom must be satisfied with an hydroxyl or some other ion such as chloride (31).

D. *Reactivity of the Metalloporphyrins.* The physiological function of heme and its derivatives centers around the capacity for the iron atom to interact with various chemical entities and groupings. The iron of hemoglobin and myoglobin can enter into a loose association with gaseous oxygen. Displacement of the oxygen by carbon monoxide effectively poisons the catalytic role of these hemoproteins. Azide and cyanide exert their effect by attaching to the iron of respiratory carriers such as cytochrome oxidase. Coordination compounds with ammonia, primary amines, hydrazine, pyridine, and imidazole compounds are also known. Once coordinated, the complex assumes characteristic light-absorption properties in the green region of the spectrum. In accordance with the suggestion of Lemberg and Legge (31), these derivatives will be designated as "hemochromes." Alkaline conditions plus the presence of reducing agents favor the formation of these coordination compounds. The hemochrome bands in the visible are often referred to as α, β, etc. The α band is usually located at 550 to 560 mμ, and the weaker β band is situated in the region of 525 mμ.

E. *The Hydroperoxidases.* The work of Theorell (43) and Chance

(44) on the mechanism of action of catalases and peroxidases shows that a common name for the two classes is desirable. Theorell has proposed the name "hydroperoxidases."

Catalase activity was found to be widely distributed in tissues by the man who discovered hydrogen peroxide, L. J. Thénard. Crystalline catalases have been obtained from liver, erythrocytes, kidney, and bacteria. Animal tissues generally show only very weak peroxidase activity, and it is likely that this usually stems from unspecified hematin compounds or hemoglobin itself. Leucocytes contain a "verdoperoxidase" or "myeloperoxidase," and milk has yielded a crystalline "lactoperoxidase." Plants contain catalase, but the concentration is not nearly as great as that of blood or liver. Some progress has been made in purifying spinach catalase. On the other hand, peroxidase is abundant in the plant kingdom. The horseradish root is an excellent source. A highly active catalase has been crystallized from *Micrococcus lysodeicticus* by Herbert and Pinsent (45). Peroxidase reactions in microbes are rare.

Catalase activity may be followed polarographically or by permanganate titration of the excess substrate. Because of destruction of enzyme by the substrate, the concentration of the latter must be kept low, and the reaction velocity is therefore first order. The first-order rate constant divided by the grams of enzyme gives the catalase "Fähigkeit," or catalase "ability." Peroxidases have been determined by following the oxidation of purpurogallin. The "Purpurogallinzahl," or "P.Z.," is the weight of this yellow dye formed in 5 minutes divided by the weight of the enzyme preparation. The catalases are very easy to crystallize, and they often crystallize accidentally when some other preparation from liver is being made. More difficulty has been experienced in crystallizing the peroxidases.

The molecular weight of crystalline liver catalase is close to 250,000, and there must be 4 atoms of iron per mole since the iron content is 0.09%. Brown (46) has demonstrated that crystalline liver catalase contains several components which are separable by careful salt fractionation. He found that a particularly active catalase was attached to the cell structure; it could be released with the Waring Blendor, however. Deutsch was able to obtain a very active erythrocyte catalase by using more gentle isolation methods than hitherto employed (47). Catalase preparations from liver contain a certain amount of bile pigment, but it is not definitely known whether this is of significance or whether the pigment is merely adventitiously associated with the enzyme.

Bonnichsen tried, and failed, to find a significant difference in the amino acid composition or immunological properties of horse liver and horse erythrocyte catalase. Tracer studies showed that radioactive iron enters liver catalase much more rapidly than erythrocyte catalase. Presumably, therefore, the two catalases are of two separate origins; i.e., the liver catalase is not simply derived from the erythrocyte during its dissolution in the liver (48).

Crystalline horseradish peroxidase has a molecular weight of 44,100. There is 1 iron atom per mole. A cytochrome *c* peroxidase has been prepared from yeast (49).

F. *The Heme-Linked Groups of the Hydroperoxidases.* The particular activity of the hemoproteins, whether enzymatic or "half-enzymatic," depends on the nature of the chemical bonding of the prosthetic group to the protein. This becomes obvious when it is recalled that all the isolated iron porphyrin enzymes contain only the same prosthetic group, namely, iron protoporphyrin IX. Theorell has prepared a lucid review dealing exclusively with this important point (50).

No simple heme model can duplicate the oxygen-holding capacity of hemoglobin or myoglobin. Such model compounds always pass over into the oxidized state whereas in hemoglobin the iron is known to remain divalent. Conant stated in his 1932 Harvey Lecture, "There are some indications that the histidine grouping may be involved in the linkage of the globin to the iron." The first conclusive experimental justification for this statement came from the titration data of Wyman, who found the heat of ionization of the heme-linked groups of hemoglobin to fit that of the imidazole nucleus.

Myoglobin contains 1 mole of iron protoporphyrin IX per mole of protein, about 16,000 grams. Hemoglobin contains the same amount of iron as myoglobin, 0.34%, but the molecular weight is about 65,000. Hence there must be 4 heme residues per mole in hemoglobin. The data on hemoglobin structure have been very useful as a background for the subsequent investigations on the hydroperoxidases and cytochromes.

Zeile and Hellström discovered ferriprotoporphyrin to be the prosthetic group of catalase (51). However, a series of unfortunate circumstances has resulted in little progress in our knowledge of the heme-linked groups of this enzyme. The prosthetic group cannot be split off reversibly as it can in some other hemoproteins. Catalase hematin cannot be reduced by ordinary reducing agents. Interpretation of various types of data is obscured by interaction of the 4 iron porphyrins in each mole of the enzyme. Agner and Theorell found that a hydroxyl group is bound to the iron atom. Anions are able to inhibit the enzyme at high *p*H, presumably by competition with the hydroxyl group for the iron atom.

Much more information is available on peroxidase. Theorell's papers on the isolation, characterization, and mechanism of action of this enzyme will remain as a great classic work. The reversible splitting of horseradish peroxidase can be achieved by adding a cold water solution of the enzyme to an acetone-HCl mixture at −5° to −10°. The colorless protein precipitates while the ferriprotoporphyrin goes into solution. Substitution of a variety of hemins on the pure apoenzyme showed that deutero- and mesohemins were active and hematohemin inactive. Apparently, therefore, the vinyl groups of protohemin may be removed (deutero-) or saturated (meso-) but not hydrated (hemato-). These results are illustrated in Fig. 19.4. There

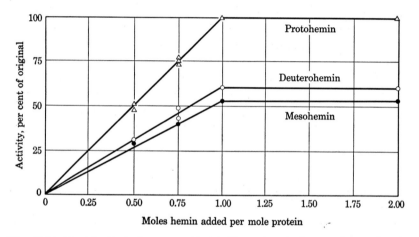

Fig. 19.4. Combination of apoperoxidase with proto-, deutro-, and meso-hemins (50). Reproduced from *Advances in Enzymology*, Interscience Publishers, New York.

is a heme-linked group with a *pKa* of 4 which is "spectrophotometrically operable" at 655 mμ and which is exactly related to the activity. The iron atom is in all probability not attached to histidine. Indications are that (*a*) a carboxyl group in the protein is bound to the iron and (*b*) one of the carboxyethyl residues is linked to the protein.

G. *Mechanism of Action of the Hydroperoxidases.* Fundamentally, the hydroperoxidases utilize hydrogen peroxide as an electron acceptor. The general reaction for a peroxidase may therefore be written:

$$AH_2 + H_2O_2 \rightleftharpoons A + 2H_2O$$

where A may be a phenol, ascorbic acid, etc. The catalase reaction involves two moles of peroxide, one acting as electron donor and the other as electron acceptor.

$$H_2O_2 + H_2O_2 \rightleftharpoons O_2 + 2H_2O$$

A great deal of basic research by Chance, Theorell, and Keilin satisfies the following general reaction mechanism for catalase:

$$Cat. FeOH + HOOH \rightleftharpoons Catalase FeOOH + H_2O$$

$$Cat. FeOOH + HOOH \rightleftharpoons Catalase FeOH + H_2O + O_2$$

Catalase reacts with ethyl hydrogen peroxide. Also, the peroxide or alkyl peroxide complex of the enzyme may react with primary alcohols. Theorell, however, does not regard the latter scheme as important for the physiological oxidation of ethanol. The very high activity of catalase may be a consequence of several factors, such as the rapidity of formation of enzyme-substrate compounds and the fact that there are 4 iron atoms per mole.

According to Chance (52) the peroxidase action may be illustrated as follows:

$$Per \cdot OH + HOOR \rightleftharpoons Per \cdot OOR(I) + H_2O$$

$$Per \cdot OOR(I) \longrightarrow Per \cdot OOR(II)$$

$$Per \cdot OOR(II) \xrightarrow[\text{decay}]{\text{Spontaneous}} Per \cdot OH$$

$$Per \cdot OOR(II) + AH_2 \longrightarrow Per \cdot OH + ROH + A$$

$Per \cdot OH$ represents the ferriperoxidase-hydroxyl group complex, and (I) and (II) are the colored enzyme-substrate compounds which may be observed spectrophotometrically. George (53) has brought forth evidence that (II) does not contain the hydrogen peroxide grouping. He thinks that complex (II) is not an enzyme-substrate compound but rather a compound in which the iron has an effective oxidation number of $+4$.

Tauber's (54) experiments show conclusively that catalase is simply a special type of peroxidase which has the additional capacity to decompose peroxide in the absence of a second substrate. He found that crystalline catalase and dilute hydrogen peroxide could oxidize α-naphthol and p-phenylenediamine to indophenol purple; p-aminobenzoic acid, sulfathiazole, adrenalin, ephedrine sulfate, and tyrosine are coupled with catechol by oxidation to form colored compounds. Pyrogallol, catechol, adrenalin, and p-phenylenediamine were all oxidized by catalase and hydrogen peroxide.

H. *The Cytochromes*. The literature on cytochromes has been covered up to 1950 by Paul (55). Two specialized reviews have appeared, one on the historical aspects of the cytochromes (56) and the other on bacterial cytochromes (57).

The cytochromes were actually discovered by MacMunn in the period 1884–1886. He found these pigments to be widely distributed in the animal kingdom and noted that they could be reversibly oxidized and reduced. He proposed for them the names "myohaematin" and "histohaematin." The Hoppe-Seyler school severely criticized MacMunn's experiments. According to them, the spectral bands described by him could only be those of hemoglobin or its derivatives.

In 1925 Keilin "rediscovered" MacMunn's pigments, renaming them "cytochrome." The most definitive work on the metabolic role of the cytochromes was Warburg's study of the "respiratory enzyme" or *Atmungsferment*. He believed this enzyme to be an iron protein for the following reasons:

1. All cells contain iron as an essential constituent for normal life.

2. From the known catalytic properties of iron it can be calculated that the iron content of certain tissues accounts for their catalytic activity.

3. Oxygen uptake in sea urchin extract is stimulated by the addition of iron.

4. Cyanide inhibits iron catalysis both *in vivo* and *in vitro*.

5. Iron catalyzes the oxidation of various substances *in vitro,* such as cysteine.

6. Cell respiratory models can be prepared from iron-containing charcoals of natural materials.

Keilin's rediscovery of the cytochromes helped to resolve the famous Warburg-Wieland controversy on the nature of tissue respiration. Warburg championed activation of oxygen, whereas Wieland, Thunberg, and others held activation of hydrogen to be the fundamental mechanism of biological oxidation. Once the concept of an extended chain had been developed for these respiratory catalysts, it was evident that the Wieland school was dealing with the dehydrogenase and Warburg with the cytochrome link in the chain.

The cytochromes are ubiquitous in nature. Cardiac muscle is a particularly rich source. It has been generally assumed that they are absent from strictly anerobic organisms. However, they have now been reported as present in certain anaerobic sulfur bacteria (58). Also, the photosynthetic organism *Rhodospirillum rubrum* contains a hemoprotein spectrally similar to cytochrome *c* (74, 59). Of great interest is the fact that this pigment could be reduced by cytochrome reductase but it could not be oxidized by cytochrome oxidase. Cytochrome c has been purified from wheat germ (60) and isolated from *Ustilago sphaerogena* (61). New components, b_3 and f, have been found in plants (62). Tint and Reiss (63, 64) found slight but significant differences in the isoelectric points of cytochrome c from the heart muscle of four animal species. The isoelectric point of *Ustilago* cytochrome c is more than 3 pH units lower than that of heart cytochrome, but spectrally the two hemoproteins are very similar and they are about equally active in the rat liver succinoxidase system.

In summary it may be stated that the cytochromes occur in bacteria, yeast, and fungi as well as in higher plants and animals. However, total chemical identity cannot be blandly assumed from spectral observations.

Generally speaking, the idea has been that, the more aerobic the cells or tissue, the more fully developed will be the cytochrome system contained therein. Figure 19.5 shows the position of the spectral bands of the main cytochrome components. The reduced spectra are far more striking than the oxidized spectra. The actual position of the bands varies slightly with species.

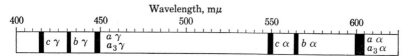

Fig. 19.5. Absorption bands of certain reduced cytochromes as revealed by the spectroscope.

The system of nomenclature is not entirely obvious from Fig. 19.5. The cytochromes with α-hemochrome bands at 605, 562, and 550 mμ were in 1925 named cytochromes a, b, and c, respectively. These compounds have weak β bands between 520 and 530 mμ. Around 1930 the Japanese workers (see reference 56) began a systematic survey of the cytochrome components of bacteria. They found the cytochrome a band to be replaced by a band at 589–590 or at 632 mμ. These new cytochromes were named a_1 and a_2, respectively. Keilin and Hartree then re-examined heart-muscle preparations and found the bands of cytochrome a at 605 and 450 mμ to be each comprised of two bands. The new component, named cytochrome a_3, was easily autoxidizable, combined in the ferric state with cyanide, and, finally, the ferrous form reacted with carbon monoxide. For these reasons, cytochrome a_3 and Warburg's *Atmungsferment* have been considered to be identical and have been called "cytochrome oxidase." The older term for this enzyme, "indophenol oxidase," was dropped when it was found that the enzyme did not react directly with indophenol but rather oxidized this substance through the cytochrome system.

I. *The Heme-Linked Groups of the Cytochromes.* The nature of the metalloporphyrins of cytochrome and their mode of attachment to the protein are of the greatest importance to the mechanism of action of these enzymes.

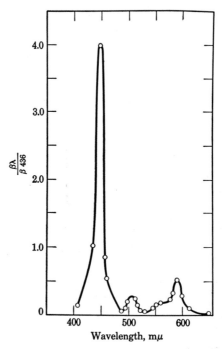

Fig. 19.6. Relative photochemical absorption spectrum of the carbon monoxide compound of cytochrome oxidase from rat heart muscle (65). Reproduced from *Journal of Biological Chemistry,* American Society of Biological Chemists, New Haven.

In general, the cytochrome spectra resemble those of the known hemoproteins such as hemoglobin. Components a and a_3 are green. Their heme must be related to chlorocruorin, in which one of the vinyl groups is replaced by a formyl group. Warburg was able to measure the spectrum of the respiratory enzyme by studying the efficiency of light of different wavelengths for dissociating the carbon monoxide complex. The photochemical absorption spectrum so obtained is recorded in Fig. 19.6 (65). It is likely that this spectrum belongs to a metalloporphyrin compound of one type or another. That the metal is iron is strongly suggested from the failure of other carbon monoxide-metalloporphyrins to dissociate in light.

Little progress has been made on the isolation of cytochrome oxidase. In his Nobel lecture, Warburg referred to this hemoprotein as being as unavailable as the "material of the stars." Solutions of sodium desoxycholate have been used to extract the enzyme, and some success has attended the preparation of the prosthetic group (66). It is similar to, but not identical with, the green heme of the *Spirographis* worm.

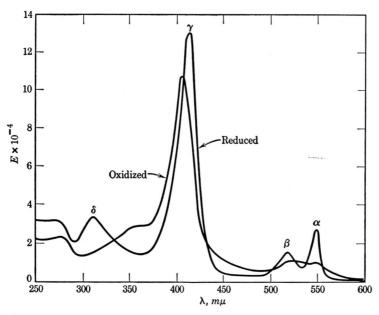

Fig. 19.7. Spectrum of cytochrome *c* in the oxidized and reduced state (56). Data of E. Margoliash. Reproduced from *British Medical Bulletin,* The Royal Society, London.

The hemochrome spectrum of cytochrome *b* closely resembles that of the pyridine hemochrome of ferriprotoporphyrin IX (67).

The component *c*, unlike the other cytochromes, is very stable and quite amenable to isolation in the pure state. The first preparations of Theorell contained 0.34% iron; later, Theorell and Åkeson (68) were able to increase the iron content to 0.43% by prolonged electrophoresis. This fascinating compound can be isolated from beef heart muscle by extraction with dilute trichloroacetic acid, precipitation of inert proteins with saturated ammonium sulfate, and collection of the enzyme by precipitation from saturated ammonium sulfate solution with dilute trichloroacetic acid. The crude material is chroma-tographed on the carboxylic acid ion-exchange resin IRC-50 to give a product containing 0.46% iron (61). This preparation is probably quite pure.

The spectrum of cytochrome *c* in the oxidized and reduced forms is shown in Fig. 19.7. The spectra are those of a typical hemochrome. The band at 550 mμ is so sharp that it may be used to calibrate spec-trophotometers! According to Theorell (68), the heme is attached to the protein in a manifold way. Two cysteine residues of the protein form thioether linkages with the vinyl groups, and histidine residues are linked to the iron atom. The prosthetic group apparently lies in a crevice in the protein; perhaps this fact explains why the enzyme is non-autoxidizable (physiological *p*H range), does not react with car-bon monoxide, and reacts only slowly with cyanide.

More recent work by Tuppy and by Tuppy and Paléus, the latter working in Theorell's laboratory, has resulted in the elucidation of the amino acid sequence around the heme moiety (97). This peptide will assume a β-helix so that the imidazole nitrogen of the histidine residue can be coordinated to the iron atom.

The protein part of cytochrome *c* is very basic. The isoelectric point is above *p*H 10. It contains an unusually high amount of lysine.

J. Mechanism of Action of the Cytochromes. The intimate mecha-nism of action of the cytochromes is completely unknown. We can say only that they transmit electrons to oxygen. There are some data which would indicate that *in vivo* they are lined up "cheek by jowl" in the particulate fraction of the cell.

K. The Copper Oxidases. The early work of Elvehjem showed that copper, as well as iron, is important in the synthesis of hemoglobin (69). Copper is also involved in the synthesis of chlorophyll (70). Several copper-containing enzymes are now known, of which the most familiar example is polyphenoloxidase or tyrosinase. Laccase and ascorbic acid oxidase also contain copper. Butyryl coenzyme A dehy-drogenase is said to contain both copper and flavin (28).

Warburg became interested in polyphenol oxidase because of its ability to react with oxygen. Unlike the Atmungsferment, the poly-phenol oxidase could be extracted from plant tissue with water. The potato enzyme contained 0.2% copper. It was inhibited by cyanide and carbon monoxide, but the latter inhibition could not be reversed with light. Dialysis of the enzyme against dilute cyanide destroyed the activity; when the excess cyanide was removed copper could be added back to give full activity. Apparently the enzyme contains no porphyrin prosthetic group of any kind.

The oxidation of a polyphenol such as catechol involves a cyclic oxido-reduction of the copper atom. Generation of a small amount of a diphenol appears to hasten the oxidation of the monophenols.

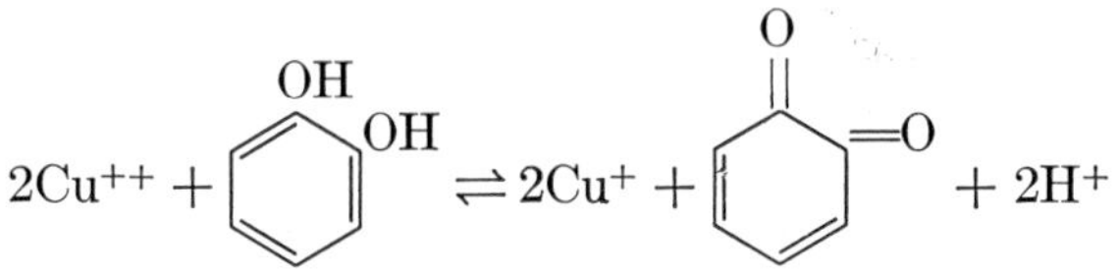

$$2Cu^{++} + \underset{\text{OH}}{\overset{\text{OH}}{\bigcirc}} \rightleftharpoons 2Cu^+ + \underset{\text{O}}{\overset{\text{O}}{\bigcirc}}{=}O + 2H^+$$

$$2Cu^+ + 2H^+ + \tfrac{1}{2}O_2 \rightleftharpoons 2Cu^{++} + H_2O$$

L-Tyrosine is first oxidized to 3,4 dihydroxy L-phenylalanine (dopa), which is eventually further oxidized to dark pigments known as melanins.

Ascorbic acid oxidase converts ascorbic acid to dehydroascorbic acid.

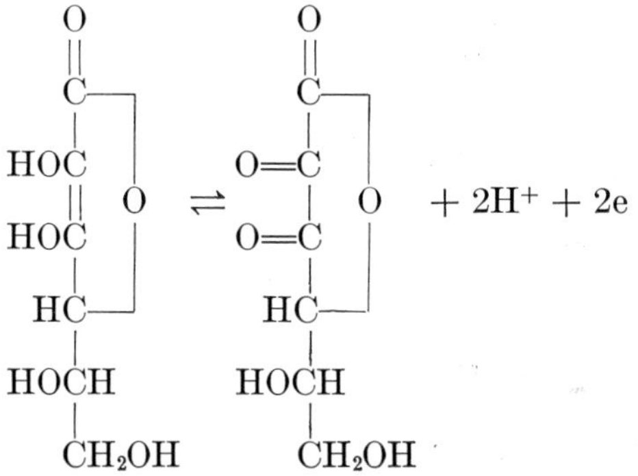

$$
\begin{array}{ccc}
\overset{O}{\overset{\|}{C}} & \overset{O}{\overset{\|}{C}} & \\
\text{HOC} & \text{O=C} & \\
\overset{\|}{\text{HOC}} \; O & \overset{}{\text{O=C}} \; O & +\,2H^+ + 2e \\
\text{HC} & \text{HC} & \\
\text{HOCH} & \text{HOCH} & \\
\text{CH}_2\text{OH} & \text{CH}_2\text{OH} & \\
\text{Ascorbic acid} & \text{Dehydroascorbic} & \\
 & \text{acid} &
\end{array}
$$

The enzyme, which is of very general occurrence in plant tissues, is a copper protein. Joselow and Dawson (73) made the discovery that isotopic copper exchanged with the copper of the acting but not the resting enzyme.

L. *The Physiological Role of the Metal Oxidases.* The biological function of the hydroperoxidases is still not entirely clear. The catalase concentration of liver or erythrocytes is far greater than that required to decompose the hydrogen peroxide which might occur in these tissues. Agner (71) observed that peroxidases could detoxify diphtheria and tetanus toxins in the presence of dilute solutions of hydrogen peroxide.

The cytochrome enzymes are concerned solely with the transport of electrons. The direction of transfer from either succinate or DPNH is shown in the diagram (56). The "Slater factor" was discovered by Slater when he observed that certain reducing agents inactivate the

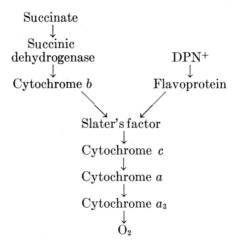

respiratory chain without affecting the other known components. According to Potter and Reif (72), the Slater factor can be specifically blocked by the antibiotic antimycin A.*

There is probably a very good physiological reason for the great difference found in the values for the dissociation constants of the enzyme-coenzyme compounds of the respiratory enzymes. The few examples which have been studied indicate that pyridine nucleotide holoenzymes may have a dissociation constant of about 10^{-6} M while that of the flavin enzymes is smaller than this by a factor of perhaps 10^2. The values for the cytochromes are still smaller. The relatively highly dissociated pyridine nucleotide dehydrogenases mean that the same coenzyme can shuttle around to different proteins. The result is the formation of a great number of fairly specific holoenzymes. However, once the hydrogen atoms have been started on their way to oxygen the need for specificity is lost since the substrate is always the same, i.e., hydrogen or electrons.†

Irradiation of the photosynthetic bacterium *R. rubrum* promotes a spectral change which is very similar to the difference spectrum of oxidized and reduced cytochrome c (75). The cytochromes, therefore, may be intimately connected with the process of photosynthesis. The cytochrome c of *R. rubrum* has been extracted from the cells and studied to some degree (74, 59).

---

* The existence of a separate factor has not yet been unequivocally demonstrated. A certain spatial arrangement may be necessary which is lost with denaturation and which allows combination with antimycin.

† Leach et al. (81) have emphasized that the oxidation chain must be considered to be "graded" with respect to both chemical mechanism and free energy change.

Table 19.5. Reactions Catalyzed by the Iron-Containing Enzymes and the Metal Oxidases

Enzyme	Substrate	Product	Prosthetic Group
	Type: $H_2O_2 + H_2O_2 \rightleftharpoons 2H_2O + O_2$ $H_2O_2 + Acceptor \rightleftharpoons H_2O + Oxidized\ acceptor$		
Hydroperoxidases			
Catalase	H_2O_2 (also acceptor)	$H_2O + O_2$	Iron protoporphyrin IX (43)
Peroxidase	H_2O_2 + Organic molecule	H_2O + Oxidized organic molecule	Iron protoporphyrin IX (43)
	(For a description of the various hydroperoxidases see ref. 43.)		
	Type: electron transport: catalyst to oxygen, catalyst to catalyst, substrate to oxygen		
Cytochromes*			
Cytochrome a_3	Cytochrome $a_{Red} + O_2$	Cytochrome $a_{Ox} + H_2O$	Iron porphyrin (56)
a	Cytochrome c_{Red} + Cytochrome a_{3Ox}	Cytochrome c_{Ox} + Cytochrome a_{3Red}	Iron porphyrin (56)
b	Succinic dehydrogenase$_{Red}$ + Slater factor$_{Ox}$	Succinic dehydrogenase$_{Ox}$ + Slater factor$_{Red}$	Iron porphyrin (56)
c	Slater factor$_{Red}$ + Cytochrome a_{Ox}	Slater factor$_{Ox}$ + Cytochrome c_{Red}	Iron protoporphyrin IX (55)
	(For other cytochromes such as the cytochrome f of chloroplasts see refs. 83, 56, and 57.)		
Copper oxidases			
Tyrosinase	Tyrosine; phenols; $+O_2$	Dihydroxyphenylalanine; oxidized phenols	Cu (40)
Ascorbic acid oxidase	Ascorbic acid $+ O_2$	Dehydroascorbic acid	Cu (40)
(For other copper oxidases see ref. 40.)			

* Yeast cytochrome b is the first cytochrome component to be obtained in crystalline form (86). Cytochrome c from a variety of sources has been crystallized by the Okunuki school (*Nature*, 178, 629, 631, 1956; 179, 250, 959, 1957).

The full biological significance of the copper oxidases is not understood. Indications are that these enzymes may play a role in the respiration of plant tissues.

M. *Reactions Catalyzed by the Iron-Containing Enzymes and Metal Oxidases.* Table 19.5 contains a list of the types of reactions catalyzed by the metal oxidases and related enzymes. Only the better-known examples have been included.

References

1. F. Schlenk, in *The Enzymes,* edited by J. B. Sumner and K. Myrbäck, Academic Press, N. Y., 1951.

2. T. Tung, L. Anderson, and H. A. Lardy, *Arch. Biochem. Biophys., 40,* 194 (1952).

3. T. P. Singer and E. B. Kearney, in *The Proteins,* edited by H. Neurath and K. Bailey, Academic Press, N. Y., 1954.

4. F. Schlenk, in *A Symposium on Respiratory Enzymes,* University of Wisconsin Press, Madison, 1942.

5. E. E. Snell, *Physiol. Revs., 33,* 509 (1953).

6. E. Negelein and H. J. Wulff, *Biochem. Z., 293,* 351 (1937).

7. J. E. Hayes and S. F. Velick, *J. Biol. Chem., 207,* 225 (1954).

8. H. Theorell and R. K. Bonnichsen, *Acta Chem. Scand., 5,* 1105 (1951).

9. D. M. Gibson et al., *J. Biol. Chem., 203,* 397 (1953).

10. J. B. Neilands, *J. Biol. Chem., 208,* 225 (1954).

11. H. Theorell and B. Chance, *Acta Chem. Scand., 5,* 1127 (1951).

12. O. Meyerhof, P. Ohlmeyer, and W. Mohle, *Biochem. Z., 297,* 113 (1938).

13. S. P. Colowick, N. O. Kaplan, and M. M. Ciotti, *J. Biol. Chem., 191,* 447 (1951).

14. J. F. Taylor et al., *J. Biol. Chem., 173,* 619 (1948).

15. A. H. Mehler et al., *J. Biol. Chem., 174,* 961 (1948).

16. F. Dickens and G. E. Glock, *Nature, 166,* 33 (1950).

17. E. J. Conway, T. G. Brady, and E. Carton, *Biochem. J., 47,* 369 (1950).

18. R. L. Coppedge et al., *J. Biol. Chem., 173,* 431 (1948).

19. H. Theorell, in *The Enymes,* edited by J. B. Sumner and K. Myrbäck, Academic Press, N. Y., 1951.

20. H. Theorell, *Biochem. Z., 278,* 263 (1935).

21. H. Theorell, *Biochem. Z., 272,* 155 (1934).

22. E. Haas, *Biochem. Z., 298,* 378 (1938).

23. T. R. Hogness, in *A Symposium on Respiratory Enzymes,* University of Wisconsin Press, Madison, 1942.

24. E. G. Ball, *J. Biol. Chem., 128,* 51 (1939).

25. W. W. Westerfeld and D. A. Reichert, *J. Biol. Chem., 184,* 163 (1950); *192,* 35 (1951); *203,* 915 (1953).

26. D. E. Green and H. Beinert, *Biochim. et Biophys. Acta, 11,* 599 (1953). See also *J. Biol. Chem., 210,* 149 (1954).

27. D. J. D. Nicholas, A. Nason, and W. D. McElroy, *Nature, 172,* 34 (1953).

28. H. R. Mahler, *J. Am. Chem. Soc., 75,* 3288 (1953).

29. H. R. Mahler and D. G. Elowe, *J. Am. Chem. Soc., 75,* 5769 (1953).

30. O. Warburg, *Heavy Metal Prosthetic Groups*, Oxford University Press, Oxford, 1949.

31. R. Lemberg and J. W. Legge, *Hematin Compounds and Bile Pigments*, Interscience Publishers, N. Y., 1949.

32. S. Granick, *Chem. Revs.*, *38*, 379 (1946).

33. B. A. Koechlin, *J. Am. Chem. Soc.*, *74*, 2649 (1952).

34. J. B. Neilands, *J. Am. Chem. Soc.*, *74*, 4846 (1952).

35. J. B. Neilands, *Abstracts*, Am. Chem. Soc. 123rd Meeting, Los Angeles, March, 1953.

36. J. B. Neilands, *Federation Proc.*, *12*, 250 (1953).

37. J. B. Neilands, *J. Biol. Chem.*, *205*, 643 (1953).

38. J. B. Neilands, *J. Biol. Chem.*, *205*, 647 (1953).

39. C. Pidacks et al., *J. Am. Chem. Soc.*, *75*, 6064 (1953).

40. C. R. Dawson and W. B. Tarpley, in *The Enzymes*, edited by J. B. Sumner and K. Myrbäck, Academic Press, N. Y., 1951.

41. D. Shemin and J. Wittenberg, *J. Biol. Chem.*, *192*, 315 (1951).

42. E. M. Jope and J. R. P. O'Brien, *Biochem. J.*, *39*, 239 (1945).

43. H. Theorell, in *The Enzymes*, edited by J. B. Sumner and K. Myrbäck, Academic Press, N. Y., 1951.

44. B. Chance, in *The Enzymes*, edited by J. B. Sumner and K. Myrbäck, Academic Press, N. Y., 1951.

45. D. Herbert and J. Pinsent, *Biochem. J.*, *43*, 193 (1948).

46. G. L. Brown, *Biochem. J.*, *51*, 569 (1952).

47. H. F. Deutsch, *Acta Chem. Scand.*, *5*, 815 (1951).

48. H. Theorell et al., *Acta Chem. Scand.*, *5*, 445 (1951).

49. R. Abrams et al., *J. Biol. Chem.*, *142*, 303 (1942).

50. H. Theorell, *Advances in Enzymology*, *7*, 265 (1947).

51. K. Zeile and H. Hellström, *Z. Physiol. Chem.*, *192*, 171 (1930).

52. B. Chance, *Advances in Enzymology*, *12*, 153 (1951).

53. P. George, *Biochem. J.*, *54*, 267 (1953).

54. H. Tauber, *Proc. Soc. Exptl. Biol. Med.*, *81*, 237 (1952).

55. K. G. Paul, in *The Enzymes*, edited by J. B. Sumner and K. Myrbäck, Academic Press, N. Y., 1951.

56. D. Keilin and E. C. Slater, *Brit. Med. Bull.*, *9*, 89 (1953).

57. L. Smith, *Bact. Rev.*, *18*, 106 (1954).

58. J. R. Postgate, *Biochem. J.*, *56*, xi (1954).

59. S. R. Elsden, M. D. Kamen, and L. P. Vernon, *J. Am. Chem. Soc.*, *75*, 6347 (1953).

60. D. R. Goddard, *Am. J. Bot.*, *31*, 270 (1944).

61. J. B. Neilands, *J. Biol. Chem.*, *197*, 701 (1952).

62. H. E. Davenport and R. Hill, *Proc. Roy. Soc.*, *B139*, 327 (1952).

63. H. Tint and W. Reiss, *J. Biol. Chem.*, *182*, 385 (1950).

64. H. Tint and W. Reiss, *J. Biol. Chem.*, *182*, 397 (1950).

65. J. L. Melnick, *J. Biol. Chem.*, *141*, 269 (1941); *146*, 385 (1942).

66. M. Kiese, *Naturwissenschaften*, *39*, 403 (1952).

67. P. Person, W. W. Waino, and B. Eichel, *J. Biol. Chem.*, *202*, 369 (1953).

68. H. Theorell and Å. Åkeson, *J. Am. Chem. Soc.*, *63*, 1804, 1812, 1818, 1820 (1941).

69. C. A. Elvehjem, *Physiol. Rev.*, *20*, 37 (1935).

70. A. L. Sommer, *Plant Physiol., 6,* 339 (1931).
71. K. Agner, quoted by Theorell, ref. 43.
72. V. R. Potter and A. E. Reif, *J. Biol. Chem., 194,* 287 (1952).
73. M. Joselow and C. R. Dawson, *J. Biol. Chem., 191,* 11 (1951).
74. L. P. Vernon, *Arch. Biochem. Biophys., 43,* 492 (1953).
75. L. N. M. Duysens, *Abstracts,* Pacific Slope Biochemical Conference, December, 1953.
76. T. P. Singer and E. P. Kearney, *Advances in Enzymology, 15,* 79 (1954).
77. K. Harrison, *Nature, 172,* 509 (1953).
78. G. H. Cookson and C. Rimington, *Biochem. J., 57,* 476 (1954).
79. A. L. Shug, P. W. Wilson, D. E. Green, and H. R. Mahler, *J. Am. Chem. Soc., 76,* 3355 (1954).
80. S. Granick, in *Chemical Pathways of Metabolism,* edited by D. M. Greenberg, Academic Press, N. Y., 1954.
81. S. J. Leach, J. H. Baxendale, and M. G. Evans, *Australian J. Chem., 6,* 409 (1953).
82. H. R. Mahler and D. E. Green, *Science, 120,* 7 (1954).
83. R. Hill, *Advances in Enzymology, 12,* 1 (1951).
84. D. J. D. Nicholas and A. Nason, *Arch. Biochem. and Biophys., 51,* 310 (1954).
85. D. E. Green, P. M. Kohout, and S. Mii, *Biochim. et Biophys. Acta, 14,* 295 (1954).
86. C. A. Appleby and R. K. Morton, *Nature, 173,* 749 (1954).
87. E. Racker, *Physiological Reviews, 35,* 1 (1955).
88. B. L. Vallee et al., *J. Am. Chem. Soc., 78,* 5879 (1956).
89. H. Theorell et al., *Acta Chem. Scand., 9,* 1148 (1955).
90. I. W. Sizer and A. Gierer, in *Discussions Farady Soc.,* No. 20 (1955).
91. N. O. Kaplan et al., *Biochem. Biophys. Acta, 23,* 221 (1957).
92. B. Vennesland, *J. Cellular Comp. Physiol., 47,* Suppl. 1, 201 (1956).
93. D. J. D. Nicholas, *Nature, 179,* 800 (1957).
94. H. Beinert, *J. Am. Chem. Soc., 78,* 5323¯(1956).
95. H. J. Lowe and W. M. Clarke, *J. Biol. Chem., 221,* 983 (1956).
96. F. Yagi et al., *J. Biochem., 39,* 669 (1956).
97. H. Theorell, *Science, 124,* 467 (1956).
98. A. P. Nygaard and H. Theorell, *Acta Chem. Scand., 9,* 1587 (1955).

20

Proteolytic Enzymes

1. Introduction[1] (References 1–3)

It was stated previously in this volume that the respiratory enzymes might be thought to enjoy an intrinsically fundamental role in biological processes since without them life would be impossible. Life on the other hand might conceivably be possible without the action of the proteolytic enzymes, i.e., if an endless supply of free amino acids were available for the synthetic and energy-requiring systems of protoplasm. Since this situation is unrealistic, a happy biological household is only maintained when the proteolytic enzymes are in the kitchen preparing food for the dining table of the synthetic and respiratory enzymes.

Further, it might be argued that in breaking substituted amide linkages, the proteolytic enzyme really does not perform as profound a reaction as many other enzymes. Thus we can break peptide bonds by means of either acid or alkaline hydrolysis. However, this argument is found on closer inspection to be entirely false. The proteolytic enzymes often exhibit extreme specificity of both the structural and optical variety. The reactions are catalyzed at low temperatures and in the pH range of 2 to 9. And even though the hydrolysis of an amide linkage can be regarded as a relatively simple biochemical event, it might be profitable to begin the study of enzyme mechanisms at this level since the detailed mode of action of not a single enzyme, proteolytic or otherwise, is known in detail.

There are several additional intriguing aspects of the behavior of proteolytic enzymes. They often occur as inactive *zymogens*. Since activation can be achieved *in vitro*, a method is hereby provided for creating the active center of an enzyme in the test tube. The proteolytic enzymes are often low molecular weight, stable, crystallizable proteins. All of these factors have made it seem desirable that, in

[1] The commonly accepted abbreviations for amino acids will be used (4)

this introductory textbook of enzyme chemistry, a special chapter
should be devoted to the proteolytic enzymes.

2. Some Characteristics of Hydrolytic Reactions

The splitting of a peptide bond will be found to be independent of
pH in the neutral region. However, at very acid or very alkaline

$$\underset{\underset{\text{Neutral }p\text{H}}{}}{-\overset{\overset{\text{O}}{\|}}{\text{C}}-\text{O}^- + \text{H}_3\text{N}^+}$$

$$-\overset{\overset{\text{O}}{\|}}{\text{C}}-\overset{\overset{\text{H}}{|}}{\text{N}}- + \text{H}_2\text{O} \underset{}{\overset{+\text{H}^+}{\rightleftharpoons}} -\overset{\overset{\text{O}}{\|}}{\text{C}}-\text{OH} + \text{H}_3\text{N}^+ \qquad \text{Acid }p\text{H}$$

$$-\overset{\overset{\text{O}}{\|}}{\text{C}}-\text{O}^- + \text{H}_2\text{N} \qquad \text{Alkaline }p\text{H}$$

values of pH, the reaction becomes dependent on the proton activity
of the solution. Thus the free energy associated with the hydrolysis
of the usual peptide bond will be at a minimum value between the
pKa levels of the α-COOH and the α-NH$_2$ groups and will increase at
extremities of pH. But even at the pH at which most proteolytic enzymes act, the hydrolysis of a peptide bond liberates between 3 and
4 kilocalories and hence the reactions go essentially to completion.

In the non-enzymatic hydrolysis of peptide linkages, a quantity
of the protein or peptide is heated at 105° for 16 hours with about a
one-hundred-fold by weight excess of either 6N HCl or 2N NaOH.
With proteolytic enzymes, comparable results can be achieved at room
temperature and at pH levels of approximately 2 to 9. Clearly the
proteolytic enzyme is either able to activate water to the extent that
it can hydrolyze peptide bonds, or what is ultimately equivalent, the
enzyme may labilize the peptide to such a degree that it is readily
hydrolyzed by water.

The inactivity of proteolytic enzymes at great extremities of pH is
hence of some interest since, as we have seen, the chemical reaction
only proceeds faster under such circumstances. Many years ago
Michaelis (5) interpreted the common bell-shaped pH *vs* activity
curves for enzymes in terms of a *Zwitterion* type of active site. Thus
the addition of either acid or alkali tends to lower the *Zwitterion* concentration with concomitant inactivation of the enzyme. Over the

years considerable support has developed for just such a view for the structure of enzyme loci. Obviously, the requirement for a proton donor and a proton acceptor group at the active site does not necessarily demand a *Zwitterion* structure.

Of particular interest in this connection is the discovery by Swain and his colleagues (6) of non-enzymatic *polyfunctional* catalysis. These investigators began with the observation that simple polar displacement reactions of uncharged substrates (such as esters, hemiacetals) may be grouped together as *concerted* reactions. That is, there is a simultaneous attack on the substrate by both nucleophilic (*N*) and electrophilic (*E*) agents. Hence, for kinetic and steric reasons it was assumed that more efficient catalysis could be achieved if the nucleophilic and electrophilic centers were combined within a single molecule.

Swain and Brown selected tetramethylglucose as the substrate and studied the effect of pyridine (*N*), phenol (*E*) and 2-hydroxyphenol (*N-E*) on the rate of mutarotation. The high rate observed with 2-hydroxypyridine was found to be some 7000 times that observed with an equivalent concentration of a mixture of phenol and pyridine. Swain and Brown (6) conclude:

> In the following respects enzymes resemble our polyfunctional catalysts closely: (1) they have both nucleophilic and electrophilic groups, but none of high general reactivity; (2) they excel especially in near neutral solution, at low temperatures and in high dilution; (3) they show high catalyst-substrate specificity; (4) they have polar rather than free radical-like reactivity; and (5) they form catalyst-substrate complexes prior to reaction.

Numerous examples can be found in the literature in which hydrolyses of esters and amides have been achieved under relatively mild conditions with the aid of metal ions or other low molecular weight catalysts. In connection with the mode of action of proteolytic enzymes, the experiments of Perenyi (7) concerning the catalysis of ester hydrolysis by thiol compounds would seem of particular interest. In the case of phosphate esters an unstable intermediate of the type

$$
\begin{array}{c}
\text{OH} \\
| \\
\text{R—O—P—S—R}' \\
\diagdown\diagup \\
\text{HO} \quad \text{OH}
\end{array}
$$

was proposed. Herr and Koshland (8) have succeeded in finding a type of ester which is hydrolyzed at a maximum rate at a pH of 2 to 4. The labile substrate is butylthiolester, $C_4H_9S\text{-}PO_3H_2$. The

Table 20.1. Classification and General Properties of the Proteolytic Enzymes

Source	Enzyme	Type	pH Optimum	Precursor System	Specificity†	Comments
Animal Gastric	Pepsin*	Endopeptidase	2	Pepsinogen (mol. wt. 42,000) $\xrightarrow{H^+}$ Pepsin (36,000) + Peptide (6000)	$-NH-\overset{R}{C}HCO-\|-NHCH-CO-$ R = aromatic	
	Rennin*	Endopeptidase	4	None known	1. Cleaves phospho amides 2. Coagulates milk 3. Hydrolyzes hemoglobin	
Pancreatic	Trypsin*	Endopeptidase	7	Trypsinogen (24,000) $\xrightarrow[\text{Trypsin}]{\text{Neutral } pH}$ Trypsin (24,000)	$-NH\overset{R}{C}H-CO-\|-NH-$ $CO-\|-OC_2H_5$ R = lysine or arginine	
	Chymotrypsin*	Endopeptidase	8	Chymotrypsinogen (22,000) $\xrightarrow{\text{Trypsin}}$ Chymotrypsin (22,000) + Small peptide No significant change in molecular weight	$-NH\overset{R}{C}HCO-\|-NH-$ $CO-\|-OC_2H_5$ R = aromatic	
	Carboxypeptidase*	Exopeptidase	7.5	Procarboxypeptidase $\xrightarrow{\text{Trypsin}}$ Carboxypeptidase No change in molecular weight	$R-CO-\|-NH\overset{R}{C}HCOOH$ R = aromatic or aliphatic	Zn^{++}
Intestinal	Amino peptidase	Exopeptidase	8–9	Known but undefined	$NH_2-\overset{R}{C}H-CO-\|-NH-$ R = leucine chain	Divalent cation required
	Dipeptidase	Exopeptidase	7.5	None known	$NH_2-\overset{R}{C}HCO-\|-NH\overset{R}{C}H$ COOH	Divalent cation required
	Aminotripeptidase	Exopeptidase	8	None known	$NH_2\overset{R}{C}HCO-\|-NH\overset{R}{C}HCONH\overset{R}{C}H$ COOH	No metal requirement

Source	Enzyme	Type	pH	Zymogen	Substrate†	Remarks
	Prolidase	Exopeptidase	7.7	None known	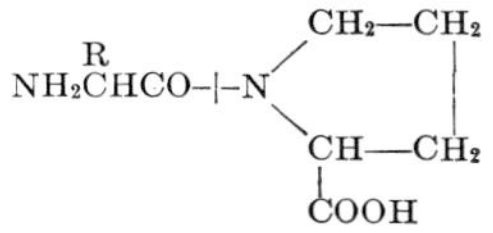 NH_2CHCO—N, CH$_2$—CH$_2$, CH—CH$_2$, COOH	Mn^{++} specific
	Enterokinase	Endopeptidase	6–9	None known	Trypsinogen → trypsin	30% by weight carbohydrate
Blood	Thrombin	Endopeptidase	—	Prothrombin	Fibrinogen → fibrin	DFP sensitive
	Plasmin (fibrinolysin)	Endopeptidase	7.5–8.6	Plasminogen (Profibrinolysin)	Acts on fibrin, casein	Urokinase activated
Other tissues	Cathepsin A	Endopeptidase	5	None known	Same as pepsin	SH activated
	Cathepsin B	Endopeptidase	5	None known	Same as trypsin	SH activated
	Cathepsin C	Endopeptidase	5	None known	Same as chymotrypsin	SH activated
Plants Latex of Carica papaya	Papain*	Endopeptidase	Wide range	None known	Wide range	Activated by SH reducing agents
Sap of fig tree	Ficin*	Endopeptidase	4–9	None known	Wide range	Activated by SH reducing system
Pineapple	Bromelin	Endopeptidase		None known	Wide range	No activation required
	Aminopeptidase	Exopeptidase	?	None known	Like animal aminopeptidase	Mn^{++}
Bacteria C. welchii	Gelatinase (κ-toxin)	Endopeptidase	?	None known	Collagen attacked; casein, albumin not attacked	
Group A streptococci		Endopeptidase		None known	Casein, gelatin, benzoyl 1-arginamid	Cysteine activated
Ps. aeruginosa	Dipeptidase	Exopeptidase	?	None known	Leucyl glycine, etc.	Metal activated
B. subtilis	Subtilisin	Endopeptidase	8	None known	Ovalbumin → plakalbumin; splits many peptides	Widespread analytical application

* Crystalline enzyme.
† The substrate specificity is generally much wider than the structures shown.

hydrolytic process is believed to proceed according to the scheme shown in Fig. 20.1. In this figure the bonds being broken are shown as dotted lines, whereas the bonds being formed are illustrated as arrows. A proton from water is transferred to the negative oxygen thereby increasing the electron-sharing capacity of the water oxygen

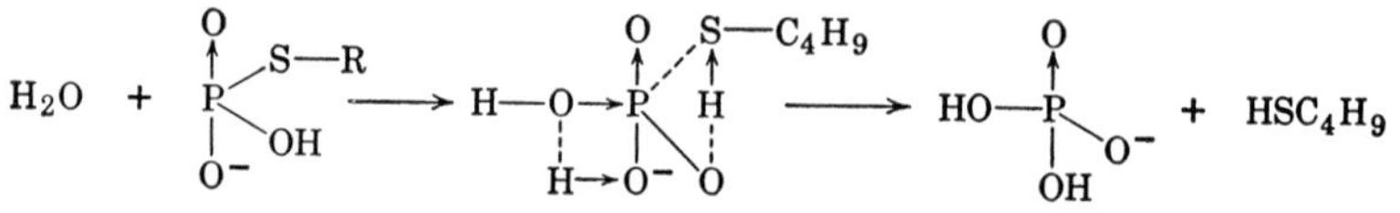

$$H_2O \; + \; \begin{matrix} O \\ \uparrow \\ P \\ | \\ O^- \end{matrix} \!\! \begin{matrix} S\!-\!R \\ \diagup \\ \diagdown OH \end{matrix} \longrightarrow H\!-\!O\!\rightarrow\! \begin{matrix} O \\ \uparrow \\ P' \\ | \\ H\!\rightarrow\!O^- \end{matrix} \!\! \begin{matrix} S\!-\!C_4H_9 \\ \diagup \uparrow \\ H \\ \diagdown O \end{matrix} \longrightarrow HO\!-\!\begin{matrix} O \\ \uparrow \\ P \\ | \\ OH \end{matrix} \!\! \diagdown O^- \; + \; HSC_4H_9$$

Fig. 20.1. Mechanism for the hydrolysis of butyl thiophosphate according to Herr and Koshland (8).

and increasing its reactivity toward the phosphorus. The hydroxyl is synchronously transferred to the thiomercaptide group. In alkaline solutions the hydroxyl is eliminated by ionization and in very acid solution a proton is bound to the primary phosphoryl hydroxyl. Thus extremities of pH would definitely inhibit the flow of protons and atoms as pictured in Fig. 20.1.

3. Classification and General Properties

Proteolytic enzymes are classified into two large groups: (*a*) *Endopeptidases*, which hydrolyze internal peptide bonds and (*b*) *Exopeptidases*, which hydrolyze terminal peptide linkages. This classification is roughly equivalent to the older definition of *proteinases* and *peptidases*, respectively. The principal members of this large and well-known group of proteolytic enzymes are listed in Table 20.1.

It will be seen from the data in Table 20.1 that several of the common proteolytic enzymes such as trypsin, chymotrypsin, and carboxypeptidase are derived from the pancreas. The remainder are mainly of peptic or intestinal origin. Intracellular proteolytic enzymes are known (e.g., cathepsins), but efforts to obtain these proteins in a nicely crystalline form have met with less success.

Papain the plant proteolytic enzyme found in the latex of *Corica papaya* has been studied extensively by Emil L. Smith (see Chapter 16).

Among the bacterial enzymes the member of greatest notoriety is subtilisin. This enzyme, from *Bacillus subtilis*, was found in Linderström-Lang's laboratory (9) to split a peptide moiety away from egg albumin; the latter then crystallizes in plates, i.e., *plakalbumin*. Subtilisin was used effectively by Tuppy (10) in his classical work in the structure of the peptide hormone oxytocin.

It will also be apparent from the inspection of Table 20.1 that the *p*H for optimum activity spans an unusually wide range. The range of *p*H at which the proteolytic enzymes are stable provides an understanding of the stability of these proteins. Trypsin, for example, may be boiled and re-cooled without loss of activity.

The substrate specificity of the proteolytic enzyme is of considerable interest. Among the endopeptidases, pepsin acts best on a peptide linkage derived from the amino group of an aromatic amino acid such as L-tyrosine or L-phenylalanine. Chymotrypsin, on the other hand, splits at the carboxyl carbon of one of these aromatic amino acids. Trypsin hydrolyzes peptide linkages in which the carbonyl group is contributed by a lysyl or arginyl residue. The exopeptidases, which attack peptide chains from either end, appear to be somewhat less exacting in their specificity requirements. Thus carboxypeptidase and intestinal (leucine) aminopeptidase have found wide application for the liberation of C- and N-terminal amino acids, respectively.

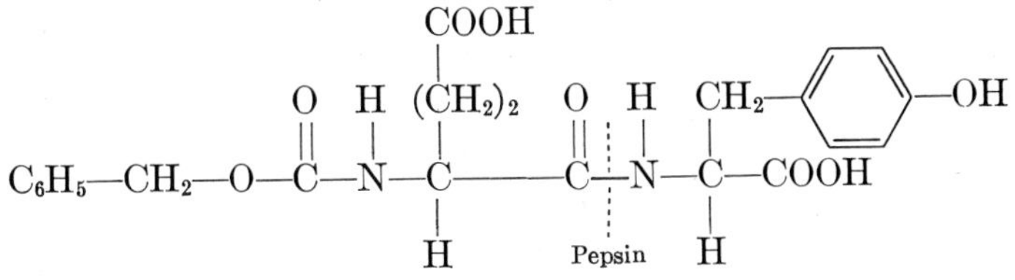

Carbobenzoxy-L-glutamyl-L-tyrosine

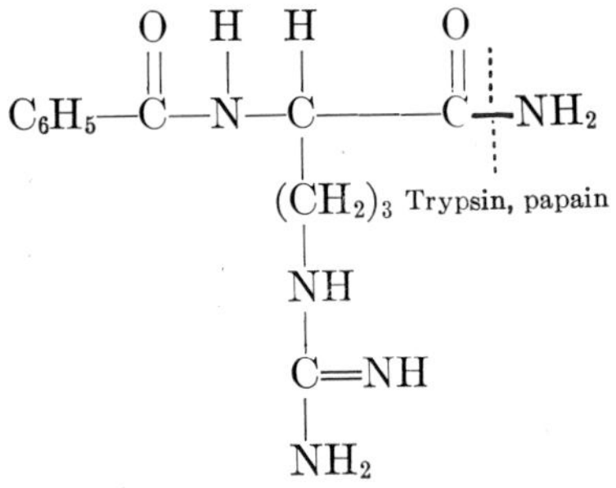

Benzoyl-L-argininamide

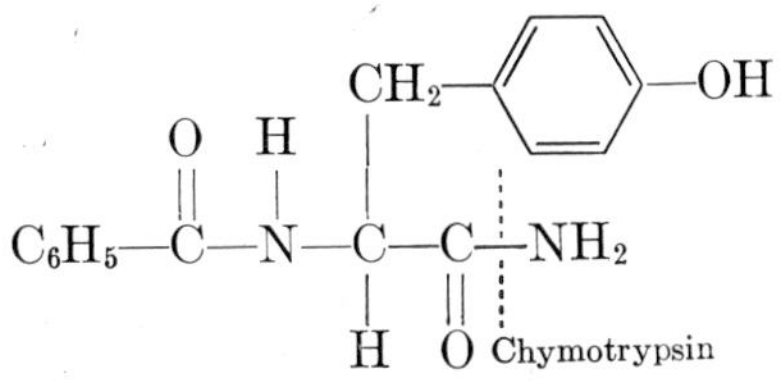

Benzoyl-L-tyrosinamide

The specificity requirements of the proteolytic enzymes suggested the use of synthetic substrates (11). Pepsin acts very well on a compound such as carbobenzoxy-L-glutamyl-L-tyrosine, where the carbobenzoxy group serves merely as an acyl substituent. Similarly, benzoyl-L-argininamide will do as a substrate for either trypsin or papain. Chymotrypsin liberates ammonia from benzoyl-L-tyrosinamide at a rapid rate, and this enzyme will even split the 2-3 carbon–carbon bond in ethyl 5-(p-hydroxyphenyl)-3-ketovalerate (26).

The ease with which the proteolytic enzymes attack these synthetic substrates might lead to the false impression that they can hydrolyze any type of native protein molecule. Such is certainly not the case. Many native proteins and even peptides are extremely resistant to enzymatic hydrolysis. Most proteins, however, become more susceptible to attack following denaturation.

As might be deduced from their sensitivity to DFP, trypsin and chymotrypsin hydrolyze ester linkages in compounds with analogous structure to the peptide substrates. A simple ester attacked by chymotrypsin is p-nitrophenylacetate. Since the acetyl moiety remains firmly bound to the enzyme, chymotrypsin can be said to commit suicide when it utilizes p-nitrophenylacetate as a substrate. In this case, as in the case with DFP, the "substrate" becomes a powerful inhibitor of the enzyme.

The optical specificity of the peptidases can be put to good use in the preparation of pure isomers. For example, Greenstein and coworkers (12) have worked out an ingenious method utilizing this principle (Fig. 20.2).

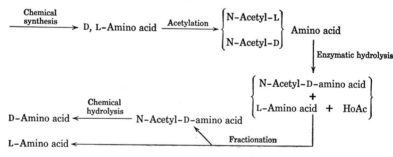

Fig. 20.2. Scheme for the enzymatic resolution of a racemic amino acid. [See Greenstein *et al.* (12).]

In addition to the cleavage of peptide linkages, the proteolytic enzymes may catalyze certain synthetic and transfer reactions (27). Of the latter, the most important is probably that of *transpeptidation.*

This reaction dates from a discovery by Bergmann and Fraenkel-Conrat (28) who observed a replacement by aniline of the amide group in benzoylglycinamide in the presence of papain.

Benzoylglycinamide + aniline $\rightleftharpoons$ benzoyglycinanilide + NH_3

Nearly all proteolytic enzymes have been found to participate in such reactions.

4. Activation

It has been recognized for many years that the proteolytic enzymes of the digestive tract are secreted in an inactive state and that activation occurs extra-cellularly. This fascinating reaction, the activation of zymogens, has been studied by a number of investigators, especially by Neurath and his group (13) in Seattle. As a result of this work the following points have been established: (a) the transformation is enzyme catalyzed and cannot be duplicated by a chemical reaction, (b) the reaction is "irreversible," and (c) the reaction involves the breaking of peptide bonds and the release of small peptide fragments.

For the purposes of illustration we shall describe the activation of trypsinogen as one of the less complex examples of this phenomenon (13). Activation of trypsinogen can be achieved with enterokinase, penicillum kinase, or trypsin itself. The latter has some advantage in that it does not introduce any new component into the reaction mixture.

Tables 20.2 and 20.3 illustrate the similarity in structure between the zymogen and active enzyme [or DFP-treated (DIP) enzyme; the inhibitor does not react with the zymogen].

From the data in Table 20.3 it might appear that a peptide fragment containing much aspartic acid was liberated from the zymogen. This peptide has been isolated and characterized as a hexapeptide, val-(asp)$_4$-lys. On the basis of these and other findings, such as the failure to locate a free COOH in trypsin, the activation process is thought to be as depicted in Fig. 20.3.

The activation of chymotrypsinogen, although more complicated, follows the same general pattern. Thus for chymotrypsin the splitting

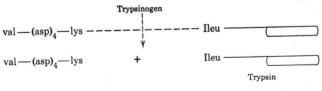

Fig. 20.3. Schematic diagram for the activation of trypsinogen (13).

Table 20.2.   Some Physical and Chemical Properties of
Trypsinogen and Trypsin (13)

	Trypsinogen	Trypsin
Molecular weight (sed; diff.)	23,800	23,800
Iso-ionic point (ion ex.)	9.3	10.1
E 1%, 280 mμ	13.9	14.4
N-terminal	1 valine	1 isoleucine
C-terminal (carboxypeptidase)	None	None

Table 20.3.   Comparison of the Amino Acid Compositions of
Trypsinogen and DIP-Trypsin* (13)

Amino Acid	Trypsinogen	Trypsin
Aspartic acid	25.4	21.5
Glutamic acid	11.0	11.1
Arginine	2.0	2.0
Lysine	14.5	14.0
Histidine	3.1	3.0
Phenylalanine	4.0	4.1
Tyrosine	9.4	9.9
Proline	8.0	8.0
½ cystine†	6.5	—
Total N		16.7%
minimum molecular weight (calculated)	23,320 ± 280	23,020 ± 340

* In terms of amino acid residues mole⁻¹. This is not the complete amino acid composition of the proteins.
† Determined as cysteic acid.

of an arginyl–isoleucine bond gives π-chymotrypsin; splitting of a second dipeptide linkage releases serylarginine to give δ-chymotrypsin; and, finally, by rupture of a third peptide linkage we get α-chymotrypsin.

The principal activating agents for the proteolytic enzymes are sulfhydryl compounds and metal ions. Papain and ficin are notoriously dependent on the presence of SH reducing agents. It is a common observation, dating from the classical work experiments of Johnson (14), that the peptidases require divalent metal ions. Carboxypeptidase has been found by Vallee and Neurath (15) to contain an atom of firmly bound zinc. Pepsin is reported to contain a molecule of diesterified phosphate (16).

Rabin (17) and co-workers have pointed out that the mechanism of metal ion activation can be interpreted in various ways. The metal ion may complex with the substrate, the enzyme, or the enzyme-substrate complex. Since amino acids form stable complexes with a number of divalent metal ions (see Chapter 3), the real substrate may be a metal-substrate chelate compound. If the metal ion must be incubated with the enzyme i.e. as is necessary in the case of leucine amino peptidase (24) it is probable that a metal ion-protein complex is formed.

Datta and Rabin (18) have also found that ionization occurs at the peptide linkage of cupric complexes of dipeptides such as glycyl-glycine and sarcosylglycine. However, when the peptide hydrogen atom was replaced by an alkyl group, as in glycylsarcosine, no acid dissociations from the cupric complexes could be detected. The metal complex is believed to possess a coordinate bond to the nitrogen and

$$
\begin{array}{c}
CH_3 \qquad O \ \ H \\
| \qquad\quad || \ \ | \\
H\!-\!N\!-\!CH_2\!-\!C\!-\!N\!-\!CH_2\!-\!COOH \\
\text{Sarcosylglycine}
\end{array}
$$

$$
\begin{array}{c}
O \ \ CH_3 \\
|| \ \ | \\
H_2N\!-\!CH_2\!-\!C\!-\!N\!-\!CH_2\!-\!COOH \\
\text{Glycylsarcosine}
\end{array}
$$

an electrostatic linkage to the carbonyl oxygen. These studies may help to elucidate the mechanism of metal binding by proteins.

$$
\begin{array}{c}
H_2C\!-\!NH_2 \\
| \qquad\qquad \searrow \\
| \qquad\qquad\quad M^{II} \\
| \qquad\qquad \nearrow \\
C\!-\!\!-\!\!-\!O \\
|| \\
N\!-\!CH_2\!-\!COO^-
\end{array}
$$

1:1 complex of a divalent metal ion and glycylglycine (18).

5. Inactivation

The inactivation of the proteolytic enzymes is of interest for at least two reasons; (a) those proteolytic enzymes with esterase activity, such as chymotrypsin and trypsin, are stoichiometrically poisoned with DFP. Thus, since the enzymes are readily obtained in a pure state, the full potential of DFP as an agent for labeling the enzyme active site may be realized; (b) the occurrence of certain natural inhibitors of the endopeptidases may represent a unique and biologically important method for the control of enzyme activity.

In spite of the ease with which inhibitors of the type $X\!-\!\overset{\overset{\textstyle O}{\textstyle \uparrow}}{P}\!-\!(OR)_2$ combine with chymotrypsin and trypsin, identification of the site of binding has not been easy. The early experiments of Balls and Jansen (19) showed that the reaction was a phosphorylation of the enzyme with concomitant liberation of HX. But since certain nucleophilic reagents (nicotinohydroxamic and picolinohydroxamic acids and their methiodides) could reverse the inhibition by displacing the alkyl phosphate from the enzyme freshly treated with DFP (but not with aged DIP enzyme), the reaction was believed to proceed in two stages: (*a*) initial phosphorylation and (*b*) transfer of the alkyl phosphate to a second stable locus. Imidazole has been suggested as the initial site of attack since: (1) the *p*H dependence of DFP inhibition indicates the participation of an ionizing group with *pKa* of 5–7; (2) histidine and tyrosine catalyze the hydrolysis of DFP; and (3) histidine derivatives accelerate the hydrolysis of *p*-nitrophenylacetate. However, the evidence in favor of serine rather than histidine as the active center is greatly strengthened by the isolation of a P^{32} labeled serine-containing peptide from DFP^{32} labeled chymotrypsin (20).

gly-asp-ser-gly
Peptide isolated from active site of chymotrypsin (20)

Hartley and Massey (21) have found that a new type of inhibitor, 1-dimethylamino-nephthalene-5-sulfonyl chloride, forms a fluorescent, unstable conjugate with chymotrypsin. Several well characterized natural inhibitors have been found. A crystalline trypsin inhibitor protein with a molecular weight of about 24,000 has been obtained from soya beans by Kunitz (22). Other natural inhibitors are found in egg white (ovomucoid), in colostrum, and in ox lung.

The common proteolytic enzymes of plant tissue, papain, ficin and bromelin are inhibited by reagents for thiol groups. Crude preparations usually contain sufficient activator for some activity. It will be recalled that in the proposed mechanism of action of papain [Stockell and Smith (23), Fig. 16.10] an acyl thiol ester is pictured as an intermediate. This thiol group can be blocked with iodoacetamide and the inhibitor apparently goes on near the C-terminal end of papain. This conclusion is supported by the previous findings of Smith that the molecule can be extensively degraded with leucine amino peptidase without loss in activity.

6. Summary

In this chapter we have attempted to sketch some of the salient features of the proteolytic enzymes. We have pointed out that they may be exploited as models for the study of the mechanism of enzyme action. It is also certain that the proteolytic enzymes will contribute greatly to our understanding of the active sites of enzymes. As analytical tools these enzymes are indispensable, i.e., enzymes can be used to "eat" enzyme, virus, or protein hormone. And the proteolytic enzymes are unsurpassed in the efficiency with which they resolve racemic amino acid derivatives.

One important question remains. It is this: How are the proteolytic enzymes synthesized? In order to answer this question we shall have

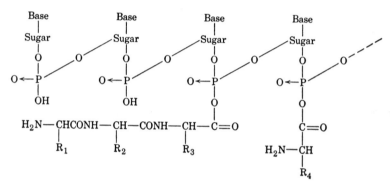

Fig. 20.4. Proposed template (incompletely fitted) for the synthesis of polypeptide chains. [See Borsook (25).]

to consider the general problem of protein synthesis, since it is likely that all proteins—enzymatically active and inactive—have a common pattern of origin. And the common reaction cannot be a simple reversal of the reaction catalyzed by proteolytic enzymes. The present evidence suggests that the amino acids must be activated perhaps by attachment to a terminal phosphate residue of polynucleotide (25). (See Fig. 20.4.)

References

General

1. *The Proteins,* edited by H. Neurath and K. Bailey, Academic Press, N. Y., 1953.

2. Physical Chemistry of Enzymes, *Discussions Faraday Soc.,* No. 20, Aberdeen University Press, Aberdeen, 1955.

3. J. H. Northrup, M. Kunitz and R. M. Herriott, *Crystalline Enzymes,* 2nd ed., Columbia University Press, N. Y., 1948.

Bibliography

4. E. Brand et al., *J. Am. Chem. Soc., 67,* 1524 (1945).

5. L. Michaelis and H. Davidsohn, *Biochem. Z., 35,* 386 (1911).

6. C. G. Swain and J. F. Brown, *J. Am. Chem. Soc., 74,* 2534, 2538 (1952).

7. L. Perenyi, *Acta Physiol. Acad. Sci. Hung., 5,* 87 (1954).

8. E. B. Herr and D. E. Koshland, *Biochem. Biophys. Acta, 25,* 219 (1957).

9. N. Egg-Larsen et al., *Arch. Biochem., 19,* 340 (1948).

10. H. Tuppy, *Biochem. Biophys. Acta, 11,* 449 (1953).

11. J. S. Fruton and M. Bergmann, *J. Biol. Chem., 127,* 627 (1939).

12. P. J. Fodor, V. E. Price and J. P. Greenstein, *J. Biol. Chem., 178,* 503 (1949).

13. H. Neurath and W. J. Dreyer, *Discussions Faraday Soc.,* No. 20, Aberdeen University Press, Aberdeen, 1955.

14. M. J. Johnston and J. Berger, *Advances in Enzymology, 2,* 69 (1942).

15. B. L. Vallee and H. Neurath, *J. Biol. Chem., 217,* 253 (1955).

16. G. E. Perlmann, *3rd Intern. Congr. Biochem., Abstr. of Communs., 7* (Brussels, Belgium) August 1955.

17. B. R. Rabin and E. M. Crook, *Biochem. Biophys. Acta, 19,* 550 (1956).

18. S. P. Datta and B. R. Rabin, *Biochem. Biophys. Acta, 19,* 572 (1956).

19. A. K. Balls and E. F. Jansen, *Advances in Enzymology, 13,* 324 (1952).

20. J. A. Cohen et al., *Discussions Faraday Soc.,* No. 20, Aberdeen University Press, Aberdeen, 1955; see also N. K. Shaffer et al., *Fed. Proc., 14,* 275 (1955) and F. Turba and G. Gundlach, *Biol. Z., 327,* 186 (1955).

21. B. S. Hartley and V. Massey, *Biochim. Biophys. Acta, 21,* 58 (1956).

22. M. Kunitz, *J. Gen. Physiol., 30,* 291, 311 (1947); *32,* 241 (1948).

23. A. Stockell and E. L. Smith, *J. Biol. Chem., 227,* 1 (1957).

24. E. L. Smith and D. H. Spackmann, *J. Biol. Chem., 212,* 271 (1955).

25. H. Borsook, in *Proteins, Biology Colloquium, No. 17,* Oregon State College, Corvallis, Ore., 1956. (Lib. Congress Cat. Card No. 52-19235.)

26. D. G. Doherty, *J. Am. Chem. Soc., 77,* 4887 (1955).

27. A. Meister, *Biochemistry of the Amino Acids,* Academic Press, N. Y. (1957).

28. M. Bergmann and H. Fraenkel-Conrat, *J. Biol. Chem., 119,* 707 (1937).

Part 4
METABOLIC PATTERNS

21

Metabolic Processes

1. Introduction (1, 2)

The study of any enzyme inevitably leads to a query concerning its role in the living cell. Its function is to catalyze metabolic reactions involved in the maintenance, growth, and reproduction of the living organism. Metabolism is a composite of two sensitively balanced processes: namely, *anabolism*, or the utilization of energy and material for chemical syntheses; and *catabolism*, or the breakdown of substrates with the release of available energy for work. Each step of these complex sequences of reactions is controlled by a specific enzyme system.

2. Methodology

Although many methods are available for the study of metabolic processes, much of the success of the experimental approach depends on the judicious choice of experimental material. The relationships of types of material available to the investigator are indicated as follows:

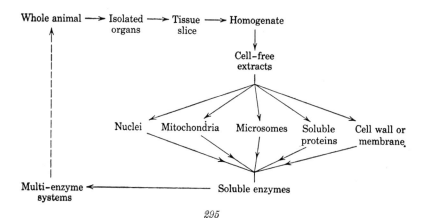

C. Cori   G. Cori   L. F. Leloir

A. von Szent-Györgyi   H. A. Krebs

M. Doudoroff   F. Lynen   F. Lipmann

In the past much information was obtained from investigations with intact animals, isolated organs, and tissue slices. More recently developed methods for tracing pathways of isotopically labeled compounds in organisms have been highly successful. But the great progress made since the 1940's toward a detailed explanation of reactions responsible for the metabolic activity of tissues has stemmed from a careful analysis of individual enzyme systems. Found first in crude homogenates, traced to their loci in cells, isolated, and purified, these enzymes have been studied thoroughly from the point of view of their properties, kinetics, and mechanism of action. Their activities have been integrated into multi-enzyme systems capable of duplicating conversion reactions originally observed in intact organs or whole organisms.

3. Multi-enzyme Systems

A multi-enzyme system may be defined as an organization of enzymes which catalyzes an orderly sequence of reactions to bring about the conversion of a substrate to the desired product (1). Examples include the TCA cycle, glycolysis, and fatty acid oxidation.

Despite the physical heterogeneity of such systems, the orderly sequence of reactions is brought about by the specificity of each enzyme for its substrate. Thus, B, the conversion product of A, would fall within the specificity requirements of enzyme b responsible for its breakdown. C, the conversion product of B, would in turn be attacked by enzyme c, which specifically handles this substrate, and thus the transformation of the initial substrate would continue to its eventual conclusion.

In Fig. 21.1 is depicted a hypothetical multi-enzyme system consisting of enzymes, cofactors, and substrates which duplicates the gross conversion of compound A to Z by an intact organism.

In general, if the system catalyzing the conversion of A to Z is a synthesizing or anabolic system, the net free-energy change will be endergonic $(+\Delta F)$; if a degradative or catabolic system, the change will be exergonic $(-\Delta F)$ (see Chapter 12). In order for an anabolic system to proceed, it must tap a source of energy which usually will be drawn from a catabolic system. In turn, to be physiologically important, multi-enzyme catabolic systems must include reactions geared to trap effectively the intrinsic free energy released during an enzyme-catalyzed reaction (1). The trapping system usually involves the adenylate or the thio ester system (see Chapter 24). However, in specialized cases such as in photosynthesis the chief pool of energy is derived from external sources.

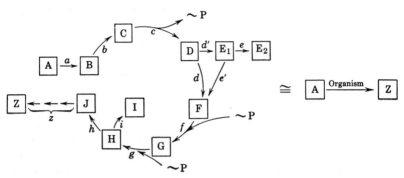

Fig. 21.1. A hypothetical multienzyme system consisting of enzymes (*a, b.* etc.), cofactors, and substrates (*A, B,* etc.) depicting the conversion of compound $A \to Z$ and the formation and utilization of high energy phosphate bonds ($\sim$P). E_2 and I represent possible side reactions.

Although of great value in revealing the details of metabolic processes, multi-enzyme systems devised by the enzyme chemist must nevertheless be viewed with a healthy skepticism. Thus, when intact tissue is homogenized, at least three factors immediately influence the enzymic activity and hence the nature of the reaction sequence in such preparations: (*a*) dilution effects by the suspending medium during homogenization, (*b*) inhibitory effects related to the liberation of substances from cell fragments, and (*c*) destructive effects such as autolytic processes which by modifying the structures of enzyme proteins decrease their enzymic activities. In addition, the inherent instability of enzyme proteins, substrates, and cofactors, the actual concentrations of these components, the mutual affinities of substrate and cofactor for enzymes, pH, temperature and salt effects, the introduction of spatial separation of enzyme from substrate and cofactors, and the possible influence of hormonal control on enzyme systems must be considered in the final interpretation of data derived exclusively from multi-enzyme systems. To determine whether isolated enzyme systems are artifacts or actually do represent the mechanism of a metabolic process, experimental results must be checked with those observed in the intact organism or in some related physiologic system.

4. Particulate Systems

Biochemical examination of the cytological components of the cell has revealed that a major portion of metabolic activity of the cell resides in small particles identified as mitochondria and microsomes (3). Although mitochondria had been recognized microscopically for some time as discrete bodies imbedded in the cytoplasm of plant and animal cells, it was not until 1934 that they were isolated from guinea pig liver (4). Almost a decade elapsed before their position in the metabolic activity of the cell was recognized. At the same time, investigations with microsomal systems have revealed the increasing importance of these particles in the total picture of metabolism. It is therefore of some value to examine the present status of mitochondria and microsomes in their relation to metabolic activity.

A. *Isolation.* Mitochondria and microsomes are obtained free of other cellular components by fractional centrifugation techniques under conditions designed to preserve as nearly as possible their original shape and activity. Tissue from which they are to be prepared is obtained as fresh as possible, chilled to a low temperature, and, in the presence of a hypertonic sucrose-phosphate buffer, is triturated by techniques mild enough to fragment the cell but not its particular components. A typical flowsheet for the preparation of mitochondria and microsomes is presented in Fig. 21.2.

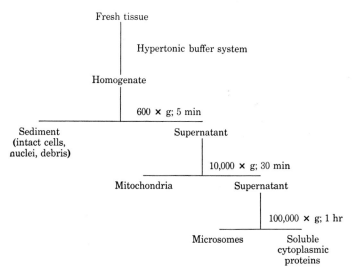

Fig. 21.2. A typical flowsheet for the isolation of mitochondria and microsomes.

Interestingly this procedure is used with only minor changes for both plant and animal cells with equal success (3, 5). Separation of particles are also effected by differential centrifugation of the homogenates in a concentration gradient (5a).

B. *Morphology of Mitochondria.* A mitochondrion is usually a cylindrical body with dimensions of 1–4 μ by 0.3–0.7 μ. Examination of extremely thin sections of cells by electron microscopy reveals a variety of mitochondrial profiles of various shapes, depending on their orientation three-dimensionally in the cytoplasm at the time of sectioning (6). These particles always appear to have a limiting membrane, that consists of two parallel membranes, each approximately 5 mμ in thickness separated by a space of about 6–8 mμ. The inner membrane is deeply folded to form a series of striations of varying lengths, parallel to each other and perpendicular to the long axis of the particle. These striations are a part of a system of internal ridges named *cristae mitochondrials*. The arrangement of the cristae internally is in some manner related to the source of the mitochondrial material. However, the same general features have been observed in material obtained from avian, amphibian, molluscan, annelid, protozoan, and leaf tissue. The space bounded by the mitochondrial membrane is called the *mitochondrial matrix*. It appears to be relatively homogeneous structurally, and presumably it contains soluble proteins.

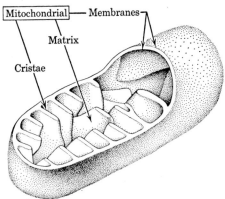

Fig. 21.3. A highly schematized diagram of a mitochondrion. After Palade (6). Reproduced from *Journal of Histochemistry and Cytochemistry*, Williams and Wilkins Company, Baltimore.

In Fig. 21.3 is depicted a highly schematized diagram of mitochondrion based on the work of Palade (6).

C. *Chemical Composition of Mitochondria*. A significant concentration of lipid and phospholipid is characteristic of mitochondria. Thus 27% of the total phospholipid of a liver homogenate is found in the particle. Thirty-nine per cent of the total nitrogen of the homogenate is associated with the particles and 60% of the total mitochondrial nitrogen is found with the soluble protein fraction which is released when the mitochondria are disrupted by sonic vibration. In Table 21.1 are summarized data concerning the vitamin content of

Table 21.1. Vitamin Content of Isolated Liver Mitochondria (7)

Compound	Concentration (whole tissue = 1)	Recovery (whole tissue = 100)
Vitamin B_6	1.3	33
Vitamin B_{12}	2.2	56
Riboflavin	1.8	53
FAD	2.3	65
Folinic acid	1.8	38
Pantothenic acid	—	43
CoA	—	52

isolated mitochondria. It is tempting to speculate that the loci of the functions of all these vitamins may be found in as yet unknown mitochondrial enzyme systems. It is already known that CoA, derived from pantothenic acid, and FAD are closely linked to the enzymes of fatty acid oxidation in mitochondria.

A further insight into the composition of these particles is obtained when the distribution of organic phosphate is studied. Of the total phosphate found in rat liver mitochondria, 21% is associated with an acid-soluble P fraction, 56% with lipid P (presumably phospholipids), and 20% with total nucleic P, of which approximately 1.5% represents DNA-P (possibly a contamination by nuclei), and 18.5% PNA-P (8).

D. *Enzymatic Activities of Mitochondria.* The enzymatic activities of mitochondrial particles are numerous and diversified, many of them being the exclusive property of these particles.

It should be stressed, nevertheless, that, before a definite activity is assigned to mitochondria, the possibility of physical adsorption of soluble cytoplasmic enzymes onto the mitochondrial membranes must be considered. In addition, isolated mitochondria are fragile structures. In hypotonic media they rapidly lose their structure as well as much of their enzymic activities. Therefore, negative tests for enzyme activity must not be regarded as positive evidence for the absence of a specific enzyme in these particles.

Though it is true that many enzymes appear localized in the mitochondria, the breakdown of a complex molecule undoubtedly requires a mutual interplay of enzymes associated not only with mitochondria but also with the soluble proteins of the cytoplasm. Thus, in the conversion of glucose to carbon dioxide and water, the initial degradation of glucose to pyruvic acid takes place in the cytoplasm before the mitochondria assume the burden of oxidation. These steps are outlined in Fig. 21.4.

Although in most cells mitochondria apparently move freely

through the cytoplasm, in some specialized cells, they appear to congregate in certain areas. Thus in the epithelium of the active segments of the nephron, a large number of mitochondria are found in the infoldings of the cell membranes of the basal pole of the cell. This suggests that mitochondria are situated in this strategic area of the cell to insure effective generation and flow of energy for the purpose of active transport of water and solute across the cell membrane.

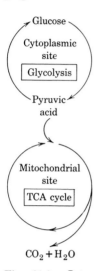

Fig. 21.4. Intracellular relation of multienzyme systems associated with soluble cytoplasmic proteins and mitochondria.

It is well known that in the mitochondria are located the extremely important activities of cyanide-sensitive respiration and oxidative phosphorylation. The orderly flow of electrons from substrate through the cytochrome system to oxygen with the simultaneous esterification of phosphate involves a complex of highly efficient but unstable enzymes which are associated with the solid phases of the mitochondrial structure. It is undoubtedly by this unique structural arrangement of enzymes that the efficiency, stability, and coordination of these vital activities are achieved.

In Table 21.2 are collected the various enzymic activities of mitochondrial particles. The table illustrates the variety of activities that these particles possess.

E. *Morphology and Chemistry of Microsomes (2)*. In most cells, in addition to the rod-like structures of mitochondria, the electron

Table 21.2.   Some Enzymic Activities of Mitochondria

Activity	Reference
Multi-enzyme systems	
TCA cycle	8
Fatty acid oxidation	8
Fatty acid synthesis (plants)	24
Oxidative phosphorylation	10
Phospholipid biosynthesis	25
Dehydrogenases and oxidases	
Succinic dehydrogenase	26
Glutamic dehydrogenase	27
Glycerolphosphate dehydrogenase	28
Cytochrome oxidase	29
Betaine aldehyde oxidase	30
Choline oxidase	31
Propionic acid oxidation (plants)	32

microscope has revealed a somewhat poorly defined network of vesicles and tubules. These elongated structures—the endoplasmic reticulum—are about 50–200 mμ wide, have membranes, and probably have a continuous internal cavity. They are covered with small, round, dense particles measuring about 10 mμ in diameter. This network appears to begin from the inner surface of the cell membrane and extends to the nuclear membrane.

A microsomal pellet prepared by differential centrifugation of a tissue homogenate (see Figs. 21.2 and 21.5), actually represents fragments of the endoplasmic reticulum and consists of isolated vesicular and tubular elements that still bear the small dense particles. If this pellet is now suspended in buffer containing sodium deoxycholate and

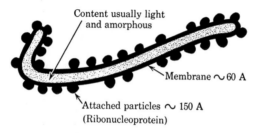

Content usually light and amorphous

Membrane $\sim$ 60 A

Attached particles $\sim$ 150 A
(Ribonucleoprotein)

Fig. 21.5. A schematized diagram of a fragment of endoplasmic reticulum from hepatic cells. Note the dense, round particles of ribonucleoprotein attached to the tubular structure. After Palade (9).

recentrifuged, the new pellet contains only small particles and is free of the membrane matrix onto which the particle had previously been associated.

These isolated particles contain 70% of the ribonucleic acid, 15% of the protein nitrogen, 10% of the phospholipid, and 5% of the hemochromogen originally found in the particle-membrane complex. Most of the ribonucleic acid of the original preparation is therefore concentrated in the small particles or "microsomes," and the other components, namely protein, phospholipid, and hemochromogen are largely associated with the membrane structure.

F. *Enzymic Activity of Microsomes.* The enzymic activities of the fragmented endoplasmic reticulum (microsomal particles) have only recently been explored and the following activities have been observed: (1) incorporation of amino acids into proteins (10), (2) glucuronide formation from uridine diphosphate glucuronic acid and suitable acceptors (11), (3) DPN and TPN-cytochrome c reductases (12), (4) glucose-6-phosphatase (13), (5) cytochrome B_5 (animals) and cytochrome b_3 (plants) (14), (6) palmitic oxidase (15), and (7) detoxification of a rather large number of unrelated compounds by the following mechanisms, (*a*) deamination, (*b*) demethylation, (*c*) dealkylation, (*d*) hydroxylation of aromatic compounds, (*e*) side chain oxidation of barbituric acid, and (*f*) cleavage of aromatic ethers (16).

G. *Other Particles.* De Duve et al. (17) and Kuff et al. (18) have presented evidence suggesting that another particle occurs in cells. Called *lysosomes*, these are approximately 100 mμ in radius and appear to contain for the most part hydrolytic enzymes such as ribonuclease, deoxyribonuclease, cathepsin, acid phosphatase, β-glucuronidase, and uricase. It would be of considerable interest if future work should show that major hydrolytic processes are associated with a specific type of particle just as the major electron transport mechanism in a cell is coupled to oxidative phosphorylation in mitochondria.

The nucleus, with its obvious importance as the carrier of chromosomes, appears to contain few enzymes. However, both nicotinamide mononucleotide pyrophosphorylase and uridine diphosphate pyrophosphorylase have been found to occur in high concentrations. Not only the nucleus but also cell walls and cell membranes need to be examined intensively for enzyme localizations in order that a more complete mapping of enzyme sites in a cell be made available.

5. Regulation of Metabolic Activity (19, 20)

Since the functioning unit of the metabolic machinery is the enzyme-catalyzed reaction, then the regulation of this unit becomes of primary importance for the economy of the cell. Conditions for metabolic regulation must involve (A) the kinetic factors which control enzymic rates, (B) the relation of the structural organization of cells to enzymic action, and (C) the action of various compounds as inhibitors or activators on enzymes.

A. *Enzymic Rates.* The kinetics of a single reaction is governed by the concentration of enzyme, substrate, cofactors, cations, anions, by the temperature, pH, the —SS—/—SH ratio, the TPNH/DPNH and TPN$^+$/DPN$^+$ ratios, the occurrence of activators and inhibitors, and by the rate and extent of conversion of proenzymes to active enzymes. In addition, the rate of synthesis and breakdown of enzyme protein and of cofactors, inhibitors, and hormones must be superimposed on the kinetic factors.

A small change of any of these factors by the physical environment, by disease, or by hormonal effects may alter rather profoundly the over-all performance of the metabolic machinery.

B. *Structural Organization.* An important number of enzymes are for the most part firmly associated with cytoplasmic particles. Thus, the cytochrome system, the major electron transport system of the cell, is subtly interlocked with the enzymes of oxidative phosphorylation in a specific geometric organization on the mitochondrial membrane or the cristae. This type of organization would inherently suggest a high order of efficiency and biochemical stability. However, physical factors, such as changes in the osmotic conditions of the surrounding medium or in the permeability of the mitochondrial membrane and biochemical factors, such as the uncoupling of phosphorylation from oxidation by dinitrophenol, may affect the structural organization of enzymes in particles and result in striking changes in the normal sequence of metabolic events.

Another consideration is the spatial separation of multi-enzyme systems from each other. Thus, in the degradation of glucose to carbon dioxide and water, at least three pathways are involved: glycolysis, pentose cycle, and the TCA cycle. The glycolytic enzymes and the enzymes of the pentose cycle are found outside the particles, whereas the tightly bound particulate enzymes of the cytochrome system and the TCA cycle are associated with mitochrondria. A close partnership must exist between the three metabolic sequences and any interference in that partnership will result in a breakdown or modification of glucose metabolism. Furthermore, any change in the concentration of phosphate and magnesium, the ratio of ADP to ATP, TPN$^+$ to TPNH, DPN$^+$ to DPNH, oxygen and carbon dioxide tension would also affect this partnership.

Still another function of particulate enzymes is the ability of mitochondria, for example, to concentrate cofactors, substrates, and enzymes far above the concentration found outside the particles (see Tables 21.1 and 21.2). By this mechanism the kinetic responses of the enzyme catalyzed reactions in mitochondria are greatly changed.

C. *Activators and Inhibitors.* Substances which decrease the rate of an enzyme catalyzed reaction are known as inhibitors. The influences of both competitive and non-competitive inhibitors on enzymic rates are simple and well known (see Chapter 9). A more complex effect is the action of dinitrophenol on the uncoupling of oxidative phosphorylation with a resultant loss of utilizable energy for the cell.

Recently, a rather subtle type of control has been recognized and has been designated as *negative feedback,* or an inhibition by an endproduct of its own synthesis. Thus, in the sequence A $\xrightarrow{\text{a}}$ B $\xrightarrow{\text{b}}$ C, product C in a sufficient concentration may strongly inhibit reaction

a. If product C is not rapidly utilized, it will build up its concentration within a given period of time to a level which will inhibit the reaction a. The formation of both B and C will then be sharply curtailed. Since there is a decreased rate of synthesis of B and a gradual utilization of endogenous C, the concentration of C gradually falls to a subinhibitory level. Once its concentration level is sufficiently low it will again release the system for its own synthesis. Such sequences have been described by Yates and Pardee (20) and by Umbarger (21) in bacterial systems.

Still another aspect is how the cell routes the metabolism of a given compound if alternate pathways are available for its transformation. For example, glucose 6-phosphate may follow either the hexose phosphate shunt pathway or the classical glycolytic sequence. It has recently been observed (22) that 6-phosphorylgluconic acid is a strong inhibitor of phosphorylglucoisomerase, which catalyzes the reaction

Glucose 6-phosphate $\rightleftharpoons$ Fructose 6-phosphate

By this effect the glycolytic pathway is blocked and the phosphorylated glucose is then channeled exclusively into the oxidative pathway:

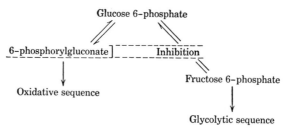

The role of hormones in metabolic regulation remain as yet a mystery. They have not been recognized either as enzymes or as cofactors nor do they have any direct activating or inhibitory effect on isolated enzymes. Because of the latent period of hormone action, the extremely low concentrations required for physiological effects, and the high degree of specificity *in vivo*, hormones probably function in controlling either the synthesis or activation of enzymes. In support of this view, Sutherland (23) has shown that the drug Epinephrine increases remarkably the concentration of active phosphorylase in rabbit liver. This effect is thus related to the conversion of the inactive form to the active enzyme *in vivo*.

In summary, the precise nature of the regulation of metabolism is still obscure. However, the new developments in the field of enzyme chemistry outlined above must be implicated as major factors in the control mechanisms of metabolism. The nature of the master mechanism that determines the over-all control or that triggers the many mechanisms at its disposal remains as yet a fertile but unexplored field.

References

General

1. M. Dixon, *Multi-Enzyme Systems,* Cambridge University Press, Cambridge, 1949.
2. O. H. Gaebler, *Enzymes: Units of Biological Structure and Function,* Academic Press, N. Y., 1956.

Bibliography

3. Chr. de Duve and J. Berthet, *Intern. Rev. Cytology,* Academic Press, N. Y., 1954, p. 225.
4. R. R. Bensley and N. Hoerr, *Anat. Rec., 60,* 449 (1934).
5. D. P. Hackett, *Intern. Rev. Cytol., 4,* 143 (1955).
5a. E. L. Kuff, G. H. Hogeboom, and A. J. Dalton, *J. Biophys. and Biochem. Cytol., 2,* 22 (1956).
6. G. E. Palade, *J. Histochem. and Cytochem., 1,* 188 (1953).
7. W. C. Schneider, *J. Histochem. and Cytochem., 1,* 212 (1953).
8. E. P. Kennedy and A. L. Lehninger, *J. Biol. Chem., 179,* 957 (1949).
9. G. E. Palade and K. R. Porter, *J. Exptl. Med., 100,* 641 (1954).
10. E. B. Keller and P. C. Zamecnik, *J. Biol. Chem., 221,* 45 (1956).
11. G. J. Dutton, *Biochem. J., 64,* 693 (1956).
12. G. H. Hogeboom and W. C. Schneider, *J. Biol. Chem., 186,* 417 (1950).
13. M. A. Swanson, *J. Biol. Chem., 184,* 647 (1950).
14. E. M. Martin and R. K. Morton, *Nature, 176,* 113 (1955).
15. T. E. Humphreys, E. H. Newcomb, A. H. Bokman and P. K. Stumpf, *J. Biol. Chem., 210,* 941 (1954).
16. J. Axelrod, *Biochem. J., 63,* 634 (1956).
17. Chr. de Duve, B. Pressman, R. Gianetto, R. Wattiaux, and F. Appelman, *Bioch. J., 60,* 604 (1955).
18. E. L. Kuff, and George H. Hogeboom, in *Enzymes: Units of Biological Structure and Function,* Academic Press, N. Y., 1956, p. 235.
19. W. E. Knox, V. H. Auerbach, and E. C. C. Lin, *Physiol. Rev., 36,* 164 (1956).
20. R. A. Yates and A. B. Pardee, *J. Biol. Chem., 221,* 757 (1956).
21. H. F. Umbarger, *Science, 123,* 848 (1956).
22. C. W. Parr, *Nature, 178,* 1401 (1956).
23. E. W. Sutherland and C. F. Cori, *J. Biol. Chem., 188,* 531 (1951).
24. P. K. Stumpf and George A. Barker, *J. Biol. Chem., 227,* 407 (1957).
25. E. P. Kennedy, *J. Biol. Chem., 201,* 399 (1953).
26. G. H. Hogeboom, W. C. Schneider and G. E. Palade, *J. Biol. Chem., 172,* 619 (1948).
27. G. H. Hogeboom and W. C. Schneider, *J. Biol. Chem., 204,* 233 (1953).

28. M. V. Dianzani, *Arch. fisiol., 50,* 187 (1951).
29. W. C. Schneider and G. H. Hogeboom, *J. Nat. Cancer Inst., 10,* 969 (1950).
30. J. N. Williams, *J. Biol. Chem., 195,* 26 (1952).
31. G. E. Palade, *Arch. Biochem., 30,* 144 (1951).
32. J. Giovanelli and P. K. Stumpf, *J. Am. Chem. Soc., 79,* 2652 (1957).

22

Glycolysis

1. Introduction (1–4)

The historical development of enzyme chemistry is inextricably associated with studies on the glycolytic pathway. The science was initiated in 1897, when Büchner prepared for the first time a cell-free extract of yeast cells and demonstrated that this extract had the capacity to ferment sugars. Many of the concepts, tools, techniques, and biochemical compounds such as ATP, DPN, and TPP now frequently used by enzyme chemists, trace their origin to the exploratory work on sugar fermentation. Many of the eminent enzyme chemists of the past and present—Meyerhof, Neuberg, the Coris, Parnas, Warburg, and Lipmann—were active participants in unraveling the mysteries of this pathway.

The pathway is, historically, the first example of a multi-enzyme system which offers a satisfactory explanation for the degradation of sugars to pyruvic acid. Although carbohydrate pathways other than the glycolytic may be dominant in the living cell, the system is nevertheless found in a large number of bacteria, in protozoa, including the acetate flagellates, trypanosomes, and the plasmodia, in a large variety of insects, fish, and in algae, higher plants, and animals. To determine the presence of the cycle in a given tissue, the age, the source, and the nutritional history must be considered since these factors have an important effect on the extent of the participation of the pathway in a given tissue.

The system as it is known today is depicted in Fig. 22.1. Table 22.1 gathers together pertinent information concerning the biochemical properties of the enzymes responsible for the degradative reactions. The energetics of the system are discussed at the end of this chapter. The physical constants of some glycolytic enzymes are found in Table 22.2.

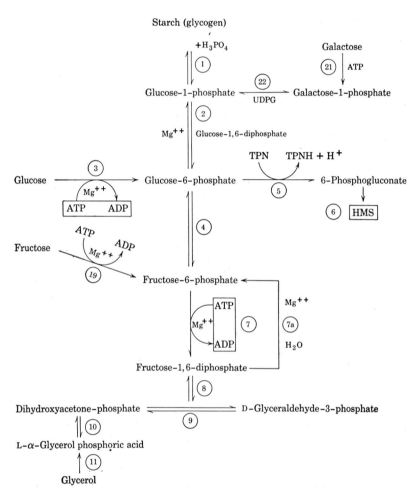

Fig. 22.1.   The glycolytic sequence. *See continuation of figure for legend.*

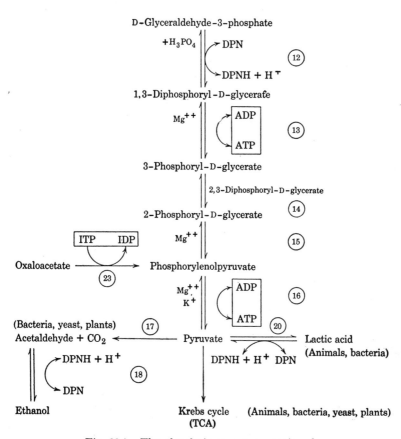

Fig. 22.1.   The glycolytic sequence, *continued.*

1. Phosphorylase.
2. Phosphoglucomutase.
3. Hexokinase.
4. Phosphohexoisomerase.
5. Glucose-6-phosphate dehydrogenase.
6. Hexose monophosphate shunt system (HMS).
7. Phosphofructokinaise
7a. Fructose diphosphatase.
8. Aldolase.
9. Triosephosphate isomerase.
10. α-Glycerolphosphate dehydrogenase.
11. Glycerol kinase.

12. Triose-phosphate dehydrogenase.
13. Phosphorylglyceryl kinase.
14. Phosphorylglyceryl mutase.
15. Enolase.
16. Phosphoenolpyruvic transphosphorylase.
17. Carboxylase.
18. Alcohol dehydrogenase.
19. Fructokinase.
20. Lactic dehydrogenase.
21. Galactokinase.
22. Galactowaldenase.
23. Phosphorylenolpyruvate carboxylase.

Table 22.1. Biochemical Properties of Glycolytic Enzymes (2–4)

Enzyme	Source	TN	Cofactor or Cosubstrate	Substrate Km M/l	Optimum pH	K_{eq}	Inhibitors
Phosphorylase	Potato* Muscle*	40,000	Amylopectin acts as primer. Pyridoxal phosphate		6	$\frac{gl\text{-}1\text{-}PO_4}{(gl)_n(PO_4)} = 0.3$ (pH 7)	Glucose
Hexokinase	Yeast*	13,000 (glucose)	Mg^{++} ATP	Glucose 1.5×10^{-4}; Mannose 1×10^{-4}; Fructose 1.5×10^{-3}	8–9	$\frac{(gl\text{-}6\text{-}P)(ADP)}{(gl)(ATP)} = 1.6 \times 10^2$ (pH 6.0)	N-acetyl glucosamine; inhibited by substrates
Phosphoglucomutase	Rabbit* muscle	16,800/30°C	Mg^{++} gl-1-6, diPO$_4$	$\left.\begin{array}{l} gl\text{-}1\text{-}PO_4 \\ gl\text{-}6\text{-}PO_4 \end{array}\right\}$ specific	7.5–9.2	$\frac{gl\text{-}6\text{-}PO_4}{gl\text{-}1\text{-}PO_4} = 19$	Fluoride; heavy metals
Phosphofructoisomerase	Rabbit muscle	Extremely rapid	None	No data	9	$\frac{gl\text{-}6\text{-}PO_4}{fr\text{-}6\text{-}PO_4} = \frac{7}{3}$	6-phosphoryl gluconic acid
Phosphofructokinase	Rabbit muscle	10,400	Mg^{++} ATP	Fructose-6-PO_4 = 10^{-4}	7.8	—	Iodoacetate
Aldolase	Rabbit* muscle	4140/30°C	None		7.5–8.5	$\frac{(triose\text{-}PO_4)^2}{HDP} = 1.5 \times 10^{-4}$ at 20°	Heavy metals
	Yeast		Zn^{++}, Co^{++}, Fe^{++}, or Ca^{++}		7.5		Pyrophosphate; cysteine
Triosephosphate isomerase	Muscle	945,000/26°C	None		7–8	$\frac{DHAP}{GA\text{-}3\text{-}P} = 22$	Phosphate
Triose phosphate dehydrogenase	Rabbit* muscle	6700/27°C	DPN^+	GA-3-PO_4— 5.1×10^{-5}	8.5	—	Iodoacetate Heavy metals Oxidants
3-Phosphorylglyceric kinase	Yeast*	320,000 forward reaction	Mg^{++}	DPGA— 1.8×10^{-6}	7	$\frac{(ATP)(3\text{-}PGA)}{(ADP)(DPGA)} = 3.3 \times 10^3$	—
Phosphoglyceromutase	Rabbit muscle	—	2,3-Diphosphoryl-D-glycerate	2-PGA—10^{-3}	60	$\frac{3\text{-}PGA}{2\text{-}PGA} = 4.5$	—

| Enolase | Yeast* | 15,000 for-ward/25° | Mg^{++} | 2-PGA—10^{-4} | 7.5 | $\dfrac{\text{PEPA}}{\text{2-PGA}} = 2.5$ | Fluoride; Ca^{++} |
| Pyruvic kinase | Yeast* | 6,000 forward reaction | K^+ Mg^{++} | Phosphoryl enol pyruvate—8.6×10^{-5} M | 7.5 | $\dfrac{\text{(Pyruvate)(ATP)}}{\text{(PEPA)(ADP)}} = 200$ | Na^+, Ca^{++} |

* Crystalline preparations.

Abbreviations: DHAP = dihydroxyacetone phosphate.
GA-3-P = D-glyceraldehyde-3-phosphate.
3-PGA = 3-phosphoryl-D-glyceric acid.
2-PGA = 2-phosphoryl-D-glyceric acid.
DPGA = 1,3-diphosphoryl-D-glyceric acid.
PEPA = phosphorylenolpyruvic acid.

Table 22.2. Physical Constants of Some Glycolytic Enzymes

Enzyme	Source	Preparation	S_{20}^0	Molecular Weight	D_{20}^0
Hexokinase	Yeast	Crystalline	3.1	96,600	2.9
Aldolase	Rabbit muscle	Crystalline	7.3	147,000	4.63
D-Glyceraldehyde-3-	Yeast	Crystalline	6.8	122,000	5.19
phosphate dehy-	Rabbit muscle	Crystalline	7.0	120,000	5.46
drogenase					
Phosphoglyceric	Rabbit muscle	Crystalline	4.21	65,700	6.1
mutase					
Phosphorylase a	Rabbit muscle	Crystalline	13.2	495,000	2.6
Phosphorylase b	Rabbit muscle	Crystalline	8.2	242,000	3.3
Phosphoglucomutase	Rabbit muscle	Crystalline	3.5	74,000	4.83

We shall now examine briefly the glycolytic sequence as it occurs in yeast, in muscle and liver tissue.

2. Alcoholic (Yeast) Fermentation

Cell-free extracts of yeast catalyze the over-all reaction

Glucose $+$ 2ADP $+$ 2 Phosphate $\rightarrow$ 2 Ethanol $+$ 2CO$_2$ $+$ 2ATP

The details of this equation are found in Fig. 22.1. Noteworthy of this fermentative scheme are the following:

1. The initial phosphorylation of free monosaccharides is catalyzed by hexokinase, an enzyme of rather broad specificity. Thus glucose, fructose, mannose, and glucosamine are phosphorylated by ATP to the corresponding hexose-6-phosphate.

2. The final products, CO$_2$ and ethanol, are derived from the decarboxylation of pyruvic acid:

$$CH_3COCOOH \xrightarrow[Mg^{++},\ TPP]{Carboxylase} CH_3CHO + CO_2$$

and by the reduction of CH$_3$CHO:

$$CH_3CHO + DPNH + H^+ \underset{dehydrogenase}{\overset{Alcohol}{\rightleftarrows}} CH_3CH_2OH + DPN^+$$

This last reaction is of considerable importance. Since alcoholic fermentation is an anaerobic process, the single oxidative step of the

D-Glyceraldehyde-3-phosphate   DPNH   CH$_3$CH$_2$OH

                                               $+$H$^+$

                            $+$PO$_4$

1,3-Diphosphoryl-D-glyceric acid   DPN$^+$ CH$_3$CHO

        I   II

cycle must be balanced by an equivalent reductive step. This coupled oxidation-reduction reaction is shown in the diagram. Reaction I represents the oxidation of triose phosphate to the unstable 1,3-diphosphoryl D-glyceric acid with a simultaneous reduction of DPN⁺. For the fermentation reaction to continue, DPNH is reoxidized back to DPN⁺ by coupling it with the reduction of acetaldehyde by the enzyme, alcohol dehydrogenase (reaction II).

3. The validity of this *in vitro* scheme has been tested by isotopic techniques with live and dried baker's yeast (5). Thus a complete fermentation of glucose-1-C^{14} was allowed to occur in the presence of yeast preparations. The fermentation products, ethanol and CO_2, were then analyzed for radioactivity. The methyl group of ethanol contained 95% of the original activity of the labeled glucose, whereas the carbinol moiety had only very slight activity. The CO_2 had a small but reproducible amount of radioactivity, averaging about 3% of the originally added activity. Thus while the classic glycolytic system dominates the fermentation process in *S. cerevisiae*, a consistently small fraction of the activity was associated with a non-glycolytic system, which may be related to the hexose monophosphate shunt, known to occur in yeasts (see Chapter 23).

3. Muscle Glycolysis

The over-all path of glycolysis in muscle tissue is represented by the reaction

$$\text{Glycogen} + 3\text{ADP} + 3\text{PO}_4 \rightarrow 2 \text{ lactic acid} + 3\text{ATP}$$

In contrast to the initial substrate in alcoholic fermentation the chief carbohydrate in muscle is glycogen. Once glycogen is converted to glucose-1-phosphate by phosphorylase, the remaining steps are identical to those of alcoholic fermentation (see Fig. 22.1).

The following points are noteworthy:

1. Since muscle functions under anaerobic conditions, an effective redox system must be available for the cycle to continue. Such a system, characteristic of muscle glycolysis, is shown herewith. System I

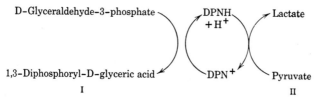

is identical to that found in alcoholic fermentation. However, lactic dehydrogenase is the specific enzyme responsible for the reoxidation of DPNH with the simultaneous reduction of pyruvic to lactic acid.

2. Skeletal muscle is a unique tissue consisting of spindle-shaped cells (myofibrils) making up the muscle fibers. These cells contain a protein, actomyosin, which appears to be the molecular contractile element in muscle. When isolated threads of this protein are treated with ATP, they rapidly contract to about one-half of their original length. Simultaneously, ATP is split to ADP and inorganic P. In some manner the chemical energy released when ~P is split is used to convert the actomyosin molecule from a fibrous to a more corpuscular form. An admirable discussion of muscle contraction will be found in Szent-Györgyi's *Chemistry of Muscle Contraction* (6).

The energy used in muscular contraction comes from the conversion of glycogen to lactic acid. However, in 1930 Lundsgaard observed that muscle tissue of animals poisoned by the triose phosphate dehydrogenase inhibitor, iodoacetic acid, could continue to contract without the formation of lactic acid. It was finally shown that the source of energy for this muscular contraction was obtained from the breakdown of creatine phosphate, an extremely labile ~P substance found in appreciable amounts in resting muscle (see Chapter 12). The interrelationship of the glycolytic cycle, ATP, creatine phosphate, and muscle contraction, is depicted in the diagram.

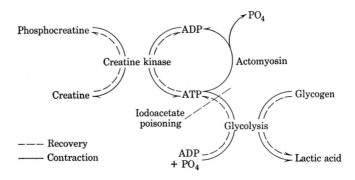

4. Liver Glycolysis

Carbohydrate metabolism in the liver cannot be reduced to the simple picture found in yeast and muscle. Suffice it to say that the metabolism of glucose, of glycogen, of lactic acid, and pyruvic acid, to name a few compounds, is complex and dynamic. However, a few pertinent data will be cited:

1. In liver, two rather unstable kinases participate in the phosphorylation of glucose and fructose:

(a) Glucokinase (7):   Glucose $+$ ATP $\rightarrow$ Glucose-6-PO$_4$ $+$ ADP
(b) Fructokinase (8):   Fructose $+$ ATP $\rightarrow$ Fructose-1-PO$_4$ $+$ ADP

2. Glucose is not formed by hydrolysis of glycogen but by the following sequence:

$$\text{Glycogen} \underset{}{\overset{\text{Phosphorylase}}{\rightleftharpoons}} \text{Glucose-1-PO}_4 \underset{}{\overset{\text{Phosphoglucomutase}}{\rightleftharpoons}} \text{Glucose-6-PO}_4$$

$$\text{Glucose-6-phosphatase} \Big\downarrow$$

$$\text{Glucose} + \text{PO}_4$$

Glucose-6-phosphatase is a highly specific enzyme found in liver tissue (9).

3. The path of fructose into the glycolytic scheme is rather indirect. Hers (10) has re-examined the nature of the reactions and has observed that fructose-1-phosphate is split by aldolase to glyceraldehyde and dihydroxyacetone phosphate (DHAP), which is partly isomerized to D-glyceraldehyde-3-phosphate (GA-3-P), and the two triose phosphates condense in the presence of aldolase to form fructose-1,6-diphosphate (F-1, 6-P). In the presence of Mg^{++}, F-1, 6-P is hydrolyzed to fructose-6-phosphate and inorganic phosphate. In the presence of ATP, glyceraldehyde is phosphorylated to GA-3-P through the action triokinase. In sharp contrast, in muscle, brain, yeast, and plants, fructose is converted directly to fructose-6-phosphate by a non-specific hexokinase (4). The liver system is depicted in the diagram.

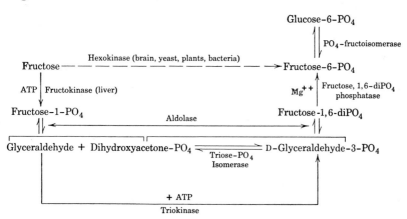

5. Muscle Phosphorylase

Of the several enzymes that participate in the glycolytic pathway, phosphorylase has received considerable attention, and a brief review of its properties will now be undertaken.

Phosphorylase specifically catalyzes the phosphorylytic cleavage or synthesis of the 1,4-α-glucosidic linkage at the non-reducing end of a glycogen or starch chain. The reversible reaction

$$\text{Glucose 1-PO}_4 + (\text{Glucose})_n \rightleftharpoons \text{PO}_4 + (\text{Glucose})_{n+1}$$

as catalyzed by phosphorylase has the following features:

(A) Muscle phosphorylase requires glycogen as a primer. The primer acts as an acceptor of glucosidic units which the enzyme transfers from the donor, α-glucose 1-phosphate to the already existing non-aldehydic terminal glucose units. Potato phosphorylase has less specific primer requirements, since maltotriose (three glucose units) can serve as primer.

(B) α-D-glucopyranosyl-1-phosphate and the α-1,4-maltosidic bond in polysaccharides are the specific substrates. β-isomers and all other α-D- or α-L-phosphorylated monosaccharides are inactive.

(C) The equilibrium of the phosphorylytic reaction is greatly influenced by the hydrogen ion concentration. The equilibrium concentration is independent of the polysaccharide concentration (since the concentration of the polysaccharide remains essentially constant throughout the course of the reaction) and is entirely determined by the ratio $\frac{\text{phosphate}^=}{\text{glucose 1-PO}_4^=}$. Although the ratio of total inorganic phosphate to total glucose 1-phosphate varies from 5.7 at pH 6.0 to 2 at pH 8.0, the ratio of the divalent ionic species for both anions remains at 2.2 throughout the pH range. The $\Delta F'$ for the reaction glucose-1-phosphate → phosphate + polysaccharide is −1460 at 30°.

(D) Phosphorylase will completely degrade under certain conditions unbranched 1,4-α linked polysaccharides (amylose) to glucose 1-phosphate units. Branched polysaccharides (amylopectin) are degraded phosphorylytically 55% to yield limit dextrins which are highly branched. Amylopectin has a branched structure in which the glucose unit at the branching point is connected by an α-1,6-glucosidic linkage. Phosphorylase will attack the side branches, cleaving off the 1,4-α-glucosidic units until the α-1,6 linkage is reached. These form a barrier and prevent further cleavage by phosphorylase.

(E) Muscle phosphorylase exists in muscle as two forms, phosphorylase *a* and *b* (12). Phosphorylase *a* exhibits 60–70% of maximal activity in the absence of 5-AMP, whereas phosphorylase *b* is inactive unless this nucleotide is present. Other nucleotides are inactive. Skeletal muscle (rat) contains mostly phosphorylase *b*, which is rapidly changed to phosphorylase *a* on injection of the animal with epinephrine. Thus, rat gastrocnemius has 31% of its total phosphorylase in the a form and after injection with epinephrine the level is increased to 78%. Muscular contraction results in a significant rise in phosphorylase a while muscle fatigue is associated with an almost complete disappearance of the a form. The conversion of b to a is rapidly accelerated by epinephrine injection (13).

(F) An enzyme, phosphorylase kinase, which converts b to a is present in muscle extracts and requires ATP and Mn^{++} or Ca^{++} as cofactors (14, 15). This enzyme catalyzes the dimerization of $2b \rightarrow a$ according to the following reaction:

$$2\text{Phosphorylase } b + 4\text{ADP}\sim\text{P*} \rightarrow \text{Phosphorylase } a \cdot 4\text{P*} + 4\text{ADP}$$
(mol. wt. 257,000)   (mol. wt. 500,000)

Phosphorylase a contains 4 gram atoms of P per mole of protein derived from ATP. If phosphorylase a is now carefully degraded with trypsin (16), a phospholhexapeptide can be isolated, which has as its structure

$$\text{Lys-glu}(NH_2)\text{-leu-val-serPO}_4\text{-arg}$$

The remaining protein, called phosphorylase b' can be reactivated by AMP specifically. This modified enzyme does not contain the PO_4 introduced by ATP in converting b to a and has a molecular weight of 242,000. Phosphate introduced by ATP ($b \rightarrow a$) does not exchange with inorganic phosphate during phosphorylation of glycogen. It is released as inorganic phosphate when another enzyme called either phosphorylase-rupturing enzyme (PR) or phosphorylase phosphatase acts on phosphorylase a:

$$\text{ph } a \rightarrow 2\text{ph } b + 4PO_4$$

If phosphorylase a is titrated with p-chloromercuricbenzoate (18) it is cleaved into four identical monomers with a molecular weight of about 125,000; with phosphorylase b two units are obtained which are identical with those derived from phosphorylase a. It would therefore appear that in some manner SH groups are involved as the bonding atoms for the tetramer.

(G) Phosphorylase a and b contain a firmly bound yellow pigment which can be released only by acid–ammonium sulfate precipitation. This pigment has been identified by Cori as pyridoxal phosphate (17). Phosphorylase a contains 4 moles of pyridoxal phosphate and the b form 2 moles per mole of protein. When pyridoxal phosphate is added to the apoenzyme in amounts slightly larger than that originally present in the protein, the a form becomes fully reactivated in the absence of 5-AMP and the b form in the presence of the nucleotide. Pyridoxamine phosphate and free pyridoxal are inert as activators.

The phosphate of pyridoxal phosphate does not exchange with inorganic phosphate in the reaction mixture.

Thus, many complex factors play interrelated roles in controlling the activity of muscle phosphorylase which participates in the breakdown and synthesis of glycogen in muscle tissue. These factors include (1) the conversion of $b \rightarrow a$ by phosphorylase kinase, (2) the cleavage of $a \rightarrow b$ by the phosphatase, (3) the activation of the b form by 5-AMP and of both a and b by pyridoxal phosphate, and (4) the acceleration of $b \rightarrow a$ in muscle tissue by epinephrine.

Fischer and Krebs have summarized the structure of phosphorylase a in the following manner:

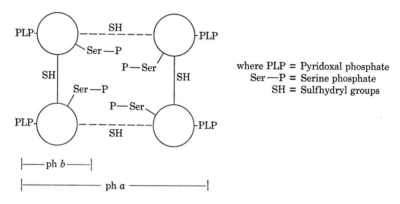

where PLP = Pyridoxal phosphate
Ser —P = Serine phosphate
SH = Sulfhydryl groups

6. Energetics

The energetics of glycolysis is closely associated with those reactions in which inorganic phosphate first combines with monosaccharides or their derivatives as an ester phosphate group of a low energy value which in turn is raised to a high energy level by a series of enzymic transformations. These energy-rich phosphate bonds are transferred to the adenylic system to be employed later for useful work.

A close inspection of Fig. 22.1 will reveal that in the anaerobic breakdown of glucose to pyruvic acid a total of four ATP molecules are synthesized from ADP corresponding to an increase of four energy-rich ($\sim$) bonds for the system. Since, of these four bonds, one is utilized in the primary phosphorylation step of glucose $\rightarrow$ glucose-6-phosphate, and a second is consumed at the fructose-6-phosphate $\rightarrow$ fructose diphosphate level, a net synthesis of only two $\sim$bonds is realized.

When either starch or glycogen is utilized, four $\sim$bonds are also generated; but, since the bond energy of the glucosidic link of the polysaccharide is preserved by means of the phosphorylytic formation of glucose-1-phosphate, the only bond utilized is at the fructose-6-phosphate → fructose diphosphate level. A net synthesis of three ∼P is thus observed.

In the glycolytic cycle there are three important systems responsible for the synthesis of ∼bonds: (*a*) the oxidation of phosphoryl-D-glyceraldehyde to phosphoryl-D-glyceric acid, (*b*) the dehydration of phosphoryl-D-glyceric acid to phosphoenolpyruvic acid, and (*c*) the transfer of electrons from DPNH aerobically to oxygen.

The free energies of hydrolysis of the phosphorylated intermediates are listed in Tables 12.1, 3, and 4. It should be noted that, with the exceptions of 1,3-diphosphoryl-D-glyceric acid and phosphorylenolpyruvic acid, all sugar intermediates contain phosphate groups of low energy value. Only when these two intermediates are formed does the energy of glycolysis become available for transfer.

A. *The Oxidation Reaction.* The oxidation of D-glyceraldehyde-3-phosphate to 1,3-diphosphoryl-D-glyceric acid represents the only oxidation step in the entire series of reactions in glycolysis. (See Chapter 16 for mechanism of action.) By the oxidation of the aldehydic group, some 12,000 calories of free energy ($\Delta F°$) are associated with the acyl phosphate bond, and this bond energy may then be transferred with little loss to the adenylate system by phosphoglycerokinase. In this manner two energy-rich bonds are formed and trapped per molecule of glucose utilized. This reaction is sensitive to iodoacetic acid and insensitive to dinitrophenol.

B. *Dehydration of Phosphoglyceric Acid.* The enolase reaction whereby water is removed,

$$\text{2-Phosphoryl-D-glycerate} \overset{\pm H_2O}{\rightleftharpoons} \text{Phosphorylenol-pyruvate}$$

is an easily reversible system. Although no oxidation occurs, this unique reaction makes possible the formation of an ∼bond by the conversion of a primary alcoholic phosphate group to a phosphorylenol group. Since the K_{eq} is 2.5 (indicating small release of free energy in the reaction), the energy localized in the phosphorylenol bond is derived from a redistribution of bond energy in the molecule by means of a dehydration reaction. In essence, then, two moles of ∼bonds, each containing approximately 12,000 calories of free energy of hydrolysis ($\Delta F°$), are synthesized per mole of glucose degraded and are trapped by ADP as the acceptor in the presence of pyruvic kinase.

C. *DPNH and Oxidative Phosphorylation.* It is well known that, in the passage of two electrons through the steps of oxidative phosphorylation, three ∼bonds are synthesized (see Chapter 24). Thus, if reduced DPN, formed by the oxidation of D-glyceraldehyde-3-phosphate, can gain access in the cell to the mitochondrial system which performs oxidative phosphorylation, three energy-rich bonds would be trapped per reduced DPN. However, since fermentations usually occur under anaerobic conditions and since the mitochondrial system is presumably competing for reduced DPN with several non-particulate dehydrogenase systems, the importance of oxidative phosphorylation as a means of trapping the energy of glycolysis is difficult to ascertain.

Table 22.3. Efficiency of Trapping of Energy in Glycolysis

Reaction	$\Delta F'$, kcal	$\sim$P Trapped	%
Glycogen (1 C_6 unit) + H_2O → 2 lactate + $2H^+$	−52	3 (× 7.5)	43
Glucose → 2 lactate + $2H^+$	−47	2 (× 7.5)	32
Glucose → 2 ethanol + $2H^+$	−56	2 (× 7.5)	27

Although at first glance the impression is gained that glycolytic reactions trap the available energy with high efficiency, only a fraction of the total available energy of the glucose molecule is extracted by glycolytic reactions (see Table 22.3). It is only by oxidation of pyruvic acid to CO_2 and water *via* the Krebs cycle that much of the total available energy is actually trapped.

References

General

1. A. Harden, *Alcoholic Fermentation*, 4th ed., Longmans, Green and Co., N. Y., 1932.

2. F. Dickens, *The Enzymes*, 2, Pt. 1, 624, Academic Press, N. Y., 1951.

3. F. F. Nord and S. Weiss, *The Enzymes*, 2, Pt. 1, 684; E. Racker, *Advances in Enzymology*, *15*, 141 (1954).

4. P. K. Stumpf, *Chemical Pathways of Metabolism*, Chapt. 3, vol. I, Academic Press, N. Y., 1954.

Bibliography

5. D. E. Koshland, Jr., and F. H. Westheimer, *J. Am. Chem. Soc.*, *72*, 3883 (1950).

6. A. Szent-Györgyi, *Chemistry of Muscle Contraction*, 2nd ed., Academic Press, N. Y., 1951.

7. M. W. Staub and C. S. Vestling, *J. Biol. Chem.*, *191*, 395 (1951).

8. H. G. Hers, *Biochim. et Biophys. Acta, 8*, 416 (1952).

9. M. A. Swanson, *J. Biol. Chem.*, *184*, 647 (1950).

10. H. G. Hers and T. Kusaka, *Biochim. et Biophys. Acta, 11*, 427 (1953).

11. W. Z. Hassid, *Chemical Pathways of Metabolism*, Academic Press, N. Y., 1954, Chapt. 6.

12. G. T. Cori and A. A. Green, *J. Biol. Chem.*, *151*, 31 (1943).

13. C. F. Cori, *Enzymes: Units of Biological Structure and Function*, Chapt. 27, Academic Press, N. Y., 1956.
14. E. H. Fischer and E. G. Krebs, *J. Biol. Chem.*, *216*, 121 (1955).
15. E. G. Krebs, A. B. Kent, and E. H. Fischer, *Fed. Proc.*, *16*, 206 (1957).
16. E. H. Fischer, D. J. Graves, and E. G. Krebs, *Fed. Proc.*, *16*, 180 (1957).
17. C. F. Cori and B. Illingworth, *Proc. Nat. Acad. Sci.*, *43*, 547 (1957).
18. N. B. Madsen and F. R. N. Gurd, *J. Biol. Chem.*, *223*, 1075 (1956).

23

The Hexose Monophosphate Shunt

1. Introduction (1)

The glycolytic scheme probably describes the main sequence for the conversion of monosaccharides to pyruvic acid. However, the existence of an alternative mechanism has become evident. Found in plants, bacteria, and animal tissue, it is called either the hexose monophosphate shunt (HMS) or the pentose cycle. It is this shunt and not glycolysis that explains the following observations:

(1) The oxidative enzymes of the glycolytic pathway are DPN+ specific. However, a number of enzymes have been found in tissues which require specifically TPN+ for the oxidation of glucose to CO_2 and triose phosphate (1). DPN+ is inert. The presence of these enzymes in tissues raises the question of their function.

(2) If glycolysis is exclusively present in a given tissue, glucose-1-C^{14} and glucose-6-C^{14} should be equivalent as substrates for the formation of pyruvic-3-C^{14}. In many tissues, however, glucose-1-C^{14} forms considerable quantities of $C^{14}O_2$ as well as labeled pentoses and hexoses, whereas glucose-6-C^{14} does not yield $C^{14}O_2$ but does contribute to the labeling of sugars (1). The distribution of C^{14} in these sugars can be predicted on the basis of the shunt pathway.

(3) In many extracts the breakdown of glucose is related to the transient appearance of pentose phosphates and heptulose phosphate and their final transformation to hexose phosphates. The glycolytic pathway does not explain these observations. Figure 23.1 presents the current view of the HMS. The first two steps are oxidative, requiring specifically TPN+. The singular function of these oxidative steps is the preparation of glucose-6-phosphate for the decarboxylation of the C_1 atom to yield ribulose-5-phosphate. Ribulose 5-phosphate must then be transformed to xylulose 5-phosphate before entry can be made into the transketolase-transaldolase sequence.

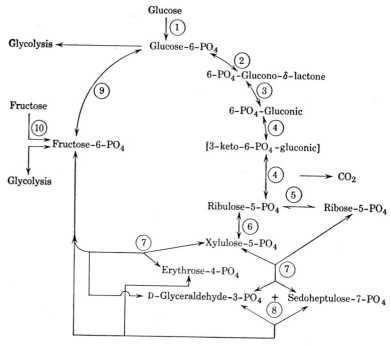

Fig. 23.1. The hexose monophosphate shunt system.

1. Glucokinase + ATP.
2. Glucose-6-phosphate dehydrogenase + TPN+.
3. Lactonase.
4. 6-Phosphogluconic dehydrogenase + TPN+.
5. Phosphoriboisomerase.

6. Phosphoketopentoepimerase
7. Transketolase.
8. Transaldolase.
9. Phosphofructoisomerase.
10. Fructokinase + ATP.

This cycle catalyzes the oxidation of glucose 6-phosphate by the following over-all reaction:

$$6 \text{ Hexose } 6\text{-PO}_4 + 12\text{TPN}^+ \rightarrow$$

$$6\text{CO}_2 + 5 \text{ Hexose } 6\text{-PO}_4 + 12\text{TPNH}_2 + \text{PO}_4$$

This reaction is actually a combination of the following complex reactions outlined in Fig. 23.2. Table 23.1 summarizes the shift of the positions of the carbon atoms of glucose after one turn of the HMS. At first there is little if any randomization of positions 1, 2, and 3 into 4, 5, and 6 of hexose. However in later phases of the pentose cycle, there may be some equilibration of the two halves of a hexose molecule through the agency of triose phosphate isomerase, aldolase, and hexose phosphatase.

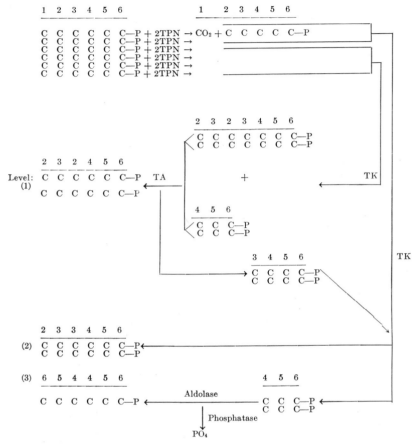

Fig. 23.2. Route of carbon atoms in HMS. After Axelrod & Beevers (2).

Table 23.1. Shift of Position of Carbons in HMS

Carbon of New Sugar—P	Level			Gl-2-C^{14}	Gl-3,4-C^{14}
	1	2	3	As Source of New Sugar	
C_1	2,2	2,2	6	67%	0
C_2	3,3	3,3	5	0	33
C_3	2,2	3,3	4	33%	25
C_4	4,4	4,4	4	0	42
C_5	5,5	5,5	5	0	0
C_6	6,6	6,6	6	0	0

Table 23.2 summarizes the biochemical properties of the enzymes involved in the shunt.

Table 23.2. Enzymes of the HMP System

Enzyme	K_{eq}*	Cofactors
Glucose-6-P dehydrogenase		TPN$^+$
Lactonase	Very large	None
6-P-Gluconic dehydrogenase	1.3 1/M	TPN$^+$
Phosphoriboisomerase	$\dfrac{\text{Ribose-5-PO}_4}{\text{Ribulose-5-PO}_4} = 2.3$	None
Transketolase	Small	Thiamine pyrophosphate, Mg^{++} (plants, yeast)
Transaldolase	0.82	None
Phosphoketopentoepimerase	0.67	None

$$* K_{eq} = \frac{\text{Product}}{\text{Reactant}}.$$

Table 23.3 presents the structural formulas of some of the unfamiliar substrates of the HMS system.

Table 23.3. Structural Formulas of Some HMS Substrates

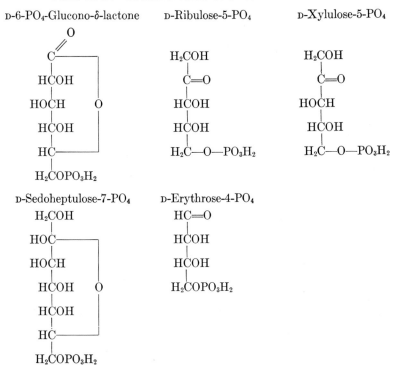

The key enzymes of this cyclic system are three enzymes named, respectively, transketolase (3), transaldolase, (4), and phosphoketo-pento epimerase (5). Transketolase has been crystallized from yeast extracts, and highly purified from spinach leaf and liver. It requires as its cofactors thiamine pyrophosphate (TPP) and Mg^{++} (only plant and yeast), and it catalyzes the reaction shown. A glycolalde-hyde-enzyme complex is assumed to arise by the cleavage of a ketol

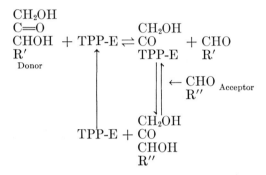

group from the donor substrate. Glycolaldehyde itself is inert since it does not serve as a donor and is never detected in a reaction mix-

Table 23.4.   Substrates for Transketolase

C$_2$-Donors	C$_2$-Acceptors
D-Xylulose-5-P	D-Glyceraldehyde-3-P
D-Sedoheptulose-7-P	D-Ribose-5-P
L-Erythrulose	Glycolaldehyde
Hydroxypyruvic acid	L-Glyceraldehyde-3-P
D-Fructose-6-P	D-Erythrose-4-P
D-Xylulose	

ture.   Table 23.4 summarizes the donor and acceptor systems for transketolase.

Donor substrates must have the configuration

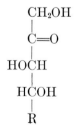

where C_1 has a free primary alcoholic group and C_2 a carbonyl group. The hydroxyl groups on C_3 and C_4 must have a *trans* configuration. The only exception to this requirement is hydroxypyruvic acid, where the carboxyl group replaces the C_3 and C_4. The acceptor must have the structure of an aldose.

Transaldolase has been demonstrated in yeast, liver, and plant tissues (4). It transfers a [$CH_2OHCOCHOH$—] group from either sedoheptulose-7-phosphate or fructose-6-phosphate, to either D-glyceraldehyde-3-phosphate or D-erythrose-4-phosphate. In contrast to the transketolase system, it does not require a cofactor. Fructose diphosphate, the substrate for aldolase in glycolysis, and dihydroxy-acetone or its phosphate ester are inert as substrates.

Phosphoketopentoepimerase (5) specifically catalyzes the reaction

$$\text{D-ribulose-5-phosphate} \rightleftharpoons \text{D-xylulose-5-phosphate}$$

and thereby connects the transketolase-transaldolase systems with the oxidative breakdown product of glucose-6-phosphate, ribulose-5-phosphate. A very active enzyme, it is found widely distributed in nature. Its only substrates are ribulose-5-phosphate and xylulose-5-phosphate. Unlike the UDP-hexose-4-hydroxyl epimerase which has bound DPN^+ as an integral part of its active site, the epimerase appears to require no cofactors. The epimerization reaction probably proceeds through an ene-diol intermediate bound to the enzyme surface.

2. Pentose Phosphates and the Path of Carbon in Photosynthesis (6)

It is well known that, when a photosynthesizing plant is exposed to $C^{14}O_2$ for a short period of time, the first stable radioactive compound which can be isolated is carboxyl-labeled 3-phosphoryl-D-glyceric acid (PGA). With increasing periods of exposure to $C^{14}O_2$, fructose-1,6-diphosphate, the hexose monophosphates and finally the free sugars become labeled predominantly in the 3,4 positions. In addition to the labeling of PGA in short exposure periods, sedoheptulose-7-phosphate, sedoheptulose-1,7-diphosphate, and ribulose-diphosphate are rapidly labeled.

The principal labeling at short exposure times are as shown.

$$
\begin{array}{cccc}
 & & \text{CH}_2\text{OH} & \\
 & & | & \\
 & & \text{C}{=}\text{O} & \text{CH}_2\text{OH} \\
 & & | & | \\
 & *\text{CH}_2\text{OPO}_3\text{H}_2 & *\text{CHOH} & \text{C}{=}\text{O} \\
 & | & | & | \\
 & *\text{C}{=}\text{O} & *\text{CHOH} & *\text{CHOH} \\
\text{CH}_2\text{OPO}_3\text{H}_2 & ***\text{CHOH} & *\text{CHOH} & *\text{CHOH} \\
| & | & | & | \\
\text{CHOH} & \text{CHOH} & \text{CHOH} & \text{CHOH} \\
| & | & | & | \\
***\text{COOH} & \text{CH}_2\text{OPO}_3\text{H}_2 & \text{CH}_2\text{OPO}_3\text{H}_2 & \text{CH}_2\text{OPO}_3\text{H}_2 \\
\text{3-Phosphoryl-} & \text{D-Ribulose-} & \text{Sedoheptulose-} & \text{Fructose-} \\
\text{D-glyceric acid} & \text{diphosphate} & \text{7-phosphate} & \text{6-phosphate}
\end{array}
$$

The characteristic pattern of labeling may be accounted for by postulating the sequence of reactions shown in Fig. 23.3, many of which are known to occur in plant tissue (7).

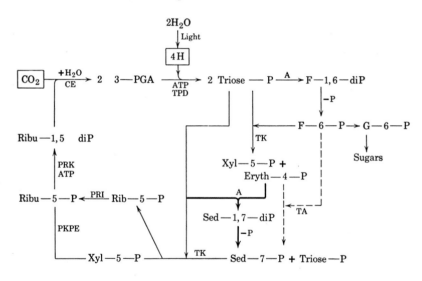

Sum: $3\text{CO}_2 + 9\text{ATP} + 5\text{H}_2\text{O} + 6\text{DPNH}_2 \longrightarrow \text{Triose}{-}\text{P} + 9\text{ADP} + 6\text{DPN} + 8\text{P}$
     (TPNH$_2$)   (TPN)

CE	Carboxylating enzyme	PRI	Phosphoribo isomerase
PKPE	Phosphoketopentoepimerase	TPD	Triose phosphate dehyd. + TPN
TK	Transketolase	A	Aldolase
TA	Transaldolase	P	Phosphatase
PRK	Phosphoribulose kinase		

Fig. 23.3. The path of CO₂ fixation in photosynthesis.

Note that the cyclic resynthesis of sedoheptulose 7-phosphate is essential for the continuation of the pentose cycle in photosynthesis.

Two possibilities exist for the formation of sedoheptulose 7-phosphate: (1) the sequential action of transketolase and transaldolase as denoted by the broken line (see Fig. 23.3), and (2) the reaction of aldolase and phosphatase as indicated by the heavy line. This second series would explain the appearance of radioactivity in sedoheptulose-1,7-phosphate when the photosynthesizing plant is exposed to $C^{14}O_2$. A continuous resynthesis is thus assured so that a supply of xylulose 5-phosphate can be fed into the carboxylation reactions. Phosphoketopentoepimerase converts xylulose 5-phosphate to ribulose 5-phosphate which is then phosphorylated by ATP in the presence of phosphoribulokinase. The kinase (8) which is activated by divalent cations, particularly Mg^{++}, catalyzes the reaction:

$$\text{Ribulose-5-phosphate} + \text{ATP} \rightarrow \text{Ribulose-1,5-diPO}_4 + \text{ADP}$$

The key substrate, ribulose-1,5-diphosphate, is the immediate acceptor for carbon dioxide. Carbon dioxide adds to the C_2 of the acceptor in the presence of the carboxylating enzyme (also called carboxydismutase) to form the unstable intermediate, 2-carboxy, 3-keto pentose diphosphate (9). Found in high concentrations in chloroplasts, this enzyme has a molecular weight of 300,000, requires a divalent cation and SH compounds or chelating agents for full activity, and has absolute substrate specificity. 2-carboxy, 3-keto pentodiphosphate presumably is cleaved to two equivalents of 3 phos-

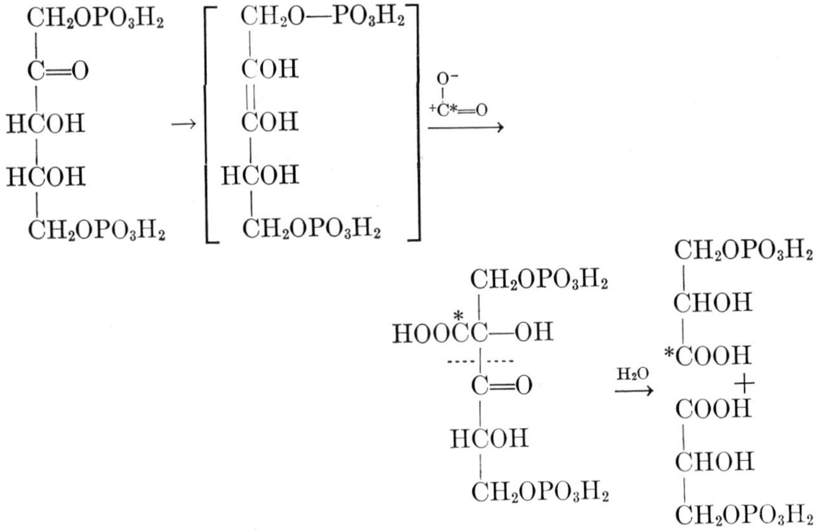

2-Carboxy, 3-ketopentodiphosphate

Fig. 23.4. Postulated mechanism of the carboxylation reaction.

phoglyceric acid (Fig. 23.4). Phosphoglyceric acid is then reduced by a specific TPN-triose phosphate dehydrogenase (7) to triose phosphate and then condensed by aldolase to the hexose phosphates. The source of hydrogen for the reduction of TPN is assumed to be derived from the photolytic cleavage of water. ATP, which is required for the synthesis of ribulose diphosphate, is generated by the process of photosynthetic phosphorylation (10). (See also Chapter 24.)

Instead of implicating the pentose cycle as a carrier of CO_2, Warburg has recently presented evidence in support of the role of the glutamic acid $\rightleftharpoons$ β-amino butyric acid + CO_2 as a key component of the path of carbon (11).

References

General

1. H. G. Wood, *Physiol. Rev., 35,* 841 (1955); I. C. Gunsalus, B. L. Horecker, and W. H. Wood, *Bact. Rev., 19,* 79 (1955).

Bibliography

2. B. Axelrod and H. Beevers. *Annual Rev. Pl. Physiol., 7,* 267 (1956).

3. B. L. Horecker, J. Hurwitz, and P. Z. Smyrniotes, *J. Am. Chem. Soc., 78,* 692 (1956).

4. G. de la Haba, I. G. Leder, and E. Racker, *J. Biol. Chem., 214,* 409 (1955); B. L. Horecker and P. Z. Smyrniotes, *J. Biol. Chem., 212,* 811 (1955).

5. P. K. Stumpf and B. L. Horecker, *J. Biol. Chem., 218,* 753 (1956).

6. W. Vishniac, B. L. Horecker, and S. Ochoa, *Adv. in Enzymol., 19,* 1 (1957).

7. J. A. Bassham, S. A. Barker, M. Calvin, and U. C. Quarck, *Biochem. Biophysics Acta, 21,* 376 (1956).

8. J. Hurwitz, A. Weissbach, B. L. Horecker and P. Z. Smyrniotes, *J. Biol. Chem., 218,* 769 (1956).

9. A. Weissbach, J. Hurwitz and B. L. Horecker, *J. Biol. Chem., 218,* 795 (1956).

10. D. I. Arnon, M. B. Allen, and F. R. Whatley, *Biochim. et Biophys. Acta, 20,* 449 (1956).

11. O. Warburg, *Angewandte Chemie, 69,* 627 (1957).

24

Tricarboxylic Acid Cycle and Oxidative Phosphorylation

PART A. TCA CYCLE

1. Introduction (1)

Into the TCA cycle is channeled a major portion of the terminal oxidation of tissue constituents. By means of this cycle the products of fat, sugar, and amino acid metabolism are eventually burned to CO_2 and water. The chemical energy released in the oxidation of these substances is captured in part as chemical bonds of high energy content.

A. *Experimental Basis.* In 1920, the famous Swedish biochemist Thunberg (2) observed that, of some 50 compounds tested, citrate, succinate, malate, and fumarate when added to a tissue homogenate were the most active in reducing methylene blue anaerobically. These initial observations stimulated other workers to search for an explanation. It was not until 1937 that H. Krebs (3), in England, aware of these and other data, proposed a hypothesis which could elegantly explain all these findings. Although this scheme, the tricarboxylic acid cycle (TCA cycle), has passed through a battery of rigorous examinations since 1937, its present form is astonishingly similar to the original hypothesis. The experimental observations employed by Krebs (3) as evidence for his cycle are as follows:

1. The catalytic effect of citric acid on the respiration of pigeon-breast-muscle homogenates is of the same order of magnitude as that of succinic acid, malic acid, and fumaric acid. All these acids in trace amounts greatly stimulate the respiration of pigeon-breast muscle.

2. Pigeon-breast-muscle homogenate rapidly oxidizes citric acid, isocitric acid, *cis*-aconitic acid, and α-ketoglutaric acid. This would imply the presence of enzymes capable of handling the oxidation of each acid.

3. In pigeon-breast-muscle homogenates, citric acid is rapidly synthesized from oxalacetic acid and pyruvic acid.

4. Pyruvic acid is readily oxidized by pigeon-breast-muscle suspensions in the presence of **trace** amounts of the di- or tricarboxylic acids. Malonate inhibits this oxidation.

5. The reductive formation of succinate from fumarate or oxalacetate can be competitively inhibited by malonate. Nevertheless, succinate accumulates oxidatively from fumarate, oxalacetate, citrate, and α-ketoglutarate in the presence of malonate. There must therefore be two pathways for the formation of succinate, one by reduction of fumarate *via* an enzyme sensitive to malonate (succinic dehydrogenase), and the other an oxidative pathway insensitive to malonate inhibition leading to a stoichiometric accumulation of succinate. The further utilization of succinate is blocked by the presence of malonate, which serves as a competitive inhibitor for succinic dehydrogenase.

6. The validity of the TCA cycle has been beautifully confirmed by the observation that, when acetate-1-C^{14} is injected into an animal, there is a rapid appearance of C^{14} in all these di- and tricarboxylic acids (4).

2. TCA Cycle

These results are best explained by the modern version of the TCA cycle as depicted in Fig. 24.1.

The uniqueness of the cycle is its versatility. Thus:

(*a*) It offers a detailed explanation for the complete oxidation of pyruvic acid to respiratory CO_2 and water.

(*b*) It defines the steps by which citric acid, isocitric acid, α-ketoglutaric acid, succinic acid, fumaric acid, malic acid, and oxaloacetic acid are synthesized and degraded. In higher plants citric acid is found in rather high concentrations in the vacuolar fluid. An explanation is now available for the net synthesis of citric acid from acetate with the discovery of the enzymes isocitritase and malic synthetase in plant and bacterial cells (5, 31). The intermediate steps can be depicted as follows:

Acetate + Isocitrate	→ Succinate + Malate
Malate + ½O_2	→ Oxaloacetate
Succinate + O_2	→ Oxaloacetate
2 Acetate + 2 Oxaloacetate	→ 2 Citrate
Citrate	→ Isocitrate
Sum: 3 Acetate + 1½O_2	→ Citrate

Additional variants of this theme may be written to explain the net synthesis of the other TCA acids which accumulate in molds and plants.

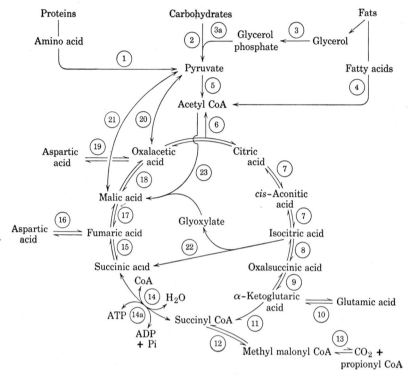

Fig. 24.1. The tricarboxylic acid cycle.

1. Amino acid degradative systems.
2. Glycolytic cycle.
3. Glycerol kinase.
3a. α-Glycerolphosphate dehydrogenase.
4. Fatty acid oxidative system.
5. Pyruvic oxidase.
6. Condensing enzyme.
7. Aconitase.
8. Isocitric dehydrogenase.
9. Oxalosuccinic decarboxylase.
10. Glutamic dehydrogenase.
11. α-Ketoglutaric oxidase.

12. Methyl malonyl CoA isomerase.
13. Propionyl CoA carboxylase.
14a. Succinyl CoA transphosphorylase.
14. Succinyl CoA deacylase.
15. Succinic dehydrogenase.
16. Aspartase.
17. Fumarase.
18. Malic dehydrogenase.
19. Aspartic glutamic transaminase.
20. Oxalacetate decarboxylase.
21. Malic enzyme.
22. Isocitritase.
23. Malic synthetase.

(*c*) Most polysaccharides and monosaccharides are ultimately metabolized to CO_2 and water. Both the glycolytic pathway and the hexosemonophosphate shunt in conjunction with TCA cycle completely describe the catabolic reactions of these sugars in living tissues. (See Chapters 22, 23.)

(*d*) Neutral fats are an important part of the daily diet. In their catabolic breakdown they are cleaved to glycerol and acyl CoA derivatives. Glycerol enters the glycolytic pathway as glycerolphosphate and is eventually converted to pyruvic acid (see Fig. 24.1), while the long-chain acyl CoA derivatives are rapidly degraded to acetyl CoA which is in turn oxidized by the TCA cycle to CO_2 and water. (See Chapter 25.)

In oil-bearing seedlings a marked conversion of fats to carbohydrates takes place. The glyoxylate by-pass, by supplying extra C_4 dicarboxylic acids from acetate, can now provide the necessary carbon skeletons for a net synthesis of carbohydrate from fats by the following sequence:

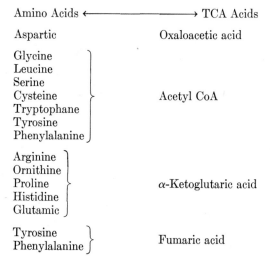

(e) Many amino acids in their later stages of catabolism enter the TCA cycle at several levels, as either acetyl CoA, α-ketoglutaric acid, oxaloacetic acid, or fumaric acid. Table 24.1 lists the amino acids in their relationship to the TCA cycle. It is quite possible that the initial steps in the synthesis of these amino acids also originate in the area of the cycle (6).

(f) The Thunberg Reaction postulated in 1920 to explain the ap-

Table 24.1. Relation of Some Amino Acids to the TCA Cycle

Amino Acids ⟵ ⟶ TCA Acids	
Aspartic	Oxaloacetic acid
Glycine Leucine Serine Cysteine Tryptophane Tyrosine Phenylalanine	Acetyl CoA
Arginine Ornithine Proline Histidine Glutamic	α-Ketoglutaric acid
Tyrosine Phenylalanine	Fumaric acid

parent condensation of two molecules of acetate to form one molecule of succinate can be considered to consist of the following complex series of reactions:

$$
\begin{aligned}
\text{Acetate} + \text{Oxaloacetate} &\rightarrow \text{Citrate} \\
\text{Citrate} &\rightarrow \text{Succinate} + \text{Glyoxylate} \\
\text{Acetate} + \text{Glyoxylate} &\rightarrow \text{Malate} \\
\underline{\text{Malate} + \tfrac{1}{2}O_2 \qquad\quad} &\underline{\rightarrow \text{Oxaloacetate} \qquad\qquad\qquad} \\
\text{Sum:} \quad 2 \text{ Acetate} + \tfrac{1}{2}O_2 &\rightarrow \text{Succinate}
\end{aligned}
$$

The basic steps developed by Krebs with pigeon-breast-muscle preparations and modified to include the glyoxylate by-pass (5) are practically identical with those found in mammalian tissue, insects, protozoans, nematodes, and in higher plants. Many bacteria possess complete TCA cycle activity, although, in some, alternative pathways are available for terminal respiration (1). The glyoxylate by-pass does not occur in mammalian tissue, but does in plants and bacteria.

3. Enzymes

Table 24.2 collects pertinent information concerning the biochemical properties of the TCA enzymes.

Table 24.2.   Enzymes of the TCA Cycle

Stage	Enzyme	Cofactor	$\Delta F'$ (1) Kcal	Inhibitors (1)
Citrate $\updownarrow$ Cisaconitate $\updownarrow$ Isocitrate	Aconitase (10)	Fe^{++}; GSH	$+2.04$ -0.45	{ Fluorocitrate *trans*-Aconitic acid O-Phenanthraline
$\updownarrow$ Oxalosuccinate	Isocitric dehydrogenase (11)	TPN^+	-0.6	Diphenyl chloro-arsine; 2'-AMP
$\updownarrow$ α-Ketoglutaric	Oxalosuccinic decarboxylase (12)	Mn^{++}	-8.6	Pyrophosphate
$\downarrow$ Succinyl CoA	α-Ketoglutaric dehydrogenase (13, 14, 15)	Mg^{++}, TPP, DPN^+, lipoic	-7.2	Arsenite, NH_2OH
$\updownarrow$ Succinic	Succinyl CoA transphosphorylase (16)	$ADP + PO_4 +$ $Mg^{++} + GDP$	-0.77	NH_2OH
$\updownarrow$ Fumaric	Succinic dehydrogenase (17)	FAD; Fe^{++}	-20	Malonate, ethyliodoacetate
$\updownarrow$ Malic	Fumarase (7)	None	-0.88	Thiocyanate, iodide
$\updownarrow$ OAA	Malic dehydrogenase (19)	DPN^+	$+7.1$	Oxaloacetate
$\updownarrow$ Acetyl CoA Citrate	Condensing enzyme (8)	—	-7.7	NH_2OH

$\Delta F' = \Delta F^\circ$ at standard conditions and pH 7.

In Table 24.3 some properties of the enzymes associated with the cycle are listed.

Table 24.3. Ancillary Enzymes

	Reaction	Cofactors	K_{eq}*	Reference
Phosphorylenolpyruvate carboxylase	Phosphorylenol pyruvate ⇌ OAA + Pi	None (plants): ITP (animal)	——	19
Malic enzyme	Malic ⇌ Pyruvate + CO₂	TPN⁺ (plants, animal) DPN⁺ (bacteria) Mn⁺⁺	19.6 (1×M⁻¹)	20
OAA decarboxylase	Oxaloacetate → CO₂ + Pyruvic	Mn⁺⁺	4.6 × 10⁻⁴ (1×M⁻¹)	21
Glutamic dehydrogenase	Glutamic ⇌ α-Ketoglutaric + NH₃	TPN⁺ (animals, yeast) DPN⁺ (animals, plants)	0.99 × 10⁻¹³ m/l 1.45 × 10⁻³ m/l	22
Aspartase	Aspartic ⇌ Fumaric	——	——	23
Glutamic-alanine transaminase	Glutamic + Pyruvate ⇌ α-Ketoglutaric + Alanine	Pyridoxal-PO₄	1.5	24
Glutamic-aspartic transaminase	Glutamic + OAA ⇌ α-Ketoglutaric + Aspartic	Pyridoxal-PO₄	6.7	24
Succinic deacylase	Succinyl CoA + H₂O → CoA + Succinyl	——	Approx. 10⁻¹⁰	25
Succinic decarboxylase	Succinic → Propionic + CO₂	ATP, Mg⁺⁺, CoA	——	26
Isocitritase	Glyoxylate + Succinate ⇌ Isocitrate	Mg⁺⁺, GSH	34 1/M	29
Citritase	Oxaloacetate + Acetate ⇌ Citrate	Mg⁺⁺	1.5 1/M	30
Malic synthetase	Glyoxylate + Acetyl CoA ⇌ Malate + CoA	Mg⁺⁺	——	31
Malonyl CoA decarboxylase	Malonyl CoA → CO₂ + Acetyl CoA	Mg⁺⁺	——	32
Propionyl CoA carboxylase	Propionyl CoA + CO₂ → Methyl malonyl CoA	Mg⁺⁺ ATP		33
Methylmalonyl CoA isomerase	Methylmalonyl CoA ⇌ Succinyl CoA	——	——	33

$$* K_{eq} = \frac{Products}{Reactants}.$$

The chemistry of the TCA enzymes has been intensively studied. Both fumarase (7) and the condensing enzyme (8) have been crystallized; others have been greatly purified. The majority of the enzymes reside in mitochondria. (See Chapter 21.) There is considerable evidence, however, that isocitric dehydrogenase (9) and aconitase (10) are found for the most part in the cytoplasmic soluble protein fraction. Over 80% of the total isocitric dehydrogenase activity and 85% of the total aconitase activity of the homogenate of liver tissue are recovered in a fraction containing the soluble material of the cytoplasm of the cell. This would imply that the TCA cycle is an integrated function of several cellular fractions and not the exclusive property of one cellular fraction.

4. Mechanism of α-Keto Acid Oxidation (30)

The mechanism for the oxidation of α-keto acids is not completely understood at present. It does seem worth while, nevertheless, to describe, as an example of this type of oxidation, the oxidation of α-keto-glutaric acid to succinic acid by a complex of enzymes called α-keto-glutaric oxidase (13–15). Equations 1 and 2 represent the over-all reactions:

(1) α-Ketoglutaric + DPN⁺ + CoA →

$$\text{Succinyl CoA} + CO_2 + \text{DPNH} + H^+$$

(2) Succinyl CoA + P + GDP ⇌ Succinic + CoA + GTP

(3) GTP + ADP   ⇌ GDP + ATP

α-Ketoglutaric dehydrogenase catalyzes equation 1. The highly puri-fied fraction obtained from pig heart muscle analyzed electrophoreti-cally and ultracentrifugally as 90% pure. Green's group (13, 14) has estimated the particle weight of ketoglutaric dehydrogenase to be about 2 million. Cofactor analysis of the protein fraction of highest purity indicates: (*a*) 1.2 moles of TPP per mole of enzyme; (*b*) no bound DPN⁺ or CoA; (*c*) 6 moles of lipoic acid per mole of enzyme. DPN⁺ is required as an additional cofactor; TPN is inert. The reaction is far to the right with little if any tendency for reversal.

In equation 2, a specific phosphorylase catalyzes the phosphoryla-tion of GDP to GTP in the presence of succinyl CoA, inorganic phos-phate, and Mg⁺⁺. Arsenate does not replace GDP, nor do inorganic pyrophosphate and GMP. The reaction is freely reversible since GTP, succinate, and CoA interact in the presence of the enzyme to form succinyl CoA, which has a thiol ester bond energy approximately equivalent to that of the ~P of ATP. In equation 3, there is a sim-ple transfer of a P from GTP to ADP.

Although these three reactions have been studied in some detail, the involvement of TPP and lipoic acid is still a matter of conjecture; their presence in the purified protein of ketoglutaric dehydrogenase suggests that they play an intimate role in the oxidation of the sub-strate.

Gunsalus (28) has postulated that in the first step TPP and Mg⁺⁺ are required. An "active succinic semialdehyde" is formed through de-carboxylation as a carboxyl-TPP complex. In the second step lipoic acid and CoA participate, the carboxyl group being transferred to the —S—S— linkage of lipoic acid to form a thiol ester linkage. The acyl group is then shifted to CoA and the reduced lipoic reoxidized by a DPN-lipoic dehydrogenase. These steps are constructed as shown in the diagram.

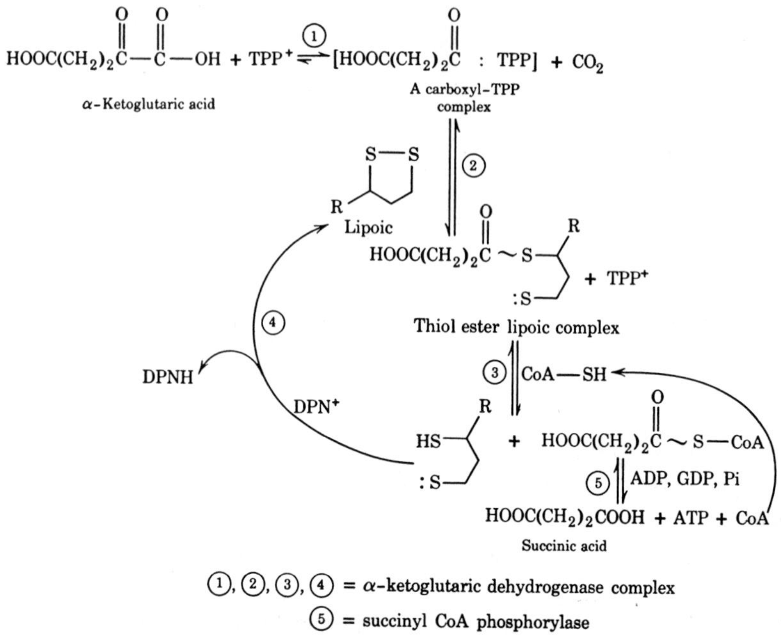

$(1), (2), (3), (4) = \alpha$-ketoglutaric dehydrogenase complex

$(5) = $ succinyl CoA phosphorylase

According to this scheme, α-ketoglutaric oxidase actually represents the following components: (1) a TPP-Mg^{++} decarboxylating enzyme; (2) a TPP-lipoic transsuccinylase system; (3) a lipoic-CoA trans-succinylase system; (4) a DPN$^+$ lipoic dehydrogenase system; (5) a succinyl CoA transphosphorylase complex. To support this view are the observations that a DPN$^+$-lipoic dehydrogenase has been obtained from cell-free extracts of *E. coli* (27) and from the α-ketoglutaric dehydrogenase complex of pig heart muscle (34). Succinyl CoA trans-phosphorylase has already been characterized in some detail (15, 16).

The importance of this complex enzyme system consisting of at least two to five discrete enzymes is centered in its role of catalyzing the oxidation of α-ketoglutaric acid with a simultaneous phosphoryla-tion of ADP. Thus the energy of oxidation is in part trapped as a thiol ester bond, succinyl CoA, which is then transferred by the phos-phorylation enzyme to the ADP + PO$_4$ → ATP system. In addition the transfer of electrons through the DPNH → O system implicates the mechanism of oxidative phosphorylation with its capacity to fix additional amounts of available energy. (See Part B, p. 342, Oxida-tive Phosphorylation.)

References for TCA Cycle

General

1. H. A. Krebs, *Chemical Pathways of Metabolism*, Academic Press, N. Y., 1954, Ch. 4; H. A. Krebs and H. C. Kornberg, *Ergebnisse der Physiologie, Biol. Chemie und Exp. Pharmicok.*, *49*, 212 (1957).

Bibliography

2. T. Thunberg, *Skand. Arch. Physiol.*, *40*, 1 (1920).

3. H. A. Krebs and W. A. Johnson, *Enzymologia*, *4*, 148 (1937).

4. J. S. Lee and N. Lifson, *J. Biol. Chem.*, *193*, 253 (1951).

5. H. L. Kornberg and H. A. Krebs, *Nature*, *179*, 988 (1957).

6. P. P. Cohen, *Chemical Pathways of Metabolism*, Academic Press, N. Y., 1954, Vol. 11, Chpt. IX; A. Meister, *Metabolism of Amino Acids*, Academic Press, N. Y., 1957.

7. V. Massey, *Bioch. J.*, *51*, 490 (1952).

8. J. R. Stern, B. Shapiro, E. R. Stadtman, and S. Ochoa, *J. Biol. Chem.*, *193*, 691, 703 (1951).

9. G. H. Hogeboom and W. C. Schneider, *J. Biol. Chem.*, *186*, 417 (1950).

10. S. Dickman and J. F. Speyer, *J. Biol. Chem.*, *206*, 67 (1954).

11. S. Ochoa, *J. Biol. Chem.*, *159*, 247 (1945).

12. S. Ochoa and E. Weisz-Tabori, *J. Biol. Chem.*, *174*, 123 (1948).

13. D. R. Sanadi, J. W. Littlefield, and R. M. Bock, *J. Biol. Chem.*, *197*, 851 (1952).

14. D. R. Sanadi, and J. W. Littlefield, *J. Biol. Chem.*, *201*, 103 (1953).

15. S. Kafman, C. Gilvarg, O. Cori, and S. Ochoa, *J. Biol. Chem.*, *203*, 869 (1953).

16. Helen Hift, L. Ouellet, J. W. Littlefield, and D. R. Sanadi, *J. Biol. Chem.*, *204*, 565 (1953); D. R. Sanadi and P. Azenyar, *Federation Proc.*, *13*, 287 (1954).

17. T. P. Singer, E. B. Kearney, and P. Bernath, *J. Biol. Chem.*, *223*, 599 (1956).

18. F. B. Straub, *Z. physiol. Chem.*, *275*, 63 (1942).

19. M. F. Utter and K. Kurshaski, *J. Am. Chem. Soc.*, *75*, 758 (1953); R. Bandurski and C. Greiner, *J. Biol. Chem.*, *204*, 781 (1953).

20. S. Ochoa et al., *J. Biol. Chem.*, *187*, 849, 863, 891 (1950).

21. L. O. Krampitz and C. H. Werkman, *Biochem. J.*, *35*, 595 (1941).

22. J. A. Olson and C. B. Anfinsen, *J. Biol. Chem.*, *197*, 67 (1952).

23. J. Erkama and A. Virtanen, *The Enzymes*, I, Part 2, 1244, 1951.

24. P. P. Cohen, *The Enzymes*, I, Part 2, 1040, 1951.

25. J. Gergely, P. Hele, and C. V. Ramakrishnan, *J. Biol. Chem.*, *198*, 323 (1952).

26. H. Whiteley, *Proc. Natl. Acad. Sci.*, *39*, 772 (1953).

27. L. P. Hager and I. C. Gunsalus, *J. Am. Chem. Soc.*, *75*, 5767 (1953).

28. I. C. Gunsalus, *Mechanism of Enzyme Action*, Johns Hopkins Press, p. 434, 1954.

29. R. A. Smith and I. C. Gunsalus, *J. Am. Chem. Soc.*, *76*, 5002 (1954).

30. R. A. Smith, J. R. Stamer, and I. C. Gunsalus, *Biochim. et Biophys. Acta*, *19*, 567 (1956).

31. D. T. O. Wong and S. Ajl, *J. Am. Chem. Soc.*, *78*, 3230 (1956).

32. O. Hayaishi, *J. Biol. Chem., 215,* 125 (1955).

33. M. Flavin, H. Castro-Mendoza, and S. Ochoa, *Biochim. et Biophys. Acta,* *20,* 591 (1956).

34. D. R. Sanadi and R. L. Searls, *Biochim. et Biophys. Acta, 24,* 220 (1957).

PART B. OXIDATIVE PHOSPHORYLATION

1. Introduction (1, 2)

The only effective means now known for coupling energy production with energy utilization is the esterification of inorganic phosphate into the adenylate system to form ATP. The $\sim$P of ATP may then be readily transferred to energy-requiring systems.

The esterification of inorganic phosphate can take place on two levels: (*a*) the substrate level, and (*b*) the electron → oxygen transfer level (e-o-t level). Substrate level phosphorylation has been known for some years and is best described by two examples:

(1) D-Glyceraldehyde-3-PO$_4$ + PO$_4$ + ADP $\underset{}{\overset{DPN^+}{\rightleftharpoons}}$

$\qquad\qquad\qquad\qquad\qquad\qquad\qquad$ 3-Phosphoryl-D-glyceric + ATP

(2) a) Succinyl CoA + PO$_4$ + GDP $\rightleftharpoons$ Succinic + GTP + CoA

$\quad$ b) GTP + ADP $\qquad\qquad\qquad \rightleftharpoons$ GDP + ATP

In both, the following points are characteristic of substrate level systems: (*a*) the formation of ATP does not require oxygen, (*b*) enzymes which catalyze these reactions are water soluble, (*c*) these systems are dinitrophenol insensitive, and (*d*) the e-o-t system does not participate.

The e-o-t system, however, involves the passage of electrons from the substrate through several electron carrier systems to the final acceptor, oxygen. Rather large amounts of utilizable energy become available and are trapped as $\sim$P. Ball (3) has depicted the sequence for the transfer of electrons to oxygen as shown in the tabulation. It

Substrate · 2H	ΔF (standard)	$\sim$PO$_4$
↓		
Pyridine nucleotides (2e + H$^+$)		
↓	−10 kcal $\cong$	$\sim$1
Flavin systems (2e + H$^+$)		
↓	−15.5 kcal $\cong$	$\sim$2
Cytochrome system (e)		
↓	−25 kcal $\cong$	$\sim$3
Oxygen → H$_2$O		
Total	−50.5 kcal	6$\sim$PO$_4$

Over-all: DPNH + H$^+$ + $\frac{1}{2}$O$_2$ → DPN$^+$ + H$_2$O $\qquad \Delta F = -52.4$ kcal

will be noted that at each level of the e-o-t system rather significant quantities of utilizable energy are theoretically available. Thus in the oxidation of DPNH a theoretical value of $6\sim PO_4$ is possible. Experimentally it has been shown that in the oxidation of DPNH by mitochondrial preparations, $3\sim P$ are formed for the transfer of the two electrons from DPNH to oxygen (4). Thus approximately 50% trapping is realized at the e-o-t level. Characteristic of the e-o-t level are the following points: (a) the system is completely inhibited by trace amounts of dinitrophenol (DNP), aging of the mitochondria, or by antimycin A; (b) oxygen uptake, however, is not inhibited by DNP; (c) the e-o-t system is found exclusively in the mitochondria of plants and animals. Mitochondria can be degraded to yield sub-particle preparation that catalyze oxidative phosporylation.

2. A Consideration of the Energetics of the Glucose → $CO_2 + H_2O$ System

This system is of primary importance because of the key role the intermediate, pyruvic acid, plays in metabolic processes. An analysis of the energetics of this system indicates that the free-energy change

Type of Phosphorylation	Reaction	$\sim P$ Trapped
Substrate	D-Glyceraldehyde-3-phosphate + PO_4 + ADP + $DPN^+ \to$ 3-PGA + DPNH + ATP	1
e-o-t	$DPNH + H^+ + \frac{1}{2}O_2 \to DPN^+ + H_2O$	3
Substrate	Phosphorylenolpyruvate + ADP → Pyruvate + ATP	1
	Pyruvate + $\frac{1}{2}O_2$ + $DPN^+ \xrightarrow{\text{CoA}}$ Acetyl CoA + DPNH + H^+	0
e-o-t	$DPNH + H^+ + \frac{1}{2}O_2 \to DPN^+ + H_2O$	3
	Isocitric + $TPN^+ \to$ TPNH + Oxalosuccinate + H^+	0
e-o-t	$TPNH + H^+ + \frac{1}{2}O_2 \to TPN^+ + H_2O$	3
	α-Ketoglutaric + $DPN^+ \xrightarrow{\text{CoA}}$ Succinyl CoA + DPNH + H^+	0
e-o-t	$TPNH + H^+ + \frac{1}{2}O_2 \to TPN^+ + H_2O$	3
Substrate	Succinyl CoA + GDP + $PO_4 \to$ Succinic + GTP + CoA	1
e-o-t	Succinate → Fumaric	2
	Malic + $DPN^+ \to$ Oxaloacetate + DPNH + H^+	0
e-o-t	$DPNH + H^+ + \frac{1}{2}O_2 \to DPN^+ + H_2O$	3
		20

Therefore: $20\sim PO_4$ per triose; $2 \times 20 = 40$ per glucose

$40 - 2$ (glycolytic phosphorylation requirements) $= 38$

$\frac{38}{85} \times 100 = 45\%$

involved in the conversion of 1 mole of glucose to CO_2 and water is approximately -688 kcal. If one $\sim PO_4$ represents a ΔF_{hydrol} of -8000 calories then $688,000/8000$ equals approximately $85 \sim PO_4$ theoretically available from the complete oxidation of glucose. The experimental values (1) obtained for this system are summarized in the tabulation. An efficiency of 45% is attained in capturing the energy theoretically available. The remaining fraction of energy is presumably lost as heat. Nevertheless, the trapping of this amount of energy is a notable achievement for the living cell.

3. Site of Oxidative Phosphorylation

Oxidative phosphorylation has always been associated with extremely sensitive systems localized in intact mitochondria. In 1955, Lehninger and his co-workers (5), by treating rat liver mitochondria with digitonin, obtained a preparation which was capable of carrying out the e-o-t transfer from β-OH butyric acid as the hydrogen donor to oxygen with a simultaneous phosphorylation of ADP to ATP.

This lipid-rich complex contains the electron-transport components usually related to oxidative phosphorylation, namely DPN^+, flavoproteins, cytochrome c, a, and a_3. It has, however, lost the capacity to oxidize many of the TCA cycle acids and has no activity toward fatty acids. With β-hydroxybutyric acid as the source of hydrogen, ADP, and inorganic phosphate, oxidation to acetoacetic acid takes place with a simultaneous fixation of inorganic phosphate at a P/O of 2.8. ADP is the specific phosphate acceptor; other purine and pyrimidine nucleotides are inert. Mg^{++}, which is required for maximum phosphorylation by intact mitochondria, surprisingly uncouples phosphorylation at this multi-enzyme level. DNP, gramicidin, and methylene blue retain their uncoupling activity.

This multi-enzyme preparation is 1/2000 the particle weight of an intact mitochondrion and shows unusual stability in hypotonic solutions in sharp contrast with intact mitochondria that are notoriously unstable under these conditions.

4. Mechanism of PO_4 Transfer in the e-o-t Level

A detailed explanation for the reaction sequence on the e-o-t level is still incomplete. The scheme depicted below brings together the existing knowledge on this subject and summarizes the many aspects of oxidative phosphorylation: concomitant with substrate phosphorylation ① is an oxidation of substrate with the removal of 2 electrons ②. This electron pair enters the e-o-t level ③ and is transferred through the carrier levels ④ to oxygen. In the meantime inorganic PO_4 is

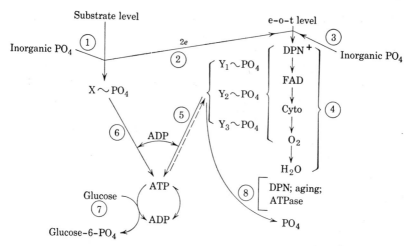

esterified at stage ④ to $Y \sim PO_4$ ⑤ which is then transferred to the acceptor ADP to form ATP. Lehninger (6) believes that the reduced carrier, AH_2, reacts with the next carrier, B, indirectly by interacting first with an enzyme protein Y:

$$AH_2 + Y \rightleftharpoons AH_2 - Y \tag{1}$$

In reaction (2) the actual oxidation-reduction occurs with the simultaneous generation of $\sim$bond thus conserving the free energy of oxidation:

$$AH_2 - Y + B \rightleftharpoons A \sim Y + BH_2 \tag{2}$$

Actual esterification of PO_4 and transfer to ADP takes place in reactions (3) and (4):

$$A \sim Y + PO_4 \rightleftharpoons A + PO_4 \sim Y \tag{3}$$
$$PO_4 \sim Y + ADP \rightleftharpoons ATP + Y \tag{4}$$

ATPase activity is depicted as being exerted by a reversal of reaction (4) and a spontaneous hydrolysis of $PO_4 \sim Y$. DNP could uncouple phosphorylation and stimulated ATPase activity by displacing PO_4 in $PO_4 \sim Y$ to form a very unstable complex $DNP \sim Y$ which would rapidly hydrolyze. Aging of the particles would probably irreversibly alter the ability of Y to participate in the complex of reactions ⑧. At ⑥, $X \sim PO_4$, formed at the substrate level, also transfers its $\sim PO_4$ to ADP. ATP is then utilized in a typical phosphorylation mechanism such as ⑦.

5. Photosynthetic Phosphorylation (7)

Photosynthetic phosphorylation describes the conversion of light energy into the energy-rich pyrophosphate bonds of ATP by isolated chloroplasts, without the aid of other cellular constituents such as leaf mitochondria. Isolated chloroplasts can carry out complete photosynthesis which can be subdivided into photolysis, photosynthetic phosphorylation, and CO_2 fixation. Photolysis is linked to photosynthetic phosphorylation by the simple reaction sequence:

$$\text{light} + P_i + \text{ADP} \to \text{ATP}$$

Under some conditions oxygen is evolved. The system has been carefully studied by Arnon and his group (7, 8) who find that the complete system in reality requires chloroplasts, ADP, TPN$^+$, FMN, vitamin K, ascorbic acid, and magnesium. Arnon pictures the system to consist of three types:

(*a*) In the presence of light, chloroplasts can cleave water to molecular oxygen and reduce added TPN$^+$ to TPNH with a simultaneous esterification of inorganic phosphate to high energy phosphate bonds. The reaction is summarized in the equation

$$\text{H}_2\text{O} + \text{TPN}^+ + \text{ADP} + P_i \xrightarrow[\text{Chloroplasts}]{\text{Light}} \text{TPNH} + \text{H}^+ + \text{ATP} + \tfrac{1}{2}\text{O}_2$$

(*b*) Upon the addition of catalytic amounts of FMN to the system represented above, oxygen evolution is abolished and phosphorylation is sharply increased. Apparently the light energy required for the photolysis of water with the concomitant formation of [2H] and [O] is trapped by the electron transfer system as $\sim$P and the electrons released in the cleavage of water are returned to the reduced and oxidized products of water photolysis, re-forming water and thereby making impossible the release of molecular oxygen.

(*c*) A third type of ATP formation in light is dependent on vitamin K. It resembles phosphorylation with FMN in that no oxygen evolution accompanies ATP formation but it differs from the FMN system in that it is insensitive to dinitrophenol.

The types may be depicted in the following diagram

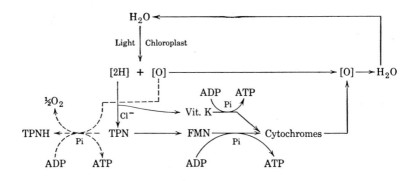

It is remarkable that the rates of photosynthetic phosphorylation with chloroplasts are so high. Thus, 500 μmoles of phosphate are esterified per hour per mgm. chlorophyll. These rates are comparable with maximum rates of conversion of light into chemical energy during photosynthesis by whole leaves in saturating light and sufficient carbon dioxide supply.

II. References

General

1. H. A. Krebs and H. L. Kornberg, *Ergebnisse du Physiol., Biol. Chemie und Exp. Pharmakol.*, *49*, 212 (1957).
2. B. Chance, and G. R. Williams, *Adv. in Enzymol.*, *17*, 65 (1956).

Bibliography

3. E. G. Ball, *Ann. N. Y. Acad. Sci.*, *459*, 363 (1944).
4. A. L. Lehninger, *J. Biol. Chem.*, *178*, 611, 625 (1949).
5. A. L. Lehninger, in *Enzymes: Units of Biological Structure and Function*, Academic Press, N. Y., 1956, p. 217.
6. C. Cooper and A. L. Lehninger, *J. Biol. Chem.*, *224*, 561 (1957).
7. D. I. Arnon, in *Enzymes: Units of Biological Structure and Function*, Academic Press, N. Y., 1956, p. 279.
8. D. I. Arnon, F. R. Whatley, and M. B. Allen, *Science*, *127*, 1026 (1958).

25

Fatty Acid Oxidation

1. Introduction (1, 2)

The first clue to the mechanism of fatty acid oxidation in animals was discovered in 1904 by Knoop. However, complete information was lacking until in 1953 Green's group in Wisconsin (3) and Lynen (4) in Munich independently identified and characterized the enzyme reactions responsible for fatty acid degradation in mammalian tissue.

Before 1953 the following data had accumulated to provide the necessary background for the final attack:

(a) Fatty acids were found to be degraded by a β-oxidation from the carboxyl end of the molecule [Knoop's classical experiments (5)].

$$R—C\text{-}|\text{-}C—C\text{-}|\text{-}C—COOH \overset{C_2}{\underset{\uparrow}{\longrightarrow}} R—C\text{-}|\text{-}C—COOH \overset{C_2}{\underset{\uparrow}{\longrightarrow}} R—COOH \rightarrow etc.$$

(b) Liver homogenates oxidize butyric acid to acetoacetic acid when supplemented by a TCA cycle intermediate, inorganic phosphate, Mg^{++}, cytochrome c and adenylic acid [Munoz and Leloir, 1943 (6)].

(c) In the cell the site of fatty acid oxidation is the mitochondrion. In the presence of Mg^{++}, oxaloacetate, ATP, and malonate, citrate and succinate accumulate; in the absence of oxaloacetate, acetoacetic acid accumulates [Kennedy and Lehninger, 1949 (7)].

(d) The discovery of a water-soluble enzyme preparation from *Clostridium kluyveri* [Stadtman and Barker, 1949 (8)], for the first time permitted a detailed investigation of the oxidative as well as the synthetic pathway of butyric acid. In essence it was observed that acetyl phosphate is condensed to butyric acid under appropriate conditions and that butyric acid is rapidly oxidized to acetyl phosphate in the presence of phosphate:

$$2 \text{ Acetyl P} \rightleftharpoons \text{C}_4 \text{ Keto acid} \underset{}{\overset{\pm 2\text{H}}{\rightleftharpoons}} \text{C}_4 \text{ Hydroxy acid} \underset{}{\overset{\text{H}_2\text{O}}{\rightleftharpoons}}$$

$$\text{C}_4 \text{ Unsaturated acid} \underset{}{\overset{\pm 2\text{H}}{\rightleftharpoons}} \text{Butyric acid}$$

(e) The discovery, isolation, and determination of the chemical structure of CoA [Lipmann and Novelli, 1949 (9)] and the demonstration that the active C_2 unit was acetyl CoA [Lynen, 1951 (10)]

$$\overset{\text{O}}{\underset{}{\overset{\|}{\text{CH}_3\text{C}}}}\text{—S—CoA}$$

with a thiol ester linkage of about 8,500 calories of $\Delta F'_{\text{hydrolysis}}$.

2. The Fatty Acid Oxidation System

It is now known that in animal and plant tissues all the enzymes for the activation and degradation of free fatty acids exist in the mitochondrion. A typical reaction sequence is presented in Table 25.1. By these reactions fatty acids are converted to acetyl CoA derivatives, which then enter the metabolic pool. The biochemical properties of the participating enzymes are summarized in Table 25.2.

The following points should be stressed:

1. For the β-oxidation of 1 mole of fatty acid only 1 mole of ATP is required, regardless of the chain length of the substrate. Once the molecule of fatty acid has been converted into the activated form, namely as an acyl CoA derivative, the CoA thiol ester grouping is preserved until the final C_2 fragment is metabolized.

2. Physiologically, acetoacetic acid accumulates in liver tissue but not in kidney or in heart tissue. This observation can now be interpreted on an enzyme basis (1). In liver a very powerful deacylase occurs which irreversibly catalyzes the reaction

$$\text{Acetoacetyl CoA} + \text{H}_2\text{O} \rightarrow \text{Acetoacetic acid} + \text{CoA}$$

In addition the β-keto acid activating enzyme which catalyzes the reaction

$$\text{Acetoacetic acid} + \text{CoA} + \text{ATP} \rightleftharpoons \text{Acetoacetyl CoA} + \text{AMP} + \text{P—P}$$

is virtually absent in liver but present in kidney and heart. Thus, once acetoacetic acid is formed in the liver it becomes metabolically inert. In contrast, in kidney and heart deacylase activity is very low. Any circulating acetoacetic acid is rapidly channeled by the β-keto acid activating enzyme into the metabolic system.

Table 25.1. Enzymic Path of Fatty Acid Oxidation (1, 4)

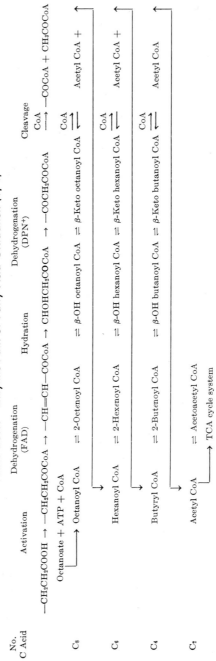

No. C Acid	Activation	Dehydrogenation (FAD)	Hydration	Dehydrogenation (DPN⁺)	Cleavage
	$-CH_2CH_2COOH \rightarrow -CH_2CH_2COCoA \rightarrow -CH=CH-COCoA \rightarrow CHOHCH_2COCoA \rightarrow -COCH_2COCoA$				$\overset{CoA}{\rightarrow} -COCoA + CH_3COCoA$
C_8	Octanoate + ATP + CoA → Octanoyl CoA	⇌ 2-Octenoyl CoA	⇌ β-OH octanoyl CoA	⇌ β-Keto octanoyl CoA	$\overset{CoA}{\rightleftarrows}$ Acetyl CoA +
C_6	Hexanoyl CoA	⇌ 2-Hexenoyl CoA	⇌ β-OH hexanoyl CoA	⇌ β-Keto hexanoyl CoA	$\overset{CoA}{\rightleftarrows}$ Acetyl CoA +
C_4	Butyryl CoA	⇌ 2-Butenoyl CoA	⇌ β-OH butanoyl CoA	⇌ β-Keto butanoyl CoA	$\overset{CoA}{\rightleftarrows}$ Acetyl CoA
C_2	Acetyl CoA	⇌ Acetoacetyl CoA → TCA cycle system			

Table 25.2. Enzymes of Fatty Acid Oxidation (1, 4)

Enzyme	Substrate Specificity	Reaction	Cofactor	T.N. (approx.)	K_{eq}*
Acyl thiokinases	(a) C_2—C_3 acids, (b) C_4—C_{12}, (c) >C_{12}	$RCOOH + ATP + CoA \rightarrow RCOCoA + AMP + P—P$	Mg^{++}, ATP, CoA	300 (b)	1.3 (heptanoic acid)
Butyryl dehydrogenase	C_4—C_6 Acyl CoA	$R—CH_2—CH_2COCoA$ $\pm 2H$	2FAD	350	0.2
General acyl dehydrogenase	C_4—C_{16} Acyl CoA	$\pm 2H$	2FAD	900	
Palmityl dehydrogenase	C_6—C_{16} Acyl CoA		2FAD	400	10
Enoyl hydrase†	General	$RC{=}CHCOCoA$ $\pm H_2O$ $RC—CH_2COCoA$ (OH)	—	1.4×10^6	0.06 (crotonyl CoA)
β-Hydroxyacyl dehydrogenase†	General	$\pm 2H$ $RCOCH_2COCoA$	DPN^+	42,000	6.3×10^{-11} (β-OH-butyryl CoA); pH 8
β-Keto-acyl thiolase	General	CoA $RCOCoA + CH_3COCoA$	CoA	700	1.7×10^4 (Acetoacetyl CoA); pH 8.5

* $K_{eq} = \dfrac{\text{Products}}{\text{Reactants}}$.

† Crystalline.

3. It is well known that, with the exception of the accumulation of acetoacetic acid, no intermediates have ever been detected when long-chain fatty acids are oxidized to CO_2 and water by the liver. Not only was this observation puzzling, but it also made extremely difficult the establishment of a scheme for the degradation of these fatty acids. It is obvious now that, rather than free fatty acids, the tissues metabolize only acyl CoA derivatives which represent the true intermediates. Once having been formed, they are rapidly degraded to acetyl CoA, which is then utilized in a very large number of reactions.

4. Reaction Sequence

(A) The first dehydrogenation step, the primary oxidation of acyl CoA, involves at least two steps, the removal of hydrogen from the α-β carbons of the acyl group by a specific dehydrogenase and the transfer of these hydrogens by a specific flavoprotein, the electron transfer flavoprotein (ETF), to a suitable acceptor. Depending on the substrate specificity, the dehydrogenases (11) are classified as butyryl dehydrogenase (C_4-C_6 acyl CoA), general acyl dehydrogenase (C_4-C_{16} acyl CoA), and palmityl dehydrogenase (C_6-C_{16} acyl CoA).

All the dehydrogenases contain FAD as the prosthetic group and are metal-free. They possess two unique characteristics: (a) the reduced flavoproteins are incapable of being reoxidized unless an additional flavoprotein, ETF, is added (12). Reduced ETF can then be readily oxidized by a mitochondrial system through cytochrome c. The following sequence summarizes these findings:

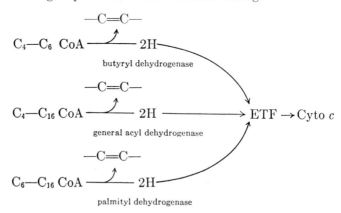

and (b) an unusually strong enzyme-substrate complex occurs between the acyl dehydrogenases and their respective substrates (13). Thus the bound substrate cannot be dialyzed, is sedimentable with the protein in the ultracentrifuge, and is precipitable with ammonium sulfate. There is no measurable dissociation of these complexes. In addition, when acyl CoA complexes with its acyl dehydrogenase, both CoA and the acyl moieties are bound. The bound substrate can be displaced by free substrate of similar affinity to the enzyme, but the substrate molecule leaves the enzyme as intact acyl CoA. There is no dynamic exchange on the enzyme of CoA and acyl moieties of different molecules. Thus $C_{16}CoA$ and $C_8CoA(P^{32})$ when added to their acyl dehydrogenase do not yield $C_{16}CoA(P^{32})$ and C_8CoA. The molar ratio of substrate bound to protein is a small number of between 1 or 2, but not larger.

(B) The hydration step—the product of the dehydrogenation step is probably an α,β unsaturated CoA derivative with a *trans* configuration. Enoyl hydrase (or crotonase) has the remarkable activity of hydrating both the *trans* and *cis* enoyl CoA derivatives, although the rate of hydration of the *cis* isomer is about 40% of the rate of the *trans* isomer. Wakil (14) presents evidence that the product of the hydration of the *trans* isomer is L(+)-β-hydroxyacyl CoA, while that of the *cis* isomer is D (−)-β-hydroxyacyl CoA. Stern, (15) however, advances evidence that the *cis* isomer is first converted to the *trans* form which is then hydrated exclusively to L (+)-β-hydroxy CoA.

Since enoyl hydrase is strongly inhibited by sulfhydryl reagents, probably the sulfhydryl groups of the enzyme protein participate in the hydration reaction. Thus, the inductive form is attacked by the nucleophilic enzyme-S: reagent to form the enzyme-substrate complex:

$$
\begin{array}{c}
RCH_2 \quad \delta^+ \quad \delta^- H \\
\diagdown C = C \diagup \\
H \diagup \quad \diagdown C - S - CoA \\
\qquad \underset{O\ \delta^-}{\overset{\|}{}}
\end{array}
$$

$$
\begin{array}{c}
RCH_2 \qquad H \\
\diagdown C - \ominus C - C - S - CoA \\
H \diagup \oplus \quad \underset{\ominus O}{\overset{\|}{}} \\
\ominus S \boxed{\oplus\ \oplus} \\
\boxed{En}
\end{array}
$$

and H+ OH− by a nucleophilic displacement of the enzyme-S: can then form the β-hydroxyacyl CoA reaction product.

(C) The second dehydrogenation step—the hydration product, L(+)-β-hydroxyacyl CoA is rapidly oxidized to the corresponding β-keto acid by DPN+ linked L(+)-β-hydroxyacyl dehydrogenase. Stern believes that the D-isomer which may be formed from *cis* crotonyl CoA is first converted to the L-isomer by a specific racemase and is then oxidized by its specific dehydrogenase (16).

D(−)-β-hydroxyacyl CoA ⇌ L(+)-β-hydroxyacyl CoA

Wakil has shown that there exists a specific DPN⁺ linked D(−)-β-
hydroxyacyl dehydrogenase which oxidizes the D acid to the corresponding β-keto acid, which can then be either further metabolized or
reduced to the L-isomer by the specific L(+)-β-hydroxyacyl dehydrogenase (11). It is conceivable that both mechanisms may be present.

$$\text{D(−)-β-hydroxyacyl CoA + DPN}^+ \underset{}{\overset{\text{D-enzyme}}{\rightleftharpoons}}$$

$$\text{β-ketoacyl CoA + DPNH + H}^+$$

$$\text{L(+)-β-hydroxyacyl CoA + DPN}^+ \underset{}{\overset{\text{L-enzyme}}{\rightleftharpoons}}$$

$$\text{β-ketoacyl CoA + DPNH + H}^+$$

L(+)-β-hydroxyacyl dehydrogenase has been obtained in crystalline
form from pig heart extracts (26). The optimum pH for reduction of
acetoacetyl CoA is about 6.5, whereas the optimum pH for oxidation
of L(+)-β-hydroxy butyryl CoA is 9.6. At the respective pH optima
the reduction reaction is 5 times more rapid than the oxidation. Both
DPN⁺ and TPN⁺ can be employed although DPN⁺ is 10 times more
effective. There is some evidence to suggest the presence of bound
pyridine nucleotide on the enzyme protein.

(D) The cleavage step β-ketoacyl thiolase reversibly cleaves a
rather large number of β-ketoacyl CoA derivatives by a thiolytic
scission. This widely distributed enzyme links the fatty acid cycle
with the TCA cycle since one of the reaction products is acetyl CoA;
it is also of fundamental importance to the concept both of β-oxida-
tion and β-condensation, since it catalyzes C_2 scission or condensation.
Since β-ketoacyl thiolase is strongly inhibited by sulfhydryl reagents,
it probably reacts with its substrate as follows:

$$\text{RCH}_2\text{COCH}_2\text{COCoA + HS—En} \rightleftharpoons \text{RCH}_2\text{CO S—En + CH}_3\text{COCoA}$$

$$\text{RCH}_2\text{CO—S En + CoA} \qquad \rightleftharpoons \text{RCH}_2\text{COCoA + HS—En}$$

This concept (2) is of considerable importance in interpreting the observations obtained when C^{14} carboxyl labeled fatty acids are oxidized by liver slices or liver mitochondria to yield acetoacetic acid
($\text{CH}_3\underline{\text{C}}\text{OCH}_2\underline{\text{C}}\text{OOH}$) with a $C^{14}O/C^{14}OOH$ ratio near unity and when
C^{14} palmitic acid labeled in the C_{15} position is oxidized to yield aceto-
acetic acid with a $C^{14}O/C^{14}OOH$ ratio of 6. It was believed at first
that in the oxidation of long-chain fatty acids, both carboxyl and odd
carbon-labeled fatty acids should release carboxyl-labeled acetyl CoA
which would enter the acetate pool and then recombine to give acetoacetic acid equally labeled in the CO and the COOH groups. The

results cited above would indicate that C_2 fragments, which are first cleaved, readily enter and mix in the acetate pool, whereas the ωC_2 fragment has properties unlike its predecessors. These results are readily explained by the reaction above, which would suggest that the terminal C_2 fragment remains as a CH_3CO-S-enzyme complex for a finite period, during which it can react with an acetate pool of low-labeled-carboxyl activity to form acetoacetic acid with a high $CO/COOH$ ratio.

3. Fatty Acid Synthesis

It has been assumed that fatty acid synthesis is simply a reversal of the fatty acid oxidation cycle, which under reductive conditions would join acetyl CoA units by a multiple head-to-tail condensation to form long chain fatty acids. In 1952 Brady and Gurin (17) prepared soluble extracts from pigeon liver which catalyzed the condensation of acetate to long-chain fatty acids in the presence of Mg^{++}, citrate, CoA, ATP, DPN^+. Popjak and Tietz (18) later obtained soluble extracts from mammary glands of goat which synthesized fatty acids in the C_6-C_{18} range from acetate and ATP, CoA, DPN^+ and α-ketoglutaric acid. Wakil et al. (19) have recently fractionated the soluble proteins of pig liver into four fractions, which, when combined with acetyl CoA, ATP, DPNH, TPN^+, Mn^{++}, isocitrate, and GSH, yielded palmitic acid, myristic acid, and decreasing amounts of the lower homologues. Either isocitrate or citrate appears to be required and is not replaced by TPNH.

With these observations at hand, the following points should be stressed:

(1) Whereas in mammalian tissues the complex of fatty acid oxidation enzymes are completely localized in mitochondria, the enzymes responsible for fatty acid synthesis have been found exclusively in soluble protein fractions. Mitochondrial particles appear to have no synthesizing capacity (20).

(2) Acyl dehydrogenase does not catalyze the conversion of α-β unsaturated fatty acyl CoA to the saturated derivative. A new enzyme, TPN^+-ethylene reductase (20), has been found to catalyze the reduction of the unsaturated to the saturated acyl CoA.

(3) In the mammalian enzyme preparations of Gurin and Wakil, either citrate or isocitrate is an essential component of the system. Although these acids would normally be expected to serve as a source of hydrogen donors for the TPN^+-reductive step, TPNH cannot completely replace this requirement. In addition, bicarbonate is a specific requirement for the synthetic system.

These observations would suggest that the synthetic pathway in mammalian tissues may be completely independent of the degradative pathway and may involve a different series of enzymes for multiple β-condensation of acetate units.

However, Seubert, Gruell, and Lynen (21) in 1957 combined highly purified preparations of the fatty acid oxidation enzymes, thiolase, β-hydroxyacyl dehydrogenase, enoyl hydrase, and the reductive enzyme, TPN+-ethylene reductase obtained from pig liver mitochondria, with labeled acetyl CoA, TPN+, DPN+, TPNH, and DPNH generating systems and have demonstrated the *de novo* synthesis of capric acid. Moreover, the cell-free extracts of *Clostridium kluyveri* (8), which oxidize short-chain fatty acids in the presence of oxygen, will also readily synthesize fatty acids from acetyl CoA under reductive conditions.

In plants the synthesizing system is localized exclusively in the mitochondrial particle (22). Thus acetate is condensed chiefly to oleic and palmitic acids in the presence of avocado mitochondrial particles, ATP, CoA, Mn++, GSH, and citrate. Citrate (or isocitrate) appears to be required for the synthesis of oleic acid, since its synthesis is greatly depressed if citrate is not added to the reaction mixture. This enzyme complex can be completely solubilized and will condense acetate to long-chain fatty acids if now in addition to the usual components a TPNH reducing system and bicarbonate are added. DPN+ is unnecessary.

In summary, part of the total picture has been revealed, but much data must be examined before the complete pattern unfolds.

4. Odd-Chain Fatty Acid Oxidation

The mechanism of long odd-chain fatty acid oxidation can be depicted as follows:

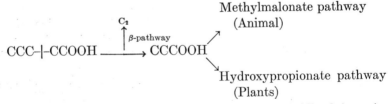

Methylmalonate pathway
(Animal)

Hydroxypropionate pathway
(Plants)

(*a*) Methylmalonate pathway. Propionate is oxidized in animal tissues (23) by the following unique sequence:

(1) Propionate + ATP + CoA $\xrightarrow{\text{Mg}^{++}}$

Propionyl CoA + ADP [propionic kinase]

(2) $HCO_3^- + ATP \xrightarrow{Mg^{++}}$ (Carbonyl phosphate) $+ ADP$

(3) Propionyl CoA $+$ (carbonyl phosphate) $\rightarrow$

$$\left. \text{Methylmalonyl CoA} + P \right\} \begin{bmatrix} \text{Propionyl} \\ \text{CoA} \\ \text{carboxylase} \end{bmatrix}$$

(4) Methylmalonyl CoA $\rightarrow$

$$\text{Succinyl CoA [Methylmalonyl CoA isomerase]}$$

In reaction (2), fluoride in the presence of CO_2 will greatly catalyze the conversion of ATP to ADP with a simultaneous accumulation of monofluorophosphate. This enzyme, fluorokinase, is rather widely distributed in mammalian tissues. Presumably, since carbonyl phosphate never accumulates, it occurs only as an enzyme-bound form; the introduction of fluoride into the system displaces the CO_2 and forms fluorophosphate, which then dissociates off the enzyme surface. This pathway completely explains the *in vivo* experiments of Wood, who showed that when labeled proponate was injected into a fasted rat, either α or β carbon atoms of propionate were equally distributed between carbons 1, 2, 5, and 6 of liver glucose.

Another mechanism for the introduction of CO_2 into fatty acids is by way of the bicarbonate-dependent cleavage of ATP to pyrophosphate and AMP-carbonate (24). In extracts of bacteria, yeast, and animal tissues, AMP-carbonate (adenosine phosphorylcarbonate) participates as the carboxylation reagent for the conversion of β-hydroxyisovaleryl CoA to β-hydroxy-β-methyl glutaryl CoA:

(1) $CO_2 + ATP \rightleftharpoons AMP{-}CO_2^- + P{-}P$

(2) $AMP{-}CO_2 + \beta\text{-hydroxyisovaleryl CoA} \rightleftharpoons$

$$AMP + \beta\text{-Hydroxy-}\beta\text{-methyl glutaryl CoA}$$

(*b*) *β-Hydroxypropionate pathway.* In several plant mitochondrial systems, propionate is readily oxidized by a modified β oxidative pathway via β-hydroxypropionate (25). The evidence supports the scheme:

(1) Propionate $+ CoA + ATP \rightarrow$ Propionyl CoA $+ AMP + PP$

(2) Propionyl CoA $\xrightarrow{-2H}$ Acrylyl CoA

(3) Acrylyl CoA $+ H_2O \rightarrow \beta$-Hydroxypropionyl CoA

(4) β-Hydroxypropionyl CoA $+ H_2O \rightarrow \beta$-Hydroxypropionate $+ CoA$

(5) β-Hydroxypropionate $\xrightarrow{-2H}$ Malonic semialdehyde

(6) Malonic semialdehyde $+ CoA \xrightarrow{-2H}$ Malonyl CoA

(7) Malonyl CoA $\rightarrow$ Acetyl CoA $+ CO_2$

Carbon dioxide is rapidly released exclusively from the carboxyl of propionate. The methyl and carboxyl groups of acetyl CoA are derived from carbon two and three respectively. No evidence is available to support the pyruvate or methylmalonate pathways in plant tissues.

References

General

1. D. E. Green, *Biol. Rev.*, *29*, 330 (1954).
2. F. Lynen, *Ann. Rev. Biochem.*, *24*, 653 (1955).

Bibliography

3. H. Beinert, R. Bock, D. Goldman, D. E. Green, H. R. Mahler, S. Mii, P. G. Stansley, and S. J. Wakil, *J. Am. Chem. Soc.*, *75*, 4111 (1953).
4. F. Lynen, *Federation Proc.*, *12*, 683 (1953).
5. F. Knoop, *Beitr. chem. Physiol. Path.*, *6*, 150 (1904).
6. J. M. Munoz and L. F. Leloir, *J. Biol. Chem.*, *197*, 355 (1943).
7. E. P. Kennedy and A. L. Lehninger, *J. Biol. Chem.*, *179*, 957 (1949).
8. E. R. Stadtman and H. A. Barker, *J. Biol. Chem.*, *180*, 1085, 1095, 1117, 1169 (1949).
9. F. Lipmann, *Harvey Lectures*, *44*, 99 (1948–1949).
10. F. Lynen and E. Reichert, *Angew. Chem.*, *63*, 47, 490 (1951).
11. F. L. Crane, S. Mii, J. G. Hauge, D. E. Green, H. Beinert, *J. Biol. Chem.*, *218*, 701 (1956).
12. F. L. Crane and H. Beinert, *J. Biol. Chem.*, *218*, 717 (1956).
13. H. Beinert, Personal communication.
14. S. J. Wakil, *Biochim. et Biophys. Acta*, *19*, 497 (1956).
15. J. R. Stern and Alice del Campillo, *J. Biol. Chem.*, *218*, 985 (1956).
16. J. R. Stern, Alice del Campillo, and A. L. Lehninger, *J. Am. Chem. Soc.*, *77*, 1073 (1955).
17. R. O. Brady and S. Gurin, *J. Biol. Chem.*, *199*, 421 (1952).
18. G. Popjak and A. Tietz, *Bioch. J.*, *60*, 147 (1955).
19. J. W. Porter, S. J. Wakil, A. Tietz, M. I. Jacob, and D. M. Gibson, *Biochim. et Biophys. Acta*, *25*, 35 (1957).
20. R. G. Langdon, *J. Biol. Chem.*, *226*, 615 (1957).
21. W. Seubert, G. Gruell, and F. Lynen, *Angew. Chem.*, *69*, 359 (1957).
22. P. K. Stumpf and George A. Barber, *J. Biol. Chem.*, *227*, 407 (1957).
23. M. Flavin, H. Castro-Mendoza, and S. Ochoa, *Biochim. et Biophys. Acta*, *20*, 591 (1956).
24. B. K. Bachhawat and M. J. Coon, *J. Am. Chem. Soc.*, *79*, 1505 (1957).
25. J. Giovanelli and P. K. Stumpf, *J. Am. Chem. Soc.*, *79*, 2652 (1957).
26. J. R. Stern, *Biochim. et Biophys. Acta*, *26*, 448 (1957).

26

Nucleotide Derivatives

1. Introduction

Until 1950, the participation of nucleotides other than the simple adenosine polyphosphates was unknown in enzymic reactions. In 1950, after a remarkable series of experiments, Leloir and his group (1) in Argentina announced the isolation of an entirely new type of nucleotide, namely uridine diphosphoglucose, which was required for the conversion of glucose 1-phosphate to galactose 1-phosphate. Since then, a host of new nucleotide derivatives have been isolated from a wide variety of tissues and include the following bases as the purine or pyrimidine nucleus: uracil, cytosine, guanine, and adenine. Simultaneously, a new series of enzymes have been described which specifically catalyze reactions in which these nucleotide derivatives participate as substrates.

In this chapter we shall outline the biosynthetic pathway of the nucleotides, the class of enzymes that catalyze the reactions in which the derivatives of these nucleosides appear as substrates, and then tabulate a wide variety of derivatives that have been described to date.

2. Biosynthetic Pathways

(a) Uridine and cytosine. Figure 26.1 summarizes the work of Kornberg and Lieberman, which is largely responsible for the elucidation of biosynthesis of these two nucleosides (2).

(b) Purine bases. Figure 26.2 depicts the biosynthetic pathways which are involved in the formation of the bases adenine, guanine, xanthine, and inosinic acid. The work of Buchanan, Greenberg, and Rabinowitz has contributed largely to this complex field (3).

For information concerning the broader subject of nucleic acids and the enzymes that are involved in their breakdown and synthesis the reviews of Carter (4), Kornberg (5), and Ochoa (6) should be

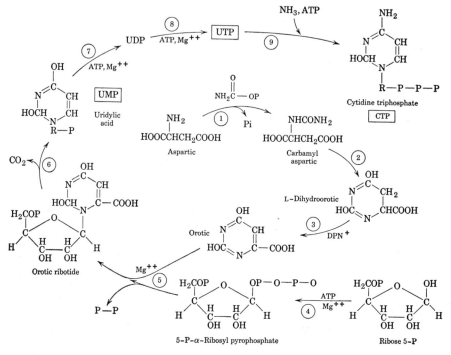

Fig. 26.1. Biosynthesis of the pyrimidine ribotides, UTP and CTP.

1. carbamylaspartic phosphorylase   6. orotidylic decarboxylase
2. dihydroorotase   7. nucleoside monophosphokinase
3. dihydroorotic dehydrogenase   8. nucleoside diphosphokinase
4. ribopyrophosphorylase   9. uridine triphosphate aminase
5. orotidylic pyrophosphorylase

consulted. *The Nucleic Acids* edited by Chargaff and Davidson (7) is the basic reference on the subject.

3. Class of Enzymes and Reactions (5)

(A) Nucleoside monophosphokinase (2): The activity of this enzyme has been found in a wide variety of tissues. However, until exhaustive purification of the enzyme protein is accomplished, little can be said concerning the specificity of the activity. The enzyme catalyzes the general reaction

$$N^1\!\!-\!\!P + N^2\!\!-\!\!P\!\!-\!\!P\!\!-\!\!P \rightleftharpoons N^1\!\!-\!\!P\!\!-\!\!P + N^2\!\!-\!\!P\!\!-\!\!P$$

where N^1 represents the nucleoside uridine, adenosine, guanosine, and cytidine and N^2, guanosine, adenine, and uridine. The equilibrium constant for this reaction is about 1.

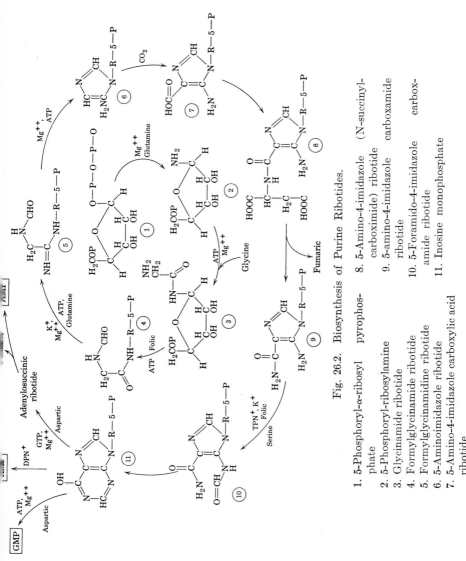

Fig. 26.2. Biosynthesis of Purine Ribotides.

1. 5-Phosphoryl-α-ribosyl pyrophosphate
2. 5-Phosphoryl-ribosylamine
3. Glycinamide ribotide
4. Formylglycinamide ribotide
5. Formylglycinamidine ribotide
6. 5-Aminoimidazole ribotide
7. 5-Amino-4-imidazole carboxylic acid ribotide
8. 5-Amino-4-imidazole (N-succinyl-carboximide) ribotide
9. 5-amino-4-imidazole carboxamide ribotide
10. 5-Foramido-4-imidazole carbox-amide ribotide
11. Inosine monophosphate

(B) Nucleoside diphosphokinase (8): Another group of kinases specifically phosphorylate the nucleotide diphosphates. Here again group specificity is apparent, but whether this is associated with one protein or a host of proteins awaits the testing of highly purified systems. The reaction

$$N^1—P—P—P + N^2—P—P \rightleftharpoons N^1—P—P + N^2—P—P—P$$

involves ATP as the phosphorylating donor and UDP, IDP, as the acceptors. The K for the reaction is approximately 1. By a combination of the reactions (A) and (B), it is possible to convert a nucleoside monophosphate to its corresponding triphosphate. This is of considerable importance, since the triphosphates are the essential participants for the synthesis of the multitude of nucleotide derivatives by reactions (D) and (H).

(C) UDP sugar pyrophosphatase (9): This reaction cleaves the pyrophosphate linkage of a UDP sugar irreversibly according to the reaction

$$\text{UDP Sugar} \rightarrow \text{UMP} + \text{Sugar 1-Phosphate}$$

Kalckar has described the enzyme for the substrate UDPG. Nucleotide pyrophosphatase is a more general enzyme with broad specificity which cleaves UDPG to the same products.

(D) Nucleoside diphosphosugar pyrophosphorylase: First discovered by Trucco in 1951 (10) and studied in more detail by Kalckar in 1953 (11), this type of enzyme pyrophosphorylyzes UDP glucose according to the reaction

$$U—P^*—P^*—G + P^x—P^x \rightleftharpoons U—P^*—P^x—P^x + \text{Glucose 1-P}^*$$

It should be noted that pyrophosphate as a unit cleaves UDPG and forms the terminal phosphates of the reaction product, UTP. There is no exchange with the phosphate of glucose 1-phosphate. The K_{eq} is approximately 1, indicating that there is little loss in the bond energetics of the system. This reaction is basic to the biochemistry of nucleotide derivatives, since by this mechanism nucleoside triphosphates and sugar phosphates are utilized for the synthesis of their derivatives. Different pyrophosphorylases catalyze the interaction of CTP, UTP, and GTP with glycosyl and other organic phosphates. The following reactions are typical examples:

UDP Galacturonic + PP ⇌ UTP + Galacturonic 1-P

GDP Mannose   + PP ⇌ GTP + Mannose 1-P

CDP Choline   + PP ⇌ CTP + Phosphorylcholine

(E) Nucleoside diphosphodonor-acceptor transferase: The term defines the nature of the reaction by which such important biochemical compounds as sucrose, lactose, and phosphatidyl choline are synthesized. There are two major types of transfer reactions in this category:

(a) Glycosyl transfer: This is illustrated by UDP glucose–fructose 6-P transglycosylase which catalyzes the synthesis of sucrose (12):

$$\text{UDP}\underline{\overset{\alpha}{}}\boxed{\text{Glucose}} + \text{Fructose 6-P} \rightleftharpoons \text{UDP} + \text{Glucose}\underline{\overset{\alpha}{}}O\underline{\overset{\beta}{}}\text{Fructose 6-P}$$

$$\text{Sucrose 6-P} + H_2O \rightarrow \text{Sucrose} + P$$

Note that the glycosyl moiety is transferred to the acceptor, fructose 6-P. The cleavage of the donor moiety is presumably at the C–O bond in UPOP-O-glucose. The α configuration of the sugar moiety is preserved in the transfer reaction although the mechanism of transfer may involve either a frontal displacement or a double inversion. However, in the synthesis of lactose, an inversion of the glucosidic bond is noted. The enzyme, UDP galactose-glucose 1-P transglycosylase (13), in transferring the galactosyl unit to the acceptor, inverts the original α configuration of UDP galactose to a β configuration in lactose:

$$\text{UDP-}\alpha\underline{}\boxed{\text{Galactose}} + \text{Glucose 1-P} \rightleftharpoons \text{UDP} + \text{Galactose}\underline{\overset{\beta}{}}\text{Glucose 1-P}$$

$$\text{Lactose 1-P} + H_2O \rightarrow \text{Lactose} + P$$

In all glycosyl transfers one of the reaction products is always a *nucleoside diphosphate:*

(b) Phosphoryldonor transfer: This class is depicted by the enzyme CDP choline–diglyceride transferase (14):

$$\text{C-P-}\boxed{\text{P-Choline}} + \text{Diglyceride} \rightleftharpoons \text{CP} + \text{Diglyceride-P-choline}$$

Here the transferred unit is a phosphorylated donor, with the cleavage at the pyrophosphate bond. The characteristic end-product is a *nucleoside monophosphate.*

(F) Glycosyl 1-P–nucleotidyl transferases: This general term has its example in galactose 1-P uridyl transferase which is a key enzyme in galactose–glucose metabolism (15). In this reaction there is a simple, freely reversible transfer of the uridyl group from UDP glucose to galactose 1-P:

UDP Glucose + Galactose 1-P $\rightleftharpoons$ UDP Galactose + Glucose 1-P

Pyrophosphate does not enter the reaction.

(G) Nucleoside diphosphosugar dehydrogenase: UDPG undergoes a two-step oxidation at the C_6 hydroxyl group of the sugar moiety:

UDP Glucose (C^6H_2OH) $\xrightarrow{-2H}$ [UDP Hexose diald (C^6HO)] $\xrightarrow{-2H}$

UDP Glucuronic (C^6COOH)

UDP glucose dehydrogenase, which catalyzes this reaction requires DPN^+ as the electron-carrying cofactor. It has been purified to a considerable extent from calf liver (16) and pea meal (17) as sources of the enzyme. However, no separation of the two-step oxidation has been achieved. It is presumably by this pathway that the uronic acids are synthesized.

Once UDP uronic acid synthesis is achieved, a glucuronyl transferase can catalyze the migration of the glucuronyl group from the donor, nucleoside diphosphoglucuronic acid, to a suitable acceptor. Thus the liver glucuronyl transferase will transfer glucuronic acid from UDP glucuronic acid to phenols, thyroxine, or sterols (18). Since glucuronides consistently have a β-glycosidic configuration, whereas the UDP-O-glucuronic acid has an α-glycosyl configuration, an inversion must take place during the transfer reaction. In contrast, in sucrose synthesis, an α-glucosidic bond is formed and thus either a simple transfer or a double inversion could occur.

(H) Nucleoside diphosphohexose-4-hydroxyl epimerase: In 1950 (1) it was observed that galactose 1-phosphate was converted to glucose 1-phosphate reversibly by the reaction

UDP Galactose $\rightleftharpoons$ UDP Glucose

This enzyme was named galactowaldenase (19), which implied that the mechanism was a walden inversion of the 4-OH of the sugar. In 1956, Maxwell (20) showed that DPN^+ participated in the conversion reaction in the following sequence:

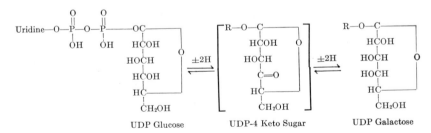

UDP Glucose   UDP-4 Keto Sugar   UDP Galactose

Four possible mechanisms suggest themselves: (a) dehydration to give C_3–C_4 or C_5–C_6 double bond and rehydration in opposite steric sense, (b) dehydrogenation to a 4-keto compound and rehydrogenation in the opposite steric sense, (c) direct inversion by a nucelophilic attack by OH⁻ from the medium, and (d) cleavage between C_3–C_4 bond and recondensation to give opposite steric configuration. Several laboratories (21) showed experimentally that H_2O^{18} and T^+OH^- do not participate in the reaction. Furthermore, enzymic dehydrogenation of deutero-labeled D—C̶—OH grouping to the corresponding —C═O with DPN⁺ as the transfer system showed complete lack of exchange of the D–C with protons of the medium. These results would rule out a, c, and d. Since DPN⁺ is very firmly associated with the enzyme protein, these results would indicate an interesting type of oxidation reduction by which the asymmetry of the H—C̶—OH of the sugar moiety is destroyed temporarily by formation of a transient —C̶═O group which is then specifically reduced to yield a HO—C̶—H grouping projected in the opposite steric sense. Similar epimerases have been discovered in plant extracts which catalyze the conversion of UDP xylose to UDP arabinose (22) and in liver extracts which convert UDP N-acetyl glucosamine to N-acetylgalactosamine (23).

(I) Adenyl acyl pyrophosphorylase: Another class of nucleotide derivatives is associated with compounds that have never been isolated from reaction mixtures but have been inferred to be formed on the basis of carefully designed experiments involving pyrophosphate exchange, hydroxamic acid formation, and biochemical activity of chemically synthesized compounds (25–30). It is puzzling that no net synthesis or accumulation of the adenyl acylates occurs in enzyme systems, but presumably the adenyl acyl derivative is formed only in concentrations equivalent to the concentration of the enzyme protein as an adenyl acyl–protein complex.

Berg (24) depicts the reaction as a nucleophilic attack by the electronegative oxygen of an acyl group, RCH_2COO^-, on the terminal pyrophosphate group of ATP with a displacement of the pyrophosphate grouping to yield inorganic pyrophosphate and an adenyl acylate:

$$ATP + RCO\ddot{O}^- \rightleftharpoons AMP—COR + PP$$

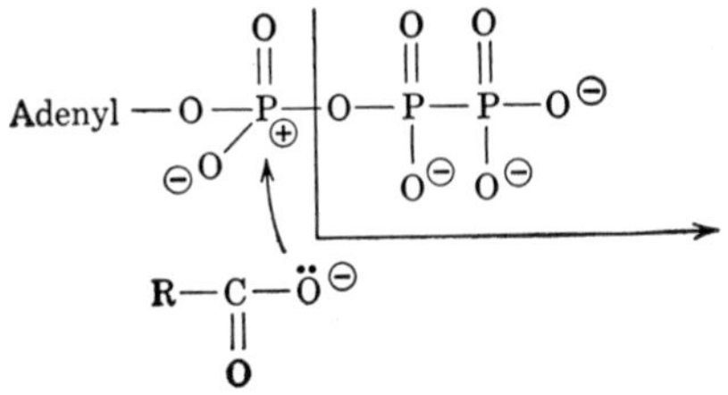

This reaction has proved to be of interest since it appears to be a general reaction for the activation of all fatty acids, of amino acids, carbonate, and sulfate (24–29). With fatty acids, the following sequence takes place:

$$RCOO^- + ATP \rightleftharpoons AMPCOR + PP$$
$$AMPCOR + CoA \rightleftharpoons RCOCoA + AMP$$

and with amino acids, presumably the adenyl amino acids participating in protein synthesis (see Chapter 27). Adenyl sulfate can un-

Table 26.1. Nucleotide Derivatives

Derivative	Class of Reactions	Reference: Isolation	Reference: Functional
UDP glucose	C, D, E, F, G, H	1	1, 12, 15–17, 20, 45, 46
UDP galactose	C, D, E, F, H	1	14, 15, 20, 22
UDP xylose	C, D, H	42	22
UDP arabinose	C, D, H	42	22
UDP glucuronic	C, D, G	32	16–18, 33, 44
UDP galacturonic	C, D	34	44
UDP N-acetylglucosamine	C, D, E, H	36, 44	23, 35
UDP N-acetylgalactosamine	C, D, E, H	23, 36	23
UDP N-acetylglucosamine phosphate	—	39	—
UDP N-acetylgalactosamine sulfate	—	39	—
UDP N-acetylaminosugar peptide	—	31	—
GDP mannose	C, D	37	38
CDP choline	C, D, E	40	13
CDP ethanolamine	C, D, E	40	13
CDP ribitol	—	41	—
CDP glycerol	—	41	—
Adenyl acetate	I	24	24
Adenyl butyrate	I	25	25
Adenyl methionine	I	26	26
Adenyl leucine	I	27	27
Adenyl sulfate	I	43	28, 30
Adenyl carbonate	I	—	29

dergo further phosphorylation by ATP to yield a 3′ phosphoryl adenyl 5 sulfate. This compound is then utilized for the introduction of sulfate into chondroitin sulfate (30).

4. Conclusion

As indicated in Table 26.1 a large number of derivatives have already been identified and they have been linked as substrates with specific enzymes. Such compounds as CDP ribitol and CDP glycerol, GDP mannose, and the interesting derivative which accumulates in organisms exposed to penicillin, UDP N-acetylamino sugar peptide (31) remain more or less functionless. However, it is safe to predict that within the near future not only will these compounds participate in new enzyme systems but new reactions will also be revealed which will employ a compound such as UDP galacturonic acid as a precusor for pectin synthesis.

References

General

1. R. Caputto, L. F. Leloir, C. E. Cardini, and A. G. Paladini, *J. Biol. Chem.*, *184*, 333 (1950); L. F. Leloir, *Proc. Third Internat. Congress of Biochem.*, Brussels, p. 154 (1955).
2. I. Lieberman, A. Kornberg, and E. S. Simms, *J. Biol. Chem.*, *215*, 403 (1953); I. Lieberman, *J. Biol. Chem.*, *222*, 765 (1956).
3. B. Levenberg and J. M. Buchanan, *J. Biol. Chem.*, *224*, 1005, 1019 (1597): D. A. Goldthwait, R. A. Peabody, and G. R. Greenberg, *J. Biol. Chem.*, *221*, 569 (1956); J. C. Rabinowitz and W. E. Pricer, Jr., *J. Biol. Chem.*, *222*, 537 (1956).
4. C. E. Carter, *Annual Rev. Biochem.*, *25*, 123 (1956).
5. A. Kornberg, *Adv. in Enzymol.*, *18*, 191 (1957).
6. S. Ochoa, *The Chemical Basis of Heredity*, edited by W. D. McElroy and B. Glass, Johns Hopkins Press, Baltimore, 1957, p. 615.
7. The Nucleic Acids edited by E. Chargaff and J. N. Davidson, vol. I and II, Academic Press, N. Y., 1955.

Bibliography

8. P. Berg and W. K. Joklik, *J. Bio. Chem.*, *210*, 657 (1954).
9. J. E. Gander, W. E. Peterson, and P. D. Boyer, *Arch. Biochem. and Biophys.*, *60*, 261 (1956). H. M. Kalckar, *Acta Chem. Scand.*, *8*, 1103 (1954).
10. R. Trucco, *Arch. Biochem. and Biophys.*, *34*, 482 (1951).
11. A. Munch-Peterson, H. M. Kalckar, E. Cutolo, and E. B. Smith, *Nature*, *172*, 1036 (1953).
12. C. E. Cardini and L. F. Leloir, *J. Biol. Chem.*, *214*, 157 (1955).
13. E. P. Kennedy and S. B. Weiss, *J. Biol. Chem.*, *222*, 193 (1956).
14. J. F. Gander, W. E. Peterson, P. D. Boyer, *Arch. Biochem. and Biophys.*, *69*, 85 (1957).
15. H. M. Kalckar, *Biochim. et Biophys. Acta*, *12*, 250 (1953); L. P. Anderson, H. M. Kalckar, and K. J. Isselbacher, *Science*, *125*, 113 (1957).

16. J. L. Strominger, E. S. Maxwell, and H. M. Kalckar, *J. Biol. Chem.*, *224*, 79 (1957).

17. J. L. Strominger and L. W. Mapson, *Biochem. J.*, *66*, 567 (1957).

18. K. J. Isselbacher and J. Axelrod, *J. Biol. Chem*, *77*, 1070 (1955).

19. L. F. Leloir, *Arch. Biochem. and Biophys.*, *33*, 186 (1951).

20. E. S. Maxwell, *J. Am. Chem. Soc.*, *78*, 1074 (1956).

21. L. Anderson, A. M. Landel, and D. E. Diedrich, *Biochim. et Biophys. Acta*, *22*, 574 (1956); A. Kowalsky and D. E. Koshland, *Biochim. et Biophys. Acta*, *22*, 575 (1956); K. M. Kalckar and E. S. Maxwell, *Biochim. et Biophys. Acta*, *22*, 588 (1956).

22. E. F. Neufeld, V. Ginsburg, E. W. Putman, D. Fanshier, and W. Z. Hassid, *Arch. Biochem. and Biophys.*, *69*, 602 (1957).

23. H. G. Pontis, *J. Biol. Chem.*, *216*, 779 (1954).

24. P. Berg, *J. Biol. Chem.*, *222*, 991, 1015 (1956).

25. C. H. L. Peng, *Biochim. et Biophys. Acta*, *22*, 42 (1956).

26. P. Berg, *J. Biol. Chem.*, *222*, 1025 (1956).

27. J. A. DeMoss, S. M. Genioth, and G. D. Novelli, *Proc. Nat. Ac. Sci.*, *42*, 325 (1956).

28. P. W. Robbins and F. Lipmann, *J. Am. Chem. Soc.*, *78*, 6409 (1956).

29. B. K. Bachhawat, M. J. Coon, *J. Am. Chem. Soc.*, *79*, 1505 (1957).

30. Furio D'Abramo and F. Lipmann, *Biochim. et Biophys. Acta*, *25*, 211 (1957).

31. J. T. Park and J. L. Strominger, *Science*, *125*, 99 (1957).

32. G. J. Dutton and D. E. Storey, *Biochem. J.*, *57*, 275 (1954).

33. E. B. Smith and G. T. Mills, *Biochim. et Biophys.*, *13*, 386 (1954).

34. E. B. Smith, G. T. Mills, and E. H. Harper, *Biochem. et Biophys. Acta*, *23*, 662 (1957).

35. L. Glaser and D. H. Brown, *Biochim. et Biophys. Acta*, *23*, 449 (1957).

36. E. Calib, L. F. Leloir, and C. E. Cardini, *J. Biol. Chem.*, *203*, 1055 (1955).

37. E. Calib and L. F. Leloir, *J. Biol. Chem.*, *206*, 901 (1954).

38. A. Munch-Peterson, *Arch. Biochem. and Biophys.*, *55*, 592 (1955).

39. J. L. Strominger, *Biochim. et Biophys. Acta*, *17*, 283 (1955).

40. E. P. Kennedy, *J. Biol. Chem.*, *222*, 185 (1956).

41. J. Baddiley, J. G. Buchanan, B. Carss, A. P. Mathias, and A. R. Sanderson, *Biochem. J.*, *64*, 599 (1956).

42. V. Ginsburg, P. K. Stumpf, and W. Z. Hassid, *J. Biol. Chem.*, *223*, 977 (1956).

43. P. W. Robbins and F. Lipmann, *J. Am. Chem. Soc.*, *78*, 2652 (1956).

44. J. Solms, D. S. Feingold, and W. Z. Hassid, *J. Am. Chem. Soc.*, 2342 (1957).

45. L. Glaser, *Biochim. et Biophys. Acta*, *25*, 436 (1957).

46. L. F. Leloir and C. E. Cardini, *J. Am. Chem. Soc.*, *79*, 6340 (1957).

27

Protein Synthesis

1. Introduction (References 1, 2, 3)

Recent years have seen very rapid advances in the elucidation of the mechanisms of biosynthesis. The biochemical pathways for the manufacture of amino acids, fatty acids, purines and pyrimidines, and carbohydrates have been largely established (see Chapters 22, 23, and 25); and in some cases (notably fatty acid synthesis) the enzymes have been studied in some detail. However, the biosynthetic process most important for the comprehension of cellular function, the synthesis of proteins, still remains largely unsolved. Over and above the biochemically familiar problems of precursors and energy supply, protein synthesis poses a new and special problem: the sequential ordering of heterogeneous building units. The magnitude of this problem becomes clear when we consider the elementary facts of protein structure.

Proteins consist of many different amino acid residues, linked primarily through peptide bonds to form long polypeptide chains. Proteins differ from one another with respect to the number, nature and sequence of the amino acids in the chain; the manner in which the chain is folded; and the nature and frequency of cross-linkages between adjacent portions of the chain. These variables permit, in theory, an almost unlimited degree of structural specificity. Although other factors may also be important, a primary determinant of specificity in proteins is the possession of *a fixed and characteristic amino acid sequence*. This fundamental conclusion is at present based largely on the analysis of the structure of insulin carried out by Sanger and his colleagues (4, 5). They have shown that the insulin from any given animal species has a constant amino acid composition and sequence; insulins from other species have the same general structure, with minor variations (Fig. 27.1). It therefore follows that the synthesis of every specific protein entails the assembly of a polypeptide

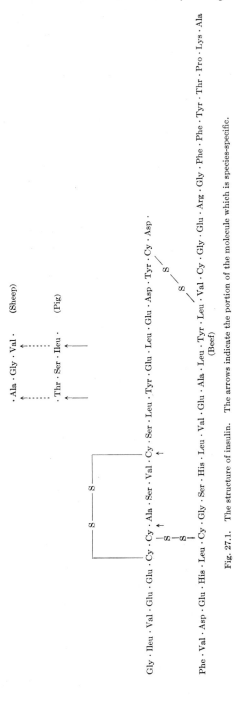

Fig. 27.1. The structure of insulin. The arrows indicate the portion of the molecule which is species-specific.

chain in which the amino acids are linked in a characteristic and invariant order. Any living organism synthesizes many hundreds of specific proteins. Enzymes cannot, so far as we know, act as sequence determinants; hence their action in protein synthesis must be coupled with the action of other, sequence-determining, components. It is now generally believed that nucleic acids perform this vital function in protein synthesis, but the inner mechanism of sequence determination is still completely unknown.

2. Systems for the Study of Protein Synthesis

Much indispensable general information about protein synthesis has been obtained through studies on intact cells and tissues. Within the past few years, attention has shifted to protein synthesis in subcellular particulate systems. In certain of these systems, it is possible to obtain net protein synthesis to a limited extent, provided that the system is suitably supplemented. Essential supplements are a complete array of amino acids, together with ATP or an ATP-generating system; in some cases, requirements for purines and pyrimidines or for nucleic acids have also been reported. Subcellular systems from plant and animal cells which are capable of making protein consist essentially of microsomes (6, 7); the analogous systems from bacteria are less well-defined structurally, but appear to be derived from the cytoplasmic membrane, possibly with certain constituents of the cytoplasm proper still attached (1, 8).

3. Measurement of Protein Synthesis

In animal and plant systems, protein synthesis has generally been estimated by gross measurements: either determination of a net protein increase, or of incorporation of isotopically labeled amino acids into protein. These two kinds of measurements are not strictly equivalent, since it has been clearly shown that labeled amino acids can enter proteins by exchange, under conditions which do not permit the occurrence of net synthesis (8). Hence, although isotopic incorporation measurements are very sensitive and easy to perform, they are not necessarily a reflection of net synthesis.

Protein synthesis can also be estimated more specifically by measuring the synthesis of a single protein, detectable as a result of its specific biological activity.

This technique has been predominantly employed in work on protein synthesis in microorganisms, where the formation of specific enzymes has been investigated. The obvious advantages are sensitivity and accuracy, coupled with the fact that in general an increase in specific catalytic power reflects net synthesis. Studies on enzyme synthesis often involve a special problem, that of *induction*. Many of the enzymes produced by microorganisms are formed at a high rate only in the presence of specific externally supplied inducers. An inducer is either a substrate for the enzyme in question, or a compound which has a close steric relation to the substrate. Enzymes which are formed in response to an inducer are known as *inducible enzymes*, in contrast to *constitutive enzymes*, the formation of which does not require an external inducer. The phenomenon of induction permits the investigator to regulate enzyme synthesis in microorganisms specifically, by providing or withholding inducer, a considerable advantage for certain types of experimental work.

4. The Amino Acid Requirement for Protein Synthesis

With a few exceptions, proteins contain an almost complete array of the 20-odd naturally occurring amino acids, which must therefore be available to the cell before a complete protein molecule can be synthesized. The cell can either synthesize its amino acids *de novo* or absorb them preformed from the external environment.

The specific requirement of many different amino acids for enzyme synthesis has been shown with particular clarity in the bacterium *Escherichia coli*. This organism can normally synthesize all its amino acids from ammonia and a suitable carbon source, but mutants can be obtained which have lost specifically the ability to manufacture one amino acid. The formation of the inducible enzyme β-galactosidase by such mutants is strictly dependent on the provision of the specific required amino acid, and ceases, under conditions otherwise favorable for enzyme synthesis, as soon as the external supply of the amino acid is depleted. By such experiments, it has been shown that each of 11 different amino acids is required for the formation of β-galactosidase (9).

5. The Formation of "False Proteins"

The absolute specificity of the amino acid requirements for protein synthesis has one very interesting exception. Certain structural analogs of the naturally occurring amino acids have long been known to act as powerful inhibitors of growth. It was originally assumed that growth inhibition reflects the blockage of incorporation of the corresponding natural amino acid into protein; this is, in fact, the basis of growth inhibition by some analogs. Other inhibitory analogs, however, have been shown recently to undergo incorporation into protein in place of the corresponding natural amino acid. Thus, among the inhibitory analogs of tryptophan, azatryptophan and tryptazan are incorporated, whereas 5-methyltryptophan is not (10). The "false proteins" formed by analog incorporation may lack biological activity, growth being eventually halted as a result of the accumulation of inactive proteins. The synthesis of false proteins does not necessarily entail a loss of functional activity, however; it has been demonstrated that in *Escherichia coli* the methionine of the cell proteins can be totally replaced by selenomethionine, without cessation of growth or loss of capacity to synthesize active β-galactosidase (11).

6. The Activation of Amino Acids

Many studies with intact cells have shown that an energy supply is required for protein synthesis. At least some of the energy requiring steps in protein synthesis appear to have been elucidated with the discovery of enzymes, present in plants, animals and microorganisms, which activate amino acids (12, 13, 14). These enzymes catalyze an exchange between ATP and pyrophosphate which is dependent on the presence of a specific amino acid. If hydroxylamine is added to the system, there is a net breakdown of ATP to pyrophosphate and AMP, accompanied by the formation of the corresponding amino hydroxamic acid. These enzymes appear to be analogous to the acetate-activating enzyme (Chapter 26). The observed reactions can be accounted for as follows:

Enzyme + Amino acid + ATP $\rightleftharpoons$ Enzyme–amino acyl–AMP +PP

Enzyme-amino acyl–AMP + Hydroxylamine $\rightarrow$

Amino hydroxamic acid + AMP + Enzyme

The assumption that amino acyl–AMP compounds are actually formed is strengthened by the observation that purified enzyme systems capable of performing a specific amino acid-dependent exchange reaction can also rapidly form ATP when furnished with the specific synthetic amino acyl–AMP and pyrophosphate.

It is probable that these amino acid activations represent the first step in protein synthesis, but the evidence is still inferential. On purely thermodynamic grounds, some type of activation of free amino acids must be postulated as a prerequisite for peptide bond synthesis. The activating enzymes have been found associated with subcellular systems capable of protein synthesis, although at least some of them can be obtained in soluble form. The best evidence for their function in protein synthesis comes from observations on the activating enzyme for tryptophan, which has been considerably purified. This enzyme can also activate the two tryptophan analogs, azatryptophan and tryptozan, which are incorporated into "false proteins" by intact cells. Other growth-inhibitory tryptophan analogs, which are not incorporated into protein by intact cells, are not activated, but inhibit competitively the activation of tryptophan (15).

7. Interrelationships Between Nucleic Acid and Protein Synthesis

The enzyme systems which activate amino acids provide a mechanism for synthesizing unstable, energy-rich derivatives of the amino acids, thus opening the way for group transfers of the amino acid residues to a suitable acceptor. The ultimate acceptor is presumably the sequence-determining component in protein synthesis, which furnishes a template on which the residues can be assembled in correct order prior to peptide bond formation. There are good reasons for excluding all cell constituents except the nucleic acids as possible sequence-determining components in protein synthesis (1), and it is believed that the RNA of the cell is the actual substance responsible for sequence determination. We must accordingly consider some of the evidence concerning the relationships of the nucleic acids to protein synthesis.

In a living cell, the storehouse of genetic information is the DNA of the nucleus. Accordingly, the ultimate potentiality of a cell to synthesize specific proteins must be conferred by its DNA. This does not necessarily mean, however, that DNA is *directly* involved in protein synthesis; indeed, two kinds of experiments lead to the conclusion that it is not. In the first place, it has been shown that cells or cell fragments deprived of DNA by removal of the nucleus can continue to synthesize both RNA and protein for considerable periods of time (16). Secondly, in a thymine-requiring mutant of *Escherichia coli* the specific arrest of DNA synthesis by thymine depletion does not prevent the formation of induced enzymes (17).

A very different picture emerges when the relation of RNA to protein synthesis is examined. In a number of different experiments, it has been shown that when the synthesis of RNA is prevented or deranged, synthesis of induced enzymes is arrested. For example, the formation of β-galactosidase by a uracil-requiring mutant of *E. coli* is strictly dependent on the presence of a supply of uracil (18) an observation which acquires added significance in view of the failure of thymine depletion to arrest enzyme synthesis by the same bacterium. In another bacterium, *Staphylococcus aureus,* the inducible formation by β-galactosidase is prevented in the presence of 8-azaguanine, an analog of guanine which competes for incorporation into RNA (19). The inhibitory effect of azaguanine is shown even after enzyme synthesis has been initiated. These observations imply that the formation of induced enzymes requires a *simultaneous*, rather than a *preceding*, synthesis of RNA. This may, however, be a phenomenon peculiar to the formation of induced enzymes, since it has been reported that formation of the constitutive enzyme, catalase, by *Staphylococcus aureus* is unaffected under certain conditions by azaguanine.

The relation between RNA and protein synthesis is not a unilateral one; there is considerable evidence that the formation of RNA is dependent on certain of the reactions of protein synthesis, although not on the complete process. Bacterial mutants with specific requirements for amino acids cease to synthesize RNA in the absence of the required amino acid; with limiting quantities of the amino acid, RNA synthesis is proportional to the quantity of amino acid supplied (20). A further very interesting feature of the relationship is revealed by the effect of chloramphenicol, an antibiotic which specifically inhibits protein synthesis. In the presence of sufficient chloramphenicol to inhibit totally protein synthesis, RNA synthesis still proceeds; but in amino acid-requiring mutants it is still dependent on the presence of the required amino acid. Chloramphenicol dramatically affects the *quantitative* aspects of the dependence of RNA synthesis on amino acid supply; with a given quantity of amino acid, the amount of RNA formed in the presence of chloramphenicol may be over 20 times as great as in the absence of the antibiotic. In effect, the inhibition of protein synthesis by chloramphenicol uncovers what appears to be a *catalytic* function of amino acids in RNA synthesis, normally concealed by the uptake of the amino acids into protein.

8. Influence of Nucleic Acids on Protein Synthesis in Subcellular Systems

Further evidence for the relationship between nucleic acid and protein synthesis has come from studies on subcellular systems. The pioneering studies in this field were carried out by Gale and Folkes (8), using sonically ruptured bacterial cells, capable of amino acid incorporation and enzyme synthesis when supplemented with an amino acid mixture and a source of ATP. The ruptured cells can be depleted to varying degrees of their nucleic acids by salt extraction or treatment with nucleases. When 93% of the RNA and 90% of the DNA are removed, little enzyme-forming ability remains unless the preparation is supplemented with nucleic acid or its derivatives. Catalase formation was observed to be stimulated by RNA, but not by purine and pyrimidine bases; β-galactosidase formation was stimulated by the bases, but not by RNA. With a higher degree of resolution, RNA and bases lost their stimulatory effects on enzyme synthesis, but a marked stimulation by DNA was reported.

More recently, some highly significant observations on a subcellular system from animal cells have been made by Zamecnik and his collaborators (21, 22). It has been found that a soluble fraction containing amino acid activating enzymes also contains RNA, which acquires radioactivity when incubated with C^{14}-labeled amino acids in the presence of ATP. The RNA-bound amino acid yields the corresponding amino hydroxamic acid on treatment with hydroxylamine and can transfer its radioactivity to protein upon incubation with microsomes in the presence of guanosine triphosphate. Experiments on incorporation *in vivo* showed that this RNA fraction acquires activity from labeled amino acids more rapidly than does any of the cellular protein. The RNA fraction is also able to incorporate adenylic acid from ATP *in vitro*, apparently in a terminal position; the incorporated adenylic acid is not, however, transferrable to the RNA of microsomes.

In view of the various types of evidence discussed above, the existence of a very close relationship between RNA and protein synthesis must be considered as established. The interpretation of the relationship remains problematical, however.

9. Stages in Protein Synthesis

It seems highly probable that the first step in protein synthesis is the formation of amino acid adenylates by the activating enzymes. The recent observations by Zamecnik and his collaborators establish that active amino acid residues can become incorporated into RNA; but, beyond this point, our biochemical knowledge of protein synthesis is inferential and entirely speculative. The dependence of RNA synthesis on the presence of amino acids, which has been demonstrated so strikingly with intact cells, suggests that the polyribonucleotide chain may be built up by successive terminal additions of nucleotides linked to amino acids. In this fashion, an amino acid sequence could be formed on the growing RNA chain. Formation of the polypeptide chain could then occur by rupture of the linkages holding the amino acids to the bases of the RNA and simultaneous peptide bond formation between adjacent amino acid residues. Since chloramphenicol blocks protein synthesis, but not amino acid activation or RNA synthesis, its most probable site of action is at the stage of peptide bond formation. The catalytic effect of amino acids on RNA synthesis in the presence of chloramphenicol would imply that even when peptide bond formation is prevented, nucleotide incorporation into RNA still requires a preliminary combination of the nucleotides with amino acids, which can be liberated spontaneously from the RNA chain and function over again in nucleotide incorporation.

This interpretation is plausible as far as it goes, but fails entirely to account for sequence determination. On formal grounds, sequence determination can be accounted for by postulating that a pre-existing RNA chain determines base sequence in the growing RNA chain and, secondarily, the sequence of the attached amino acid residues. There is still a very wide gap, however, between such formal speculations and the observations of the biochemist.

10. The Regulation of Protein Synthesis

The complexity of the problem of protein synthesis cannot be fully grasped without a consideration of its regulatory aspects (see also Chapter 21). Most of the proteins made by an organism are enzymes, which must be produced in a balanced array to permit the correct integration of biochemical functions. Furthermore, the enzymatic constitution of an organism is never static, undergoing both qualitative and quantitative changes through time. In higher organisms, the morphological differentiation which occurs during development is accompanied by a differentiation of enzymatic pattern, with the result that in the mature organism, each tissue region contains a distinctive and characteristic array of enzymes (Table 27.1). The adaptation of an organism to changes in the external environment may also involve changes of enzymatic constitution. For example, facultatively

Table 27.1. Specific Enzymatic Activities in Normal Mouse Tissues (23)

Tissue	Arginase	Catalase	Acid Phosphatase	Alkaline Phosphatase	Esterase
Liver	246	8.00	12	4	411
Lymph nodes	20	0.02	49	8	25
Bone marrow	4	0.01	22	23	—
Spleen	6	0.12	73	17	106
Kidney	42	3.20	15	1072	108
Skeletal muscle	4	0.01	19	2	13
Cardiac muscle	7	0.01	18	12	13
Skin	27	0.01	30	5	3
Lung	50	0.22	33	36	68
Intestinal mucose	80	0.00	34	2789	973
Gastric mucose	4	0.00	27	17	48
Thymus	2	0.00	5	3	3
Pancreas	8	0.01	10	1	1820
Brain	3	0.00	15	12	7

anaerobic yeasts and bacteria may show marked changes of enzymatic constitution which are correlated with growth in the presence and absence of air (24, 25). Aerobically grown cells possess enzyme systems for electron transport to oxygen and for the operation of the TCA cycle. Under anaerobic conditions, the rates of synthesis of many of these enzymes fall, in many cases, often to negligible values, and after a few generations of anaerobic growth the cells can lose completely their respiratory capacity (Table 27.2). Re-exposure to air causes a very rapid resynthesis of the enzyme systems of respiratory metabolism.

Table 27.2. Levels of Enzymatic Activities in *Pasteurella pestis**

Enzyme	Aerobic	Anaerobic
Condensing enzyme	82.3	7.9
Isocitric dehydrogenase	73.6	1.2
Fumarase	50.3	11.1
Malic dehydrogenase	13.4	4.9
Cytochrome system	Present	Absent

* Cells grown aerobically and anaerobically. Activities of enzymes are expressed as micromoles of substrate transformed per hour per milligram of cell nitrogen (25).

How are such changes in enzymatic constitution produced? There appear to be several different mechanisms. One, which has been already mentioned, is specific induction of enzyme synthesis by substrates or substrate-analogs. Induced enzyme synthesis is well known in microorganisms, which have been almost exclusively employed for its study. However, it also occurs in other biological groups; mammalian tryptophan peroxidase, for example, is a largely inducible enzyme. A second control mechanism, also so far largely studied in microorganisms, is the specific suppression of enzyme synthesis (26, 36). Specific suppression operates very strikingly in the control of certain biosynthetic pathways; the endogenous synthesis of amino acids and pyrimidines by bacteria is suppressed when the cells are furnished with an external supply of these materials. Analyses on an enzymatic level have shown in several such cases that the suppression of endogenous synthesis by the end-product of the biosynthetic pathway operates through suppression of enzyme formation, and not merely through inhibition of enzyme action. A third control mechanism, of considerable importance in higher animals, is the hormonal regulation of enzyme synthesis (35).

11. The Mechanism of Induction

Of the above-mentioned regulatory mechanisms, induced enzyme synthesis is the only one so far subjected to a detailed study. Inducible enzymes are formed by an organism at a high rate in the presence of an appropriate, specific external inducer; when the inducer is withheld, enzyme formation occurs at a very low, sometimes undetectable, rate. Although most inducers are substrates for the enzymes whose formation they elicit, inducers and substrates are not necessarily identical. The most comprehensive study of this question has been made with the inducible β-galactosidase of *Escherichia coli* (27). This enzyme can be extracted from the cells by toluene treatment and assayed by a very sensitive and precise optical method: measurement of the yellow compound *o*-nitrophenol, formed by hydrolysis of the colorless synthetic substrate, *o*-nitrophenyl-β-D-galactoside. The induction of β-galactosidase was studied by growing *E. coli* for 5 hours in the presence of different sugars, then treating the cells with toluene, and assaying β-galactosidase activity as described above. The compounds tested as inducers were also tested as growth substrates for the bacterium, and as substrates and complexants for the isolated and purified enzyme. Complexing ability ("relative affinity") is defined in terms of the degree of competitive inhibition of the hydrolysis of *o*-nitrophenyl-β-galactoside shown by the compound in question. Some results of this study are shown in Table 27.3. It can be seen that the β-galactosides and galactose can combine with the enzyme and also act as inducers, although there is no necessary quantitative correlation between relative affinity and inducing capacity. Of the α-galactosides tested, two—melibiose and methyl-α-galactoside—induce enzyme formation even though they are neither substrates nor complexants for the enzyme. Indeed, melibiose is almost as good an inducer as lactose, which is the natural substrate for β-galactosidase. Two of the compounds tested are substrates for the enzyme but are wholly devoid of inductive power. They are phenyl-β-D-thiogalactoside, in which the galactosidic residue has been modified by the substitution of an S atom for the O atom of the pyranose ring, and *o*-nitrophenyl-α-L-arabinoside, which (despite the difference in nomenclature) is structurally identical with *o*-nitrophenyl-β-D-galactoside except that C-6 of the galactosidic residue has been removed.

These results reveal a fundamental fact about the nature of induction. Since the ability to combine with the active site of the enzyme

Table 27.3.   Inducer and Substrate Function of Different Sugars for
β-Galactosidase (27)

		Properties with Regard to Isolated Enzyme	
Compound	Inducer Function*	Relative Affinity†	Hydrolysis
Galactose	420	30	
β-D-Galactosides			
methyl	2800	10	+
n-butyl	2800	400	+
o-nitrophenyl	1060	1000	+
naphthyl	42	200	+
4-glucose-(lactose)	2500	100	+
mannose	2500	10	+
Phenyl-β-D-thiogalactoside	0	700	0
α-D-Galactosides			
methyl	140		
6-glucose (melibiose)	2400	0	0
6-sucrose (raffinose)	0	0	0
o-Nitrophenyl-α-L-arabinoside	0	50	+

* Activity induced by exposure of cells to sugars at a concentration of $10^{-3} M$, measured as rate of hydrolysis of o-nitrophenyl-β-D-galactoside per milligram of dry weight.

† Determined by measuring the competitive inhibition of o-nitrophenyl-β-D-galactoside hydrolysis. The affinity of the enzyme for this substance is arbitrarily taken as 1000.

being synthesized is neither a necessary nor a sufficient property of the inducer, induction clearly cannot be brought about by a combination of the inducer with pre-existing enzyme molecules in the cell. In other words, the *formation* of an induced enzyme is in no way connected with its *function*. This suggested that the inducer might play a catalytic role in enzyme synthesis by becoming incorporated in the enzyme-forming system.

Direct evidence for the catalytic role of inducer has been obtained through studies on another inducible bacterial enzyme, the penicillinase of *Bacillus cereus* (28–30). This enzyme cleaves the antibiotic penicillin hydrolytically to penicilloic acid, and its only known inducer is penicillin. The inductive process has a unique feature (28). As a rule, the continuance of induced enzyme synthesis is strictly dependent on the maintenance of an external supply of the inducer, but the formation of penicillinase constitutes an exception. When cells of *B. cereus* are exposed briefly to penicillin, washed, and transferred to a penicillin-free broth medium, the growing population synthesizes penicillinase at a rate about 30 times as great as the basal rate of synthesis by an untreated control population, and this increased rate of penicillinase formation continues unchanged for at least ten generations. Even if the exposure to penicillin is made at 0°C, the subsequent induction occurs. The amount of penicillin required is very small: maximal induction is achieved by exposure of the cells to the inducer at a concentration of 1 unit/ml (approximately 10^{-8} M). The kinetics of induction are curious. Since the treated population is placed in a growth medium, the total number of cells increases exponentially during enzyme synthesis; but penicillinase formation, after a brief lag, proceeds linearly with respect to time. This implies that the *enzyme-forming capacity* of the total population remains at a fixed level, established by the penicillin pretreatment, and hence that the specific penicillinase activity of the individual cells rises to a maximum early in growth, and then steadily declines.

These findings suggest that the pretreatment with penicillin results in the establishment of a fixed number of enzyme-forming sites in the treated population, and that these sites remain indefinitely active, although undergoing dilution as a result of subsequent increase in cell numbers. The most reasonable explanation is that during penicillin treatment a certain number of penicillin molecules are more or less irreversibly fixed in the treated cell, occupying sites where they can continue to function as inducers, but are immune to penicillinase attack. Study of the fixation of S^{35}-labeled penicillin by the bacteria revealed the existence of a receptor site which has a very high affinity for penicillin and is saturated at low concentrations of the antibiotic. Additional penicillin can be fixed by the cells at higher concentrations, but the kinetics of fixation indicate that a different site is involved. The former type of fixation has been termed "specific fixation" and the latter, "non-specific fixation." At a penicillin concentration sufficient to produce maximal induction of enzyme synthesis, only about 80 molecules of penicillin are specifically fixed in each bacterial cell. Since penicillinase has been crystallized and its turnover number is known, the number of molecules of enzyme formed by each cell as a result of induction can be determined. Calculations show that between 30 and 40 molecules of penicillinase are produced for each molecule of penicillin that is specifically fixed by the cell (31). For this particular system, therefore, the catalytic function of the inducer is established.

12. Constitutive Enzyme Synthesis

Even in microorganisms, the levels of many enzymes in the cell remain more or less constant under all environmental conditions.

Since the synthesis of these so-called "constitutive" enzymes cannot be affected by external induction, it might seem as if they are formed by a mechanism fundamentally different from that which governs inducible enzyme formation. An experimental study of this question became possible when it was found that bacteria which synthesize an enzyme inducibly can give rise to spontaneous mutants in which the synthesis of the same enzyme is constitutive (31, 32). Mutants of this nature, constitutive for the enzyme β-galactosidase, were first discovered in *E. coli* (32). Subsequently, mutants constitutive for penicillinase were obtained in *B. cereus*. A very detailed comparison of the constitutive and inducibly formed penicillinases of *B. cereus* (31) has failed to reveal any difference between them; even immuno-chemical analysis, by far the most sensitive technique for the detection of minor differences in protein structure, indicates that they are identical. The conclusion seems inescapable that they are synthesized by the same mechanism.

The explanation for the fact that an enzyme may require induction in one bacterial strain, but not in another, is at present obscure. The known facts about induced enzyme synthesis indicate that the inducer is incorporated into the enzyme-forming system, such incorporation being necessary for the activation of the enzyme-synthesizing process. Constitutive enzyme synthesis could also proceed under the influence of induction, provided one makes the assumption that the inducer is endogenously formed, and therefore at all times present in the cell. There is no direct evidence in support of this assumption, but a possible model for constitutive enzyme synthesis mediated by endogenous inducers is provided by the phenomenon of sequential induction (Section 12 of this chapter). An equally plausible alternative explanation of constitutive enzyme synthesis can be made by assuming that the enzyme-forming system requires no inducer, in itself possessing the structure necessary to confer catalytic specificity on the protein which it forms.

12. Sequential Induction (33)

When a series of enzymes, catalyzing the successive steps in a metabolic pathway, are all inducibly formed, exposure of the cell to a single inducer can produce a very complex inductive situation. If the inducer also serves as the primary substrate in the metabolic pathway, its dissimilation by the enzyme whose formation it evokes produces a metabolic intermediate which can serve as both inducer and substrate for the second enzyme in the sequence. In this fashion, a single inducer-substrate may serve as a trigger for the synthesis of a whole series of enzymes. With the exception of the first member of the series, all these enzymes are formed as a result of endogenous induction by the intermediary metabolites produced within the cell from the primary substrate. This phenomenon is known as sequential induction. The magnitude of some sequential inductions is well illustrated by the oxidation of tryptophan by bacteria of the *Pseudomonas* group (34). This oxidation is catalyzed by a sequence of at least eight inducible enzymes, all of which are synthesized by the cell in response to a single external inducer, L-tryptophan. The fact that endogenous induction has been shown to play such an important part in the synthesis of induced enzymes provides some experimental basis for the hypothesis that constitutive enzyme formation might also reflect endogenous induction.

References

General

1. S. Spiegelman, *The Chemical Basis of Heredity,* Johns Hopkins Press, Baltimore, 1957, p. 232.
2. E. F. Gale and K. McQuillen, *Ann. Rev. Microbiol., 11,* 283 (1957).
3. F. Lipmann, *Currents in Biochemical Research, 1956,* Interscience Publishers, N. Y., 1956, p. 241.

Bibliography

4. F. Sanger and H. Tuppy, *Biochem. J., 49,* 463 (1951).
5. F. Sanger and E. O. P. Thompson, *Biochem. J., 53,* 353 (1953).
6. P. C. Zamenick and E. B. Keller, *J. Biol. Chem., 209,* 337 (1954).
7. G. C. Webster and M. P. Johnson, *J. Biol. Chem., 217,* 641 (1955).
8. E. F. Gale and J. P. Folkes, *Nature, 173,* 1223 (1954).
9. J. Monod, A. M. Pappenheimer and G. Cohen-Bazire, *Biochim. et Biophys. Acta, 9,* 648 (1952).
10. A. B. Pardee, V. G. Shore and L. S. Prestidge, *Biochim. et Biophys. Acta, 21,* 406 (1956).
11. G. N. Cohen and D. B. Cowie, *Comptes Rendus Acad. Sci., 244,* 670 (1957).
12. M. B. Hoagland, *Biochim. et Biophys. Acta, 16,* 288 (1955).
13. J. A. DeMoss, S. M. Genuth and G. D. Novelli, *Proc. Nat. Acad. Sci., 42,* 325 (1956).
14. P. Berg, *J. Am. Chem. Soc., 77,* 3163 (1955).
15. N. Sharon and F. Lipmann, *Federation Proc., 16,* 246 (1957).
16. J. Brachet and H. Chantrenne, *Cold Spring Harbor Symposia on Quantitative Biology, 21,* 329 (1956).
17. S. S. Cohen and H. D. Barner, *J. Bact., 68,* 80 (1954).
18. A. B. Pardee, *J. Bact., 69,* 233 (1955).
19. E. H. Creaser, *J. Gen. Microbiol., 12,* 288 (1955).
20. F. Gros and F. Gros, *Biochim. et Biophys. Acta, 22,* 200 (1956).
21. M. B. Hoagland and P. C. Zamecnik, *Federation Proc., 16,* 197 (1957).
22. P. C. Zamecnik, M. L. Stephenson, J. F. Scott and M. B. Hoagland, *Federation Proc., 16,* 275 (1957).

23. J. P. Greenstein, *Research Conference on Cancer,* Publ. of Am. Assoc. Adv. Sc., p. 192 (1945).

24. P. Slonimski, *"La formation des enzymes respiratoires chez la Levure,"* *Actualités Biochim., 17* (1953).

25. E. Englesberg and J. B. Levy, *J. Bact., 69,* 418 (1955).

26. J. Monod and G. Cohen-Bazire, *Compt. Rend. Acad. Sci., 236,* 530 (1953).

27. J. Monod, G. Cohen-Bazire and M. Cohn, *Biochim. et Biophys. Acta, 7,* 585 (1951).

28. M. R. Pollock, *Brit. J. Exptl. Path., 31,* 739 (1950).

29. M. R. Pollock, *Brit. J. Exptl. Path., 32,* 387 (1951).

30. M. R. Pollock, *Brit. J. Exptl. Path., 33,* 587 (1952).

31. M. Kogut, M. R. Pollock and E. J. Tridgell, *Biochem. J., 62,* 391 (1956).

32. G. Cohen-Bazire and M. Jolit, *Ann. Inst. Pasteur, 84,* 937 (1953).

33. R. Y. Stanier, *J. Bact., 54,* 339 (1947).

34. O. Hayaishi and R. Y. Stanier, *J. Bact., 62,* 691 (1951).

35. W. E. Knox, *Cellular Metabolism and Infections,* Academic Press, N. Y., 1954, p. 35.

36. H. J. Vogel, in *The Chemical Basis of Heredity,* Johns Hopkins Press, Baltimore, 1957, p. 276.

APPENDIX

Alphabetical List of Enzymes and Some of Their Properties[1,2,3]

Enzyme	Reaction	Source	Cofactor	pH	Reference
Acetoacetate decarboxylase	Acetoacetic acid → Acetone + Carbon dioxide	Cl. acetobutylicum	—	5	I, I, 625
Acetoarylamine kinase	RNH_2 + AcCoA → RNHAc + CoA	Liver	SH	6–9.5	I, I, 608
Aceto-CoA-kinase	ATP + CoA + HAc → Ac~SCoA + AMP + PP	Yeast	Mg^{++}	7.2	I, I, 585
Acetokinase (acetate kinase)	Acetate + ATP → Acetyl-P + ADP	E. coli	Mg^{++}	7.4	I, I, 591
Acetokinase	Ac~SCoA + D-Glucosamine → N-Acetyl-D-glucosamine + CoA	Pigeon liver	—	—	I, I, 612
Acetylcholinesterase	Acetyl choline → Choline + Acetic acid	Nerve tissue	—	—	I, I, 642
Acetyl CoA deacylase	Ac~SCoA + H_2O → HAc + HSCoA	—	—	—	I, I, 606
N-Acetyl-β-glucosaminidase	Degradation of oligosaccharides	Rat kidney	—	4.3	IV, 65, 464 (1957)
Acetylornithinase	N^α-Acetyl-L-ornithine → L-ornithine + Acetic acid	E. coli	Co^{++}, GSH	7.0	II, 218, 97 (1956)
Acetyl phosphatase	Hydrolysis of acyl phosphates	Horse muscle	—	7.4	I, I, 555
Aconitase	Citrate ⇌ cis-Aconitate → D-Isocitrate	Pig heart	Fe^{++}	5.9	II, 226, 703 (1957)
Aconitic decarboxylase (cis)	cis-Aconitic acid → Itaconic acid + CO_2	A. terreus	—	—	VII, 71, 356 (1956)
Aconitic hydrase	cis-Aconitate + H_2O → Citrate	—	—	—	I, II, 109
Acylase I	General deacylation	Kidney	Zn^{++}, Co^{++}	6.7–7.7	III, 79, 630 (1957)
Adenine deaminase	Hydrolytic deamination of adenine	A. vinelandii	—	—	
Adenosine deaminase (non-specific)	Adenosine compound + H_2O → Inosine compound + NH_3	—	—	5–8	I, II, 475
Adenosine deaminase (specific)	Adenosine + H_2O → Inosine + NH_3	Intestine	—	7±	I, II, 473
Adenosine-5-Phosphatase	Adenosine-5-Phosphate → Adenosine + Phosphate	Potato	—		I, II, 550
Adenosine phosphokinase	Adenosine + ATP → 5'-AMP + ADP	Yeast	Mg^{++}	6.0	I, II, 497
Adenylate kinase* (myokinase)	2ADP → ATP + AMP	Rabbit skeletal muscle	Mg^{++}, Ca^{++}	6.0–7.5	I, II, 598

NOTE: See p. 406 for table notes.

385

Enzyme	Reaction	Source	Cofactor	pH	Reference
5'-Adenylic acid deaminase	5'-AMP + H_2O → 5'-IMP + NH_3	Rabbit muscle	Certain anions	6.4	II, *227*, **987, 993, 999** (1957)
Adenylosuccinase	AMP + Fumaric → Adenylosuccinic	Yeast	—	6.5	II, *222*, 17 (1956)
Adenyl sulfurylase	ATP + SO_4 → AMPS + PP	Liver	—	—	III, *78*, 2652 (1956)
Alanine dehydrogenase	Alanine → Pyruvic + NH_3	B. subtilis	DPN^+	—	IX, *176*, 1073 (1955)
Alanine racemase	L-Alanine → DL-Alanine ← D-Alanine	S. faecalis	Pyridoxal phosphate, GSH	8.5	I, II, 212
Alcohol dehydrogenase*	Alcohol + DPN → Acetaldehyde + DPNH + H^+	Horse liver	DPN^+	8	I, I, 495
Alcohol dehydrogenase	Alcohol + TPN^+ → RCHO + TPNH + H^+	L. mesenteroides	DPN^+ or TPN^+	7.5-9.2	I, I, 504
Alcohol dehydrogenase*	RCH_2OH + DPN^+ → RCHO + DPNH + H^+	Baker's yeast	DPN^+	7.9	I, I, 500
Aldehyde dehydrogenase	CH_3CHO + CoA + DPN^+ → Ac~SCoA + DPNH + H^+	C. kluyveri	DPN^+	7.5-8.8	I, I, 518
Aldehyde dehydrogenase	RCHO + DPN^+ → RCOOH + DPNH + H^+	Beef liver	DPN^+	9.3	I, I, 514
Aldehyde dehydrogenase	RCHO + $\begin{Bmatrix} DPN^+ \\ or \\ TPN^+ \end{Bmatrix}$ + H_2O → RCOOH + $\begin{Bmatrix} DPNH \\ or \\ TPNH \end{Bmatrix}$ + H^+	Yeast	K^+	8.0	I, I, 508
Aldehyde dehydrogenase	CH_3CHO + TPN^+ + H_2O → CH_3COOH + TPNH + H^+	Baker's yeast	TPN, Ca^{++}, Mg^{++}	7.5-8.0	I, I, 511
Aldehyde oxidase	RCHO + $3OH^-$ → RCO_2^- + $2H_2O$ + $2e^-$	Pig liver	FAD	7.0-8.0	I, I, 523
Aldolase	F-1-P ⇌ Dihydroxyacetone phosphate (DAP) + Glyceraldehyde	Rat liver	—	6.7-7.8	I, I, 320
Aldolase*	FDP ⇌ GAP + Dihydroxyacetone phosphate	Rabbit muscle	—	7-8	I, I, 310
Aldolase	FDP ⇌ GAP + DAP	Yeast	—	7-8	I, I, 315
ω-Amidase	$RCONH_2$ + H_2O → RCOOH + NH_3 ; $RCONH_2$ + NH_2OH → $RCONHOH$ + NH_3 } etc.	Liver	—	7	II, *215*, 441 (1955)
Amine oxidase	RCH_2NH_2 + O_2 → RCHO + H_2O_2 + NH_3	Steer plasma	—	6.2-7.5	I, II, 390
Amino acid acetylase	Ac~SCoA + Glycine → Acetyl glycine + HSCoA	Cl. kluyveri	CN^-, azide	7.7-8.3	I, I, 616
Amino acid acylase I	$R^1CH_2CONHCHR^2COOH$ → R^1CH_2COOH + $NH_2R^2CHCOOH$	Hog kidney	—	—	I, II, 115
Amino acid acylase II	$R^1CH_2CONHCHR^2COOH$ → R^1CH_2COOH + $NH_2R^2CHCOOH$	Hog kidney	—	—	I, II, 115
Amino acid amidase	$RCHNH_2CONH_2$ → $RCHNH_2COOH$ + NH_3	Hog kidney	Mn^{++}	8	I, II, 397
Amino acid decarboxylase	DOPA → Dihydroxytyramine + CO_2	Pig kidney	Pyridoxal phosphate	6.8	I, II, 195
D-Amino acid oxidase	$RCHNH_2COOH$ + O_2 + H_2O → RCOCOOH + NH_3 + H_2O_2	Kidney	—	8.8	I, II, 199
L-Amino acid oxidase	Oxidation of L-amino acids and related compounds	Snake venom, rat kidney	FAD, FMN	7.0-7.5	I, II, 204

Enzyme	Reaction	Source		pH	Reference
Amino acid reductase	$CH_3CHNH_2COOH + 2CH_2NH_2COOH + 2H_2O \rightarrow 3CH_3COOH + 3NH_3 + CO_2$	Cl. sporogenes		—	I, II, 217
Aminolevulinic dehydrase	δ-Aminolevulinic → Porphobilinogen	Ox liver	GSH	6.7	IV, 61, 618 (1955)
Aminotripeptidase	Hydrolysis of tripeptides to amino acids + a dipeptide	Calf thymus		—	I, II, 83
α-Amylase*	α-1,4-polyglucosans → dextrins, maltose	Human saliva	Cl^-	6.9	I, I, 149
β-Amylase*	Hydrolysis of α-1,4-glucosidic bonds of polyglucosans	Sweet potato		4-6	I, I, 154
Amylo-1,6-glucosidase	Phosphorylase limit dextrin → Glucose + polysaccharide	Muscle		—	I, I, 211
Amylomaltase	Maltose → Amylose type polysaccharide + Glucose	E. coli		6.8	I, I, 189
Amylosucrase	Sucrose → Glycogen type polysaccharide + fructose	N. perflava		6.4	I, I, 184
Amylo-1,4 → 1,6-transglucosidase	Amylopectin branching	Rat liver		—	I, I, 222
Anserinase	Anserine → β-Alanine + Methyl histidine	Codling muscle	Zn^{++}	7.3	IV, 60, 81 (1955)
Apyrase	$ATP + 2H_2O \rightarrow 5\text{-}AMP + 2P_i$	Potato		—	I, II, 591
Arginase	Arginine → Ornithine + Urea	Beef liver	Mn^{++}	9.5	I, II, 368
Arginine decarboxylase	Arginine → CO_2 + Agmatine	E. coli		4.4	VI, 53, 370 (1954)
Arginine decarboxylase	Arginine → Agmatine + CO_2	E. coli		5.3	VI, 53, 370 (1954)
Arginine desiminase	Arginine → Citrulline + NH_3	S. faecalis		6.8	VI, 69, 186 (1957)
Arginine-ornithine transamidase	Arginine + En. ⇌ Ornithine + Amidine-En.	Hog kidney		7.2	II, 221, 771 (1956)
Arginine phosphokinase	Arginine + ATP → Phospho-arginine + ADP	Sea crayfish muscle	Mn^{++}, GSH	7-8	IV, 65, 143 (1957)
Arginine synthetase	L-Citrulline + L-aspartic + ATP → L-arginine + Fumaric + ADP + P_i	Beef liver, pig kidney		—	I, II, 356
Argininosuccinate synthetase	L-Citrulline + L-Aspartic + ATP → L-Arginosuccinate + ADP + P_i	Liver, yeast	Mg^{++}	—	I, II, 359
Arylsulfatase	Arylsulfate + H_2O → SO_4 + ArylOH	Rabbit liver		6.1	VI, 53, 29 (1954)
Ascorbic oxidase	Ascorbic + O → Dehydroascorbic	Squash		5.6	I, II, 813
Asparaginase	Asparaginase + H_2O → Aspartic + NH_3	Guinea pig serum		7.5-8.5	I, II, 383
Aspartase	Fumaric + NH_3 → Aspartic	E. coli		7.0-7.5	VIII, 42, 443 (1955)
Aspartic decarboxylase	Aspartic → β-alanine + CO_2	Cl. welchii	Co^{++}, folic	5.5	I, II, 188
Aspartic β-Semialdehyde dehydrogenase	Aspartic β-semi CHO + TPN^+ + P_i → β-Aspartyl P + TPNH	Yeast	TPN^+	8-9	II, 213, 39 (1955)
Aspartokinase	Aspartic + ATP → Aspartyl PO_4 + ADP	Yeast	Mg^{++}	5-9	II, 213, 27 (1955)
ATPase	ATP → AMP + $2P_i$	Thoracic muscle of flying insects	Mg^{++}, GSH	7.8-8.0	I, II, 597
ATPase	ATP + H_2O → ADP + P_i	Rabbit muscle	Mg^{++}	6.8-7.0	I, II, 588
ATPase	ATP + H_2O → ADP + P_i	Mitochondria (mouse liver)	Mg^{++}	8.5	I, II, 593

Enzyme	Reaction	Source	Cofactor	pH	Reference
ATPase myosin*	ATP + H₂O → ADP + Pi	Rabbit skeletal muscle	Ca^{++}	6.5-9.2	I, *II*, 582
ATP-Creatine transphosphorylase*	ATP + Cr → ADP + Cr~P	Rabbit back and leg muscles	Mg^{++} or Mn^{++}	6-9	I, *II*, 605
Barbiturase	Barbituric + 2H₂O → Urea + Malonic	*Mycobacteria*	—	8-9	I, *II*, 492
Benzaldehyde dehydrogenase	Benzaldehyde → Benzoic	Aerobic bacteria	DPN^+ TPN^+	DPN^+-8.5 TPN^+-9.0	I, *II*, 280
Benzoylformic carboxylase	Benzoylformic → Benzaldehyde + CO₂	Aerobic bacteria	TPP	6.0-6.5	I, *II*, 278
Betaine-homocysteine transmethylase	Betaine + Homocysteine → Methionine + Dimethylglycine	Rat liver	Unknown cofactor	7.8	II, *222*, 537 (1955)
Biotin oxidase	Biotin oxidation	Pig kidney cortex	—	—	I, *II*, 631
Bromelin	Proteolytic	Pineapple	—	—	II, *127*, 643 (1939)
Butyryl dehydrogenase	AcylCoA → α,β-Unsat. acyl CoA (trans.)	Beef liver	FAD	7.0	I, *II*, 553
Canavaninosuccinase	Canavanine + Fumarate → Canavaninosuccinic	Hog kidney, jack bean meal	—	6.5	VI, *59*, 233 (1955)
Carbamyl phosphate-aspartate transcarbamylase	L-Aspartate + Carbamyl P → Carbamylaspartate	Liver	—	9.2	IV, *63*, 11p (1956)
Carbonic anhydrase	CO₂ + H₂O ⇌ H₂CO₃	Red cells, leaf tissue	Zn^{++}	10	I, *II*, 836
α-Carboxylase	RCOCOOH → RCHO + CO₂	Wheat germ, yeast	TPP, Mg^{++}	6.3	I, *I*, 465
			TPP, Mg^{++}	6.0	I, *I*, 460
Carboxylating enzyme	Ribulose diP → 2,3-PGA	Plant bacteria	Mg^{++}, SH	8	II, *218*, 795 (1956)
Carboxymethylcellulase	Hydrolysis of CMC	Rumen microorganisms	—	—	IV, *65*, 23p (1957)
Carboxypeptidase*	Exopeptidase	Beef pancreas	Zn^{++}	7.5	II, *223*, 457 (1956)
Carnosinase	Dipeptidase activity	Swine kidney	Mn^{++}	8.0	I, *II*, 93
Catalase*	H₂O₂ → H₂O + ½O₂	Liver	—	6.8	I, *II*, 775
Cathepsin	Peptide bond hydrolysis	Animal tissues	—	5	II, *218*, 59 (1956)
Cathepsin B	Peptide bond hydrolysis	Spleen	SH	4.2-5.8	II, *226*, 173 (1957)
Cathepsin C	Proteinase	Beef spleen	Cysteine	5	I, *II*, 64
	Transamidation	Beef spleen	Cysteine	7.4	I, *I*, 64
Cellobiase	Cellobiose hydrolysis	Snails, *A. oryzae*	—	4-5	I, *I*, 177
Cellulase	Cellulose → Glucose	Snails	—	5.2	I, *I*, 173
		M. verrucaria	—	5.4	II, *218*, 131 (1956)

Enzyme	Reaction	Source	Prosthetic group / Cofactor	pH	Reference
Cholesterol dehydrogenase	Cholesterol + $\frac{1}{2}O_2 \rightarrow$ Cholestenene-3-one	Myobacteria	—	6.5–9	I, I, 678
Choline acetylase	Acetyl CoA $\rightarrow$ Choline $\rightarrow$ Acetyl choline	Squid ganglia	CoA, Mg^{++}	7.0	I, I, 619
Choline dehydrogenase	Choline $\rightarrow$ Choline Aldehyde	Rat liver mitochondria	—	6.8	IV, 60, 644 (1955)
Choline esterase	Acetyl choline $\rightarrow$ Acetic + Choline	Electric eel	Mg^{++}	—	II, 168, 223 (1947)
Chymotrypsin*	Endopeptidase	Beef pancreas	—	6.5	I, II, 8
Citritase	Citric $\rightarrow$ Oxaloactate + Acetate	A. aerogenes	Mg^{++}	7.5–8.5	V, 19, 567 (1956)
Citrullinase	Citrulline $\rightarrow$ Ornithine + NH_3 + CO_2	Bacterial cells	Mg^{++}, AMP, P	6.2	I, II, 376
Citrulline synthetase	Ornithine + CO_2 + $NH_3 \rightarrow$ Citrulline	Rat liver	Mg^{++}, ATP	7.2	I, II, 350
CoA transferase	Succinyl CoA + Acetoacetic $\rightarrow$ Succinate + Acetoacetyl CoA	Pig heart	—	9	II, 221, 15 (1956)
CoA transphorase	Butyryl CoA + Acetate $\rightleftharpoons$ Butyrate + Acetyl CoA	Cl. kluyveri	—	6.8	I, I, 599
Condensing enzyme*	Acetyl CoA + OAA $\rightarrow$ CoA + Citric	Pig heart	—	7.4	I, I, 685
Convertin	Prothrombin conversion	Blood	—	7.3–7.4	I, II, 155
Creatine phosphokinase	ATP + Cr $\rightarrow$ CrP + ADP	Rabbit muscle	—	9	II, 209, 191, 203 (1954)
Crotonase*	Crotonyl CoA $\rightarrow$ β-Hydroxybutyryl CoA	Liver	—	9.4	II, 218, 971 (1956)
Cyanase	HCNO + $H_2O \rightarrow NH_3$ + CO_2	Wheat germ	—	6.8	Chem. Abstr. 51, 1147 (1957)
Cystathionine cleavage enzyme	Cystathionine $\rightarrow$ Cysteine + NH_3 + α-Ketobutyric	Liver	**Citric, SH**	9–10	I, II, 311
Cysteine desulfhydrase	Cysteine $\rightarrow H_2S$ + Pyruvic + NH_3	E. coli, liver	Pyridoxal P	7.8	VII, 70, 735 (1956)
		Liver	Pyridoxal P	7.4–7.6	I, II, 315
Cysteine sulfinic decarboxylase	Cysteine sulfinic $\rightarrow$ Hypotaurine + CO_2	Liver	Pyridoxal P. SH	—	V, 23, 624 (1957)
Cytochromes a, a₁, a₂, a₃ (a₃ = oxidase)	Terminal respiration	Heart muscle, etc.	Heme prosthetic group	ca. 7	I, II, 732
Cytochrome b group	Terminal respiration	Yeast, bacteria	Heme prosthetic group	ca. 7	I, II, 744
Cytochrome b₂	Terminal respiration; lactic ox.	Yeast	Heme prosthetic group	7.4	VI, 56, 487 (1955)
Cytochrome c*	Terminal respiration	Heart muscle, yeast	Heme prosthetic group, Fe	7.4	I, II, 749, VIII, 44, 453 (1957)
Cytochrome c₁	Terminal respiration	Heart muscle	Heme prosthetic group	—	IX, 176, 200 (1955)
Cytochrome c peroxidase	Leucochlorophenol + $H_2O_2 \rightarrow$ Chlorophenol Light	P. fluorescens	—	7.0	II, 220, 967 (1956)

Enzyme	Reaction	Source	Cofactor	pH	Reference
Cytochrome c photooxidase	Cytochrome c FeII + O₂ → Cytochrome c FeIII	Spinach chloroplasts	—	7	XI, _125_, 353 (1957)
Cytochrome c reductase	DPNH + 2 Cytochrome c FeIII → DPN⁺ + 2 Cytochrome c FeII	Rabbit muscle	—	7.5	II, _222, 497_ (1956)
	DPNH + 2 Cytochrome c FeIII → DPN⁺ + 2 Cytochrome c FeII	Pig heart	—	8.5	I, _II_, 688
	DPNH + 2 Cytochrome c FeIII → DPN⁺ + 2 Cytochrome c FeII	E. coli	—	8.0	I, _II_, 693
	DPNH + 2 Cytochrome c FeIII → DPN⁺ + 2 Cytochrome c FeII	Hog liver	FAD	7.8	I, _II_, 704
Cytochrome c reductase	TPNH + 2 Cytochrome c FeIII → TPN⁺ + 2 Cytochrome c FeII	Yeast	FMN	—	I, _II_, 699
Cytochrome h	Terminal respiration	Liver	FAD	7.8	I, _II_, 704
		Snail hepatopancreas	Heme prosthetic group	—	IX, _180, 427_ (1957)
Cytosine nucleoside deaminase	CR + H₂O → UR + NH₃ CDR + H₂O → UDR + NH₃	E. coli	—	—	I, _II_, 478
Dehydroascorbic reductase	DHA + 2GSH → GSSG + AA	Plant tissue	—	6.9	I, _II_, 847
5-Dehydroquinase	5-Dehydroquinic → Dehydroshikimic + H₂O	E. coli	—	8.0	V, _15_, 54 (1954)
5-Dehydroshikimic reductase	5-DHS + TPNH → Shikimic + TPN	E. coli	TPN⁺	8.5	II, _213, 787_ (1955)
Deoxyribonuclease	Hydrolysis of DNA	Beef pancreas	Mg⁺⁺	6-7	I, _II_, 437
		Spleen	—	5.2	I, _II_, 444
		Group A hemolytic streptococci	Mg⁺⁺	7.5	I, _II_, 446
		Thymus	—	7.2	I, _II_, 443
Deoxyribophosphate aldolase	DR-5-P → G-3-P + CH₃CHO	E. coli	—	6-8	I, _I_, 384
Dephospho CoA kinase	ATP + DP CoA → CoA + ADP	Pigeon liver	Mg⁺⁺	8.5	I, _II_, 649
Dephospho-CoA pyrophosphorylase	ATP + P-Panthethine → Dephospho-CoA + PP	Hog liver	Mg⁺⁺	7.5	I, _II_, 667
Desulfinases	Sulfinylpyruvic → Pyruvic + SO₂	Animal tissues	—	—	I, _II_, 333
Dextransucrase	Sucrose + Acceptor → Dextran + Fructose	_Leuconostoc mesenteroides_	—	4-6	I, _II_, 178

Enzyme	Reaction	Source	Cofactor	pH	Reference
Diacetylmethylcarbinol synthetase	2 Diacetyl → Diacetylmethylcarbinol + Acetic	Micrococcus ureae	TPP, Mn++	6-8	VII, 72, 746 (1956)
Dialkylphosphofluoridases	Dialkylfluoro P → Dialkyl P + HF	Hog kidney	Mn++	7.5-8	I, II, 651
Diamine oxidase	Histamine + O_2 → RCHO + NH_3 + H_2O_2	Hog kidney	—	7.2	I, II, 394
Diaminopimelic decarboxylase	Mesodiaminopimelic → L-Lysine + CO_2	E. coli	—	8.5	IV, 65, 448 (1957)
Diaminopimelic racemase	LL-Diaminopimelic → Mesodiaminopimelic	E. coli	GSH	7.7-8.3	IV, 65, 448 (1957)
Diaphorases	DPNH + A + H+ → DPN+ + AH_2	Pig heart	FAD	7.2	IV, 67, 147 (1957)
Diaryl pyrophosphatase	Aryl-P-P aryl → 2 Aryl-P	Pig liver	—	7-8	VIII, 43, 683 (1956)
Dihydro-orotic dehydrogenase	Orotate + DPNH → Dihydro-orotate + DPN	Zymobacterium oroticum	DPNH	6.5	V, 12, 223 (1953)
Dihydrouracil dehydrogenase	Dihydrouracil + DPN+ → Uracil + DPNH	Cl. uracilicum	DPN+	7.4-7.8	II, 227, 693 (1957)
DPNase	NRPPRA + H_2O → N + RPPRA	Beef spleen	—	7.2	I, II, 660
DPNase		Neurospora crassa	—	3-9	I, II, 664
DPNH oxidase	DPNH + $\frac{1}{2}O_2$ → DPN+ + H_2O	Pig heart	—	10-10.5	II, 213, 951 (1955)
DPN kinase	ATP + DPN+ → TPN+ + ADP	Pigeon liver	Mg++	7.5	I, II, 652
DPN pyrophosphorylase	NMN + ATP → DPN+ + PP	Rat liver. yeast	Mg++	7.4	I, II, 670
Elastase	Elastin breakdown	Hog pancreas		8.8	II, 222, 705 (1956)
Enolase*	2-PGA → PEP + H_2O	Brewer's yeast	Divalent cations	7.2	I, II, 427
Esterases	Methyl butyrate → Butyric + Methanol	Horse liver	—	8.0	I, II, 657
ETF (electron transferring flavoprotein)	Reduced fatty acyl dehydrog. + ETF → Oxidized fatty acyl dehydrogenase + Reduced ETF	Pig liver	FAD	7.0	II, 218, 717 (1956)
Fatty acid peroxidase	Palmitate → CO_2 + RCHO	Cotyledons of germinating seeds	—	6.3	II, 222, 643 (1956)
Fatty acid synthesis system	Synthesis of fatty acids from acetate	Beef liver	Several, see Chapter 25	—	V, 24, 453 (1957)
Fibrinogen	Fibrinogen → Fibrin	Blood	—	6.4-6.6	I, II, 158
Ficin*	Endopeptidase	Fig tree	SH	4-9	I, II, 61
FAD pyrophosphorylase	FMN + ATP → FAD + PP	Yeast	Mg++	7.5	I, II, 673
Flavin-linked aldehyde oxidase	RCHO + 3OH- → RCO_2^- + $2H_2O$ + 2e	Pig liver	—	7-8	I, I, 523
Flavin peroxidase	DPNH + H+ + H_2O_2 → DPN + $2H_2O$	S. faecalis	FAD	5.4	II, 225, 557 (1957)
Flavokinase	Riboflavin + ATP → FMN + ADP	Brewer's yeast	Mg++	7.8-8.5	I, II, 640
Folic acid conjugase	Folic conjugates → Folic acid activity	Chicken pancreas	—	7-8	I, II, 629

Enzyme	Reaction	Source	Cofactor	pH	Reference
Formaldehyde dehydrogenase	$DPN^+ + H_2CO \rightarrow HCOOH + DPNH + H^+$	Beef liver	DPN^+, GSH	7.9–8.2	II, *213*, 447 (1955)
Formic dehydrogenase	$DPN^+ + HCOOH \rightarrow DPNH + CO_2 + H^+$	Dried pea seeds	DPN^+	5.5–8.0	I, *I*, 536
Formic hydrogenlyase	$HCOOH \rightarrow H_2 + CO_2$	E. coli	Fe^{++}, Mn^{++}	6.0–6.2	I, *I*, 539
Formyl-L-glutamic deformylase	Formyl-glutamic → Glutamic + Formic	Liver	—	—	VIII, *41*, 771 (1954)
β-Fructofuranosidase (invertase)	Fructosyl transfer to H_2O or sugar acceptor	Yeast	—	4.5–5.5	I, *I*, 251
Fructokinase	Fructose + ATP → F-1-P + ADP	Beef liver	Mg^{++}	5.5–7.8	V, *8*, 416 (1952)
Fructose-1,6-diphosphatase	$FDP + H_2O \rightarrow F-6-P + P$	Rabbit muscle	—	—	I, *I*, 289
Fumarase*	$Fumarate + H_2O \rightarrow Malate$	Rabbit liver	Mg^{++}	9.5	II, *221*, 909 (1956)
Fumarylacetoacetate hydrolase	Fumarylacetoacetate → Fumarate + Acetoacetate	Pig heart	—	6–7.5	I, *I*, 729
		Rat liver	—	—	I, *II*, 298
Galactitol dehydrogenase	Polyol → Keto-sugar	Pseudomonas sp.	DPN^+	10	IV, *64*, 394 (1956)
Galactokinase	Galactose + ATP → ADP + Galactose-1-P	Galactose adapted yeast	Mg^{++}	6.0	I, *I*, 290
α-Galactosidase	Melibiose → Hexose	Sweet almond emulsin	—	3.5–5.3	I, *I*, 249
β-Galactosidase*	β-Galactosides hydrolysed	E. coli	Na^+	7.3	I, *I*, 241
Gluconic dehydrogenase	Gluconic + ½O_2 → 2-Ketogluconic	P. aeruginosa	Dye	5.6	V, *17*, 122 (1955)
Gluconokinase	Gluconate + ATP → Gluconate 6-P + ADP	E. coli (B), yeast	Mg^{++}	7.2	I, *I*, 352
Gluconolactonase	Gluconolactone → Gluconate	Baker's yeast	Mg^{++}	6.0	II, *212*, 677 (1955)
Glucosamine-6-P acetylase	Gluconolactone-6-P → Gluconic-6-P Acetyl CoA + Glucosamine-6-P → N-acetylglucosamine-6-P + CoA	Yeast	—	7.5	V, *16*, 429 (1955)
Glucosamine 6-P deaminase	Glucosamine 6-P → NH_3 + Fructose 6-P	E. coli	—	7.9	V, *21*, 193 (1956)
		Hog kidney	Mg^{++}	6.2	II, *225*, 125 (1957)
		P. fluorescens	Mg^{++}	7.4	II, *220*, 45 (1956)
Glucose dehydrogenase	Glucose + DPN^+ → Gluconate + DPNH	Liver	DPN^+	9.8	I, *I*, 335
Glucose oxidase	Glucose + H_2O + O_2 → Gluconic + H_2O_2	Penicillium notatum	FAD	5.6	I, *I*, 340
Glucose 6-phosphatase	Glucose-6-P → Glucose + P_i	Liver	—	6.5	I, *II*, 541
Glucose 6-P dehydrogenase	Glucose-6-P → Gluconic-6-P	Leuconostoc	DPN^+, TPN^+	7.8	I, *I*, 330

Enzyme	Reaction	Source	Activators/Cofactors	pH	Reference
Glucose 6-P dehydrogenase (Zwischenferment)	Glucose-6-P → Gluconic-6-P	Brewer's yeast	TPN⁺	8.5	II, *216*, 67 (1956)
Glucose 1-P kinase	G-1-P + ATP → G-1,6-diP	Yeast	Mn⁺⁺	6.8	I, *I*, 354
Glucose 1-P transphosphorylase	2 G-1-P → G-1,6-diP + glucose	Rabbit muscle	—	7.6	II, *222*, 89 (1956)
β-Glucosidase	Hydrolysis of glucosides	Sweet almond emulsin	Anions, cations	5.0	I, *I*, 234
Glucosidase, oligo-1,6	Hydrolysis of 1,6 linkages	Hog small intestines	—	6.2	II, *215*, 723 (1955)
β-Glucuronidase	Hydrolysis of β-Glucuronides	Calf liver	—	5.0	I, *I*, 262
Glucuronolactone decarboxylase	Glucuronolactone → CO₂ + Pentose	Rat kidney	Mg⁺⁺, ATP, UTP, DPN⁺, TPP	7.0	V, *23*, 289 (1957)
Glutamic decarboxylase	Glutamic → Aminobutyric + CO₂	Plants	Pyridoxal P	5.5-5.8	I, *II*, 190
Glutamic dehydrogenase*	Glutamic → Ketoglutaric + NH₃	Beef liver	DPN⁺	8.5-8.6	I, *II*, 220
		Chicken liver	DPN⁺	8.0	II, *223*, 271 (1956)
Glutamic racemase	L-Glutamic → DL-Glutamic ← D-Glutamic	L. arabinosus	Pyridoxal P	6.8	I, *II*, 215
Glutamic semi-CHO reductase	Glutamic semi-CHO → Proline	Rat liver	DPN⁺	6.6-7.0	II, *226*, 317 (1957)
Glutamic synthetase	Glutamic + NH₃ + ATP → Glutamine + ADP + P	Pea seed, brain	Mg⁺⁺	7.3	I, *II*, 337
Glutaminase	Glutamine → Glutamic + NH₃	E. coli	—	4.7-5.1	I, *II*, 380
Glutamyl transferase	Glutamine + NH₂OH → Glutamohydroxamate + NH₃	Sheep brain, pig liver	Mn⁺⁺, ATP	5.5	I, *II*, 269
Glutamyl transpeptidase	Transpeptidation reaction	Beef kidney cortex	Fe⁺⁺	8.5	II, *221*, 895 (1956)
Glutathione reductase	GSSG + TPNH → TPN + 2GSH	Wheat germ	TPN⁺	7.8	I, *II*, 719
		Liver or yeast	TPN⁺	7.6	I, *II*, 722
		E. coli	TPN⁺, FAD	6.9	II, *213*, 77 (1955)
Glutathione synthetase	Glutamylcysteine + Glycine → GSH	Brewer's yeast	ATP, Mg⁺⁺, K⁺	8.3	II, *213*, 825, 813 (1955)
Glutathione-homocysteine transhydrogenase	GSH + Hcystine → GSSG + Hcysteine	Beef liver	DPN⁺	—	II, *217*, 867 (1955)
Glyceraldehyde 3-P dehydrogenase	GAP → PGA	Muscle	DPN⁺, (Pᵢ)	9.0	I, *I*, 401
		Yeast	DPN⁺, (Pᵢ)	8.3-8.5	I, *I*, 407
		Sugar beet leaf	TPN⁺, (no Pᵢ)	8.3-8.6	II, *217*, 361 (1955)
Glyceric kinase	Glyceric + ATP → 3PGA + ADP	Horse liver	Mg⁺⁺	7.4-7.7	II, *225*, 949 (1957)
Glycerol Dehydrogenase	Glycerol → Dihydroxyacetone	A. aerogenes	DPN⁺	6.8-11	I, *I*, 397
α-Glycerol phosphate dehydrogenase	DHAP + DPNH → L-α-glycerol P + DPN⁺	Rabbit muscle	DPN⁺	7.5	I, *I*, 391

Enzyme	Reaction	Source	Cofactor	pH	Reference
Glycerolphosphorylcholine diesterase	$GPC \rightarrow GP$ + Choline	Nerve tissue	Mn^{++}	9.5	IV, *65*, 374 (1957)
Glycine-glyoxylate transaminase	Amino acid + Glyoxylate $\rightarrow$ Glycine + Keto acid	Pseudomonad strain 2RCC-1	Pyridoxal P	8-9	VII, *71*, 81 (1956)
Glycine oxidase	Glycine $\rightarrow$ Glyoxylic + NH_3	Rat kidney	FAD	8.3	I, *II*, 225
Glycocyamine-P-kinase	Glycocyamine $\rightarrow$ P-Glycocyamine	*N. diversicolor*	ATP	7.1-8.9	*Chem. Abstr.*, *51*, 12169 (1957)
Glycolic oxidase	Glycolic $\rightarrow$ Glyoxylic + H_2O_2	Spinach leaves	FMN	8.3	I, *I*, 528
Glycylglycine dipeptidase	Hydrolysis of glycylglycine	Rat muscle	Co^{++}	7.6	I, *II*, 107
Glycyl-l-leucine dipeptidase	Hydrolysis of peptide	Intestinal mucosa	Zn^{++}, P_i	7.8	I, *II*, 105
Glyoxylase I	Keto-aldehyde + GSH $\rightarrow$ Thioester	Baker's yeast	—	6-8	I, *I*, 454
Glyoxylase II	Thioester $\rightarrow$ Hydroxyacid $\rightarrow$ GSH	Beef liver	—	6.6	I, *I*, 458
Glyoxylic reductase	Glyoxylate $\rightarrow$ Glycolic	Tobacco leaves	DPN^+	6.4	I, *I*, 532
Guanase	Guanine + H_2O $\rightarrow$ Xanthine + NH_3	Rat liver	—	6-10	I, *II*, 480
Guanidinobutyramidase	Guanidinobutyramide $\rightarrow$ Guanidinobutyric + NH_3	*S. griseus*	—	6.5	*Chem. Abstr.*, *51*, 10605 (1957)
Guanidoacetic methylpherase	S-Adenosylmethionine + Guanidinoacetic $\rightarrow$ Creatine + S-Adenosylhomocysteine	Liver	GSH	7.5	I, *II*, 260
Hexokinase*	Hexose + ATP $\rightarrow$ Hexose-6-P + ADP	Animal tissue	Mg^{++}	6-8	I, *I*, 277
	Hexose + ATP $\rightarrow$ Hexose-6-P + ADP	Yeast	Mg^{++}	8-9	I, *I*, 269
Hippuric acid synthetase	S-Benzoyl CoA + Glycine $\rightarrow$ Hippuric acid + CoA	Liver	ATP, Mg^{++}	—	I, *II*, 346
Histidase	l-Histidine $\rightarrow$ Urocanic acid + NH_3	*P. fluorescens*	—	7-9.5	I, *II*, 228
Histidine decarboxylase	Histidine $\rightarrow$ Histamine + CO_2	*Cl. welchii*	—	4.5	I, *II*, 187
Histidinol phosphatase	Histidinol P $\rightarrow$ Histidinol + P	*N. crassa*	—	9.0	II, *226*, 583 (1957)
Homocysteine desulfhydrase	Homocysteine $\rightarrow$ α-Ketobutyric + NH_3 + H_2S	Rat liver	Pyridoxal P	7.5	I, *II*, 318
Homogentisate oxidase	Homogentisate + O_2 $\rightarrow$ Maleylacetoacetate	Rat liver	Fe^{++}	—	I, *II*, 292
Homoserine dehydrogenase	Aspartic β-semi CHO $\rightarrow$ Homoserine	Yeast	—	6.8	II, *213*, 51 (1955)
Homoserine kinase	l-Homoserine + ATP $\rightarrow$ O-Phosphohomo-serine + ADP	Yeast	Mg^{++}	7-7.5	VIII, *44*, 299 (1957)
Hyaluronidase	Hydrolysis of hyaluronic acid	Bull testes	—	—	I, *I*, 166
Hydrazine dehydrogenase	Hydrazine oxidation	*P. savitum* seedlings	—	—	*Chem. Abstr.*, *51*, 14910 (1957)
Hydrogenase	$H_2 \rightarrow 2H^+$ + 2e	*D. desulfuricans*	Fe^{++}, SH	7.4-8.6	V, *19*, 440 (1956)
		Cl. butylicum	Fe^{++}, Mo, FAD	5.2	VII, *73*, 569 (1957)

Enzyme	Reaction	Source	Activators, coenzymes	pH	Reference
Hydrolase (riboflavin)	Riboflavin → Lumichrome + Ribitol	Pseudomonas	—	5.8-7.0	II, *221*, 593 (1956)
Hydropyrimidine hydrase	Carbamyl β-Analine → Hydrouracil	Calf liver	Mg^{++}	5.5	II, *226*, 277 (1957)
L(+)β-Hydroxy acyl dehydrogenase	L(+)βOH acyl CoA → β-Keto acyl CoA	Pig liver	DPN^+ or TPN^+	6-8	V, *26*, 448 (1957)
Hydroxyisobutyric dehydrogenase*	β-HO butyric + DPN^+ → Methylmalonate-semi CHO + DPNH + H^+	Pig kidney	SH	9.0	II, *225*, 511 (1957)
Hydroxylamine reductase	NH_2OH + DPNH + H^+ → NH_3 + DPN + H_2O	N. crassa	FAD	8-9	I, *II*, 416
p-Hydroxyphenylpyruvate enol-keto tautomerase	HO C_6H_4 $CH_2COCOOH$ → HO C_6H_4 CH=COHCOOH	Pig liver	Fe^{++}, Cu^{++}	6.2	I, *II*, 289
Hydroxyphenylpyruvate oxidase	Hydroxyphenylpyruvate → Homogentisate	Beef liver	—	5.5-7.0	II, *225*, 935 (1957)
Imidazoleacetol-P transaminase	Histidinol-P + α-KG → Imidazoleacetol-P + Glutamic	N. crassa	Pyridoxal P	8.1	II, *220*, 113 (1956)
Iminodipeptidase	Hydrolysis of N-terminal L-proline or HO proline peptides	Swine kidney	Mn^{++}, Cd^{++}	8.0	I, *II*, 97
Inosinediphosphatase	IDP → IMP + P_i	Beef liver	Mg^{++}	6.9	II, *217*, 235 (1955)
Inosine-5-P-dehydrogenase	I-5'-P → X-5'-P	A. aerogenes	K^+, NH_4^+, DPN^+, SH	8.1	II, *226*, 339 (1957)
Inositol dehydrogenase	Myo- inositol → Monoketone	A. aerogenes	DPN^+	7.4-9	VI, *60*, 352 (1956)
Insulinase	Hydrolysis of insulin	Pancreas	—	—	III, *79*, 755 (1957)
Isocitric dehydrogenase (DPN)	D-Isocitric acid → α-Ketoglutaric + CO_2	Beef liver	Mn^{++}, Mg^{++}, DPN^+	6.5	I, *I*, 710
	D-Isocitric acid → α-Ketoglutaric + CO_2	Yeast	Mn^{++}, Mg^{++}, AMP, DPN^+	7.5	I, *I*, 707
Isocitric dehydrogenase (TPN)	D-Isocitric acid → α-Ketoglutaric + CO_2 (Oxalosuccinate intermediate)	Yeast	Mg^{++}, Mn^{++}, TPN^+	—	I, *I*, 705
	D-Isocitric acid → α-Ketoglutaric + CO_2	Pig heart	TPN^+, Mn^{++}	7-7.5	I, *I*, 699
Isocitritase	Isocitrate → Succinate + Glyoxylate	P. aeruginosa	Mg^{++}, SH	7.6	V, *19*, 567 (1956)
α-Keto acid ω amidase	$H_2NCO(CH_2)_2COCOOH$ → α-Keto acid + NH_3	Rat liver	—	8.5-9.5	I, *II*, 384 (1955)
β-Ketoacyl reductase	Acetoacetyl CoA + DPNH + H^+ → β-HO-butyryl CoA + DPN	Liver	DPNH	—	I, *I*, 566
β-Ketoacyl thiolase	Acetoacetyl CoA + CoASH → 2 Acetyl CoA	Heart	—	—	I, *I*, 581
α-Ketogluco kinase	α-Ketogluconic + ATP → 6-P-α-Ketogluconic	P. fluorescens	Mg^{++}	7.4	II, *220*, 45 (1956)
α-Ketoglutaric dehydrogenase	α-KG + DPN^+ + CoASH → Succinyl CoA + CO_2 + DPNH	Pig hearts	TPP, Lipoic, DPN^+	—	I, *I*, 714
2-Ketophosphogluconate reductase	2-K-6-PG + H^+ + TPNH → TPN^+ + 6PG	A. cloacae	TPN^+	—	Naturwiss. *42*, 584 (1955)

Enzyme	Reaction	Source	Cofactor	pH	Reference
Kynureninase	L-Kynurenine → Anthranilic acid + Alanine	P. fluorescens	Pyridoxal P	8.5	I, II, 249
	L-Kynurenine → Anthranilic acid + Alanine	Liver	Pyridoxal P	8.0	I, II, 249
Kynurenine formamidase (formylase)	Formylkynurenine → Formic + Kynurenine	Liver	—	6–8	I, II, 246
Kynurenine transaminase	Kynurenine + Keto acid → Amino acid + Kynurenic acid	N. crassa	Pyridoxal P	7.5	II, 221, 689 (1956)
Laccase	Oxidation of polyphenols	Latex	Cu	6.5	IX, 163, 480 (1949)
Lactase	Lactose → Glucose + Galactose	Calf intestine	None	5.5–6.0	V, 9, 283 (1952)
Lactic dehydrogenase*	L(+)-Lactate + DPN^+ → Pyruvate + DPNH + H^+	Heart muscle	DPN^+	7–10	I, I, 448
Lactic dehydrogenase*	L-Lactate + A → Pyruvate + AH_2	Yeast	—	5.2–8.0	I, I, 444
Lactic dehydrogenase	Pyruvate + DPNH + H^+ → Lactate + DPN^+	Rabbit muscle	DPN^+	—	I, I, 441
Lactic oxidative decarboxylase	Lactate + O_2 → Acetate + CO_2	Mycobacterium pheli	FMN	5.6–6.0	II, 216, 749 (1955)
Lactonizing and lactone-splitting enzyme	cis, cis, muconic acid → Ketoadipic acid	Aerobic bacteria	Mg^{++} or Mn^{++}	7–8	I, II, 282
Lactoperoxidase*	Oxidation of phenols and aromatic amines (H_2O_2 present)	Skim milk	—	—	I, II, 813
Leucine aminopeptidase	Hydrolysis of amino acids	Swine kidney	Mn^{++}	8–8.5	II, 212, 255 (1955)
Levansucrase	Sucrose + Acceptor → Levan + Glucose	A. levanicum	—	5.0–5.8	I, I, 186
Lipase	$RCOOR' + H_2O → RCOOH + R'OH$	Hog pancreas	Surface-active compounds, Ca^{++}	5–8	I, I, 634
Lipase	$RCOOR' + H_2O → RCOOH + R'OH$	Fusarium lini Bolley	—	7	I, I, 640
Lipoprotein lipase	Hydrolysis of triglyceride	Chicken adipose tissue	NH_4^+	8.5	II, 226, 833 (1957)
Luciferase*	DPNH + FMN + RCHO + O_2 → light or $FMNH_2$ + RCHO + O_2 → light	Luminiscent bacteria	FMN	6.8	I, II, 857
Luciferase	Luciferin → light (hν)	Photinus pyralis (firefly)	Mg^{++}, ATP	7.8	V, 20, 170 (1956)
ε-Lysine acylase	ε-Acetyl lysine → Lysine + Acetic	Rat kidney	—	7–7.02	VI, 69, 56 (1957)
L-Lysine decarboxylase	Lysine → CO_2 + Cadaverine	E. coli	Pyridoxal phosphate	—	VI, 53, 354 (1954)
Lysozyme*	Hyaluronic acid hydrolysis	Papaya latex	—	4.65	II, 215, 67 (1955)
Maleylacetoacetate isomerase	Maleylacetoacetate → Fumarylacetoacetate	Rat liver	GSH	8.5–9.0	I, II, 205
Malic dehydrogenase	L-Malate + DPN^+ → Oxalo-acetate + DPNH + H^+	Pig heart	DPN^+	—	I, I, 735
"Malic" enzyme	L-Malate ⇌ L-Lactate + CO_2 (1) Oxaloacetate → Pyruvate + CO_2 (2)	L. arabinosus	Mn^+, DPN^+	4.5–6.0	I, I, 748

Enzyme	Reaction	Requirement	pH	Reference
"Malic" enzyme	L-Malate + TPN^+ ⇌ Pyruvate + CO_2 + TPNH (1); Oxaloacetate → Pyruvate + CO_2 (2)	TPN, Mn^{++}	(1) 7.3 (2) 4.5–5.2	I, I, 739
Malic synthetase	Acetyl CoA + Glyoxalate → Malic + CoA	—	8.0	III, 78 3230 (1956)
Maltase	Maltose → 2 Glucose	—	6.3–7.2	II, 225, 899 (1957)
Maltose phosphorylase	D-Maltose + P_i ⇌ β-D-Glucose-1-P + Glucose	—	6.5	I, I, 229
L(+)Mandelic acid dehydrogenase	$C_6H_5CHOHCOOH$ + ½O_2 → $C_6H_5COCOOH$ + H_2O		—	I, II, 277
D(−)Mandelic acid racemase	$D(-)C_6H_5CHOHCOOH$ ⇌ $L(+)C_6H_5CHOHCOOH$		—	I, II, 276
D-Mannitol-1-P dehydrogenase	Mannitol-1-P + DPN^+ → F-6-P + DPNH + H^+	DPN^+	10	II, 218, 849 (1956)
Mannitol-P dehydrogenase	F-6-P + DPNH + H^+ → DPN^+ + Mannitol-1-P	—	6–9	I, I, 346
Mannose isomerase	Mannose → Fructose	SH	7.5	II, 218, 535 (1956)
Metaphosphatase	Hydrolysis of polyphosphate	Divalent metals	4.5–5.7	I, II, 577
Metaphosphate synthetase	$XATP + [(PO_3^-)_n] \rightarrow XADP + (PO_3^-)_n$	Mg^{++}	7.2	V, 20, 215 (1956); Chem. Ab. 49, 5540 (1955)
Methioninase	L-Methionine → NH_3 + Mercaptan + α-Oxobutyric	—	—	—
Methionine activating enzyme	L-Methionine + ATP → S-Adenosylmethionine + 3P_i	SH, Mg^{++}	7.4	I, II, 254
Methylase, serine HO	Serine → Glycine + CH_2O	DPN^+, TPN^+, GSH, Pyridoxal P, Folic	7.5	II, 224, 435 (1957)
Migratase	β → α Fatty acid migration, Lysolecithin	—	6.0	II, 226, 789 (1957)
Mucopolysaccharase	Hyaluronate hydrolysis	—	5.1	II, 226, 267 (1957)
Mutarotase	α,β-Glucose → Equilibrium mixture	—	5.6	V, 50, 341 (1952)
Mutase, di-P-glyceric	1,3 di-P-GA → 2,3 di-P-GA	3-PGA	7.2	I, I, 425
Myeloperoxidase	Peroxidation of dyes, etc.	—	—	I, II, 794
Neuraminase	Neuraminylgalactose(amine) → Neuraminic acid + Galactose(amine)	—	6	V, 23, 645 (1957)
New yellow enzyme	H^+ + TPNH + N.Y.E. → TPN^+ + Leuco enzyme	FAD	7.4	I, II, 715
Nicotinamide methyl pherase	S-Adenosyl methionine + Nicotinamide → N-Methylnicotinamide	—	5.1	I, II, 257
Nicotinamide riboside phosphorylase	Nicotinamide riboside + P_i → Nicotinamide + Ribose-1-P	—	8	I, II, 454
Nitrate reductase	Organic nitrate esters $\xrightarrow{\text{GSH}}$ Inorganic NO_3	—	7–8	I, II, 403
Nitrate reductase	$TPNH + H^+ + NO_3^- \rightarrow TPN^+ + NO_2^- + H_2O$	FAD	7	I, II, 411

(Organisms, as listed: Pigeon liver; Wheat germ; E. coli; Equine serum, N. meningitidis; P. fluorescens; Aerobic bacteria; E. coli; E. coli; P. saccharophila; Yeast, animal tissue; E. coli; Pseudomonas; Liver; Beef liver; Pancreas; Bovine testes; P. notatum; Erythrocytes; Empyema; V. cholerae, Flu virus; Yeast; Liver; Liver; Liver; Neurospora.)

Enzyme	Reaction	Source	Cofactor	pH	Reference
Nitric oxide reductase	$NO \rightarrow N_2$	P. stutzeri	TPNH or DPNH; FAD; Cu++ or Fe+++	7	II, 218, 627 (1956)
Nitrite reductase	Nitrite → Hydroxylamine	A. agile	TPNH or DPNH; FAD	7.1	VII, 73, 553 (1957)
Nitroethane oxidase	$C_2H_5NO_2 + O_2 + H_2O \rightarrow C_2H_4O + HNO_2 + H_2O_2$	N. crassa	—	7.0	I, II, 400
Nitro reductase	Chloramphenicol; p-Nitrobenzene → Arylamine	E. coli E26	FMN, Mn++	—	II, 223, 285 (1956)
Nucleosidases	$PuR' + H_2O \rightarrow {Pu \atop Py} + R'$ PyR'	L. pentosus	—	—	I, II, 456
Nucleoside diphosphatase	GDP (IDP, UDP) → GMP (IMP, UMP)	Pig kidney cortex	Mg++	—	V, 16, 536 (1955)
Nucleoside diphosphokinase	ATP + IDP → ITP + ADP	Yeast, rabbit muscle	—	8	IX, 172, 1008 (1953)
Nucleoside phosphorylase	Inosine + P_i → Hypoxanthine + Ribose-1-P	Calf spleen	—	7.0	I, II, 448
Nucleoside phosphorylase	4-Amino-5-imidazolecarboxamide + ribose-1-P → 5-Amino-4-imidazole carboxamide riboside	Beef liver	—	—	II, 217, 183 (1955)
Nucleoside phosphotransferase	Nucleoside + Phenylphosphate → 5-Nucleotide + Phenol	Plants, animals, bacteria	—	5-6	V, 15, 549 (1954)
Nucleoside transdeoxyribosidase	Pu-deoxyribose + Pu' → {Pu'-deoxyribose + Pu; Py-deoxyribose + Py' → Py'-deoxyribose + Py}	Various bacterial species	—	5-9	I, II, 464
Nucleotidase (3')	Nucleoside-3'-P → Nucleoside + P_i	Rye grass	—	7.5	I, II, 551
Nucleotidase (5')	5'-AMP → Adenosine + P_i	Bull seminal plasma	Mg++	8.5	I, II, 547
Nucleotidase (5')	5'-AMP → Adenosine + P_i	Snake venom	—	—	I, II, 549
Nucleotide pyrophosphatase	Nucleoside pyrophosphates → Nucleotides + P_i or PP	Maine potatoes	—	6.5-8.5	I, II, 655
Old yellow enzyme*	H+ + TPNH + Yellow enzyme → TPN + Leuco enzyme	Yeast	FMN	7.4	I, II, 712
Ornithine decarboxylase	Ornithine → Putresine + CO_2	Cl. septicum	Pyridoxal P	5.25	I, II, 189
Ornithine peptidase (amino)	L-Ornithine peptides hydrolyzed	B. brevis	Mn++, Co++	9	II, 224, 1073; (1957)
Orotate decarboxylase	O-5-P → U-5-P + CO_2	Brewer's yeast	Mg++	8.0	II, 215, 403 (1955)
Orotate pyrophosphorylase	Orotic + PRPP → O-5-P + PP	Brewer's yeast	Mg++	6-7	II, 215, 403 (1955)
Oxalic decarboxylase	Oxalic → CO_2 + Formic	C. veltipes	—	2.5-3.0	VIII, 42, 321 (1955)
Oxaloacetic (de)carboxylase	Oxaloacetic → Pyruvic + CO_2	M. lysodeikticus	Divalent cations	5-6	I, I, 753
Oxaloacetic synthesizing enzyme	$PEP + GDP + CO_2 \rightarrow OAA + GTP$ (IDP, ITP)	Liver	Mn++	7	II, 226, 1059 (1957)
Palmityl dehydrogenase	α,β Dehydrogenation of fatty acyl CoA	Pig liver	FAD	7	II, 219, 727 (1956)

Enzyme	Reaction	Source	Activator	pH	Reference
Pankrin	Protein hydrolysis	Pancreas	—	3.5-8.5	III, *78*, 5888 (1956)
Pantetheine kinase	Pantetheine → 4'-Phosphopantetheine	Pigeon liver	Mn^{++}, Mg^{++}	6.5-7.2	I, II, 633
Pantothenate-synthesizing enzyme	Pantoate + β-Alanine → Pantothenic	*Brucella abortus*	ATP, Mg^{++}	8-8.5	VI, *56*, 537 (1955)
Pantothenate-synthesizing enzyme	Pantoate + β-Alanine + ATP → Pantothenate + AMP + PP	*E. coli*	K^+, Mn^{++}	8.5	I, II, 619
Papain*	Peptide bond hydrolysis	Papaya latex	SH	7	II, *207*, 515 (1954)
Pectinesterase	Pectin + H_2O → Pectic acid + CH_3OH	Higher plants	Certain salts	4-7	I, I, 159
Penicillinase*	Penicillin + H_2O → Penicilloic acid	*B. cereus* 5/B	None	7	IV, *62*, 387 (1956)
Pentokinase	Ribose + ATP → R-5-P + ADP	Yeast	Mg^{++}	5.8-8.4	I, I, 357
Pentose isomerase	D-Arabinose ⇌ D-Ribulose / D-Xylose ⇌ D-Xylose	*E. coli*	Mn^{++} or Mg^{++}	8-8.5	I, I, 366
Pentose phosphate isomerase	Ribose-5-P ⇌ Ribulose-5-P	Yeast, pea leaves	—	7.0	I, I, 363
P enzyme	Succinyl-SCoA + ADP + P ⇌ Succinate + ATP + HSCoA	Pig heart	—	—	I, I, 718
Pepsin*	Hydrolysis of peptide bonds	Swine mucosa	—	—	I, II, 3
Peptidase (carboxy, basic)	Peptide bond hydrolysis	Pancreas	—	7.6-7.7	III, *78*, 3541 (1956)
Peroxidase*	H_2O_2 + HA → HOA + H_2O	Beef liver	—	—	I, II, 791
Peroxidase*	ROOH + AH_2 → H_2O + ROH + A	Horseradish	—	—	I, II, 801
Peroxidase	Oxidation of leuco dye by H_2O_2	Rat uterus	—	6	II, *214*, 775 (1955)
Phenolase complex	Monophenol + O_2 → Diphenol + H_2O	Mushroom	Cu^+	7	III, *77*, 2914 (1955)
Phenylalanine hydroxylase	Phenylalanine + H^+ + DPNH $\xrightarrow{O_2}$ Tyrosine + DPN^+	Rat liver	Fe^{++}	7	VI, *60*, 476 (1956)
Phosphatase, acid	P-Ester hydrolysis	Wheat	—	5.7	II, *226*, 751 (1957)
Phosphatase, acid, prostatic	ROP → ROH + P_i	Prostate glands	—	5.3-5.6	II, *216*, 81 (1955)
Phosphatase, alkaline	ROP + H_2O → ROH + P_i	Milk	Mg^{++}	9.7	IV, *60*, 573 (1955)
Phosphatase, alkaline	ROP + H_2O → P_i + ROH	Calf intestine	Mg^{++}	9.6	V, *8*, 162 (1952)
Phosphoacetylglucosamine mutase	N-Acetylglucosamine-1-P → N-Acetylglucosamine-6-P	Neurospora	Mg^{++}, Glucose-1,6-diP	7.7	II, *219*, 753 (1956)
Phosphoamidase	Amidophosphate + H_2O ⇌ NH_3 + P_i	Human semen	—	6.7	V, *16*, 162 (1955)
Phosphodiesterase	Cyclic ribomononucleotides → 3'-Mononucleotides	Calf intestine	—	7	I, II, 569
Phosphodiesterase	Hydrolysis of RNA, various dinucleotides, etc.	Spleen	—	7.0	I, II, 565
Phosphodiesterase	$R-O-P(O_2H)-O-R'$ + H_2O → $R-O-PO_2H_2$ + R'OH	Snake venom	—	9.3	I, II, 561
Phosphoglucomutase*	G-1-P ⇌ G-6-P	Rabbit muscle	Mg^{++}	—	I, I, 294
6-Phosphogluconate dehydrase	6-P-Gluconate $\xrightarrow{-H_2O}$ 2-Keto-3-deoxy-6-P-gluconate	*P. fluorescens*	Fe^{++}, GSH	8	II, *213*, 745 (1955)

Enzyme	Reaction	Source	Cofactor	pH	Reference
6-Phosphogluconic dehydrogenase	6-P-Gluconate → Ribulose-5-P + CO_2 + 2H	L. mesenteroides	DPN	7.8	I, I, 332
6-Phosphogluconic dehydrogenase	6-P-Gluconate → Ribulose-5-P + CO_2 + 2H	E. coli	TPN	7.6	IV, 65, 686 (1957)
Phosphoglucosamine isomerase	$G-NH_2-6-P$ → F-6-P + NH_3	E. coli	SH	8	VI, 66, 333 (1957)
Phosphoglucose isomerase	G-6-P ⇌ F-6-P	Muscle	—	8.6	I, I, 304 (1955)
Phosphoglucose isomerase	G-6-P ⇌ F-6-P	S. mansoni	—	8.2–8.6	II, 215, 507 (1955)
Phosphoglycerate kinase*	D-1,3-Diphosphoglycerate + ADP ⇌ D-3-Phosphoglycerate + ATP	Brewer's yeast	Mg^{++}, Mn^{++}	—	I, I, 415
3-Phosphoglyceric acid mutase*	3-PGA → 2-PGA	Baker's yeast	Mg^{++}	7.0	V, 20, 394 (1956)
3-Phosphoglyceric acid mutase*	3-PGA → 2-PGA	Rabbit muscle	2,3-diPGA	7.0	II, 223, 885 (1956)
Phosphohexokinase	F-6-P + ATP → F-1,6-diP + ADP	Rabbit muscle	Mg^{++}	—	I, I, 306
Phosphoketo-pentoepimerase	Xu-5-P ⇌ Ru-5-P	L. pentosus	—	7–8	II, 223, 993 (1956)
Phospholipase A*	Lecithin + H_2O → Lysolecithin + Unsaturated fatty acid	Venom of Crotalus terrificus	Ca^{++}	7.0	I, I, 660
Phospholipase B	Lysolecithin → GPC + Fatty acid	Liver	—	6.2	IV, 64, 192 (1956)
Phospholipase B*	Lysolecithin + H_2O → GPC + Sat'd. fatty acid	Pancreas	—	5–6	I, I, 665
Phospholipase C	Lecithin + H_2O → Diglyceride + Phosphorylcholine	Cl. welchii	Ca^{++}	6.0–7.6	I, I, 670
Phospholipase D	Lecithin + H_2O → Phosphatidic acid + Choline	Cabbage leaves	—	5.1–5.9	I, I, 672
Phospholipase D	Phospholipids → N Base + Phosphatidic acid	Cottonseed	—	5–6	II, 218, 213 (1956)
Phosphomannose isomerase	M-6-P ⇌ F-6-P	Rabbit muscle	—	5.5	I, I, 299
Phosphomonoesterase	Hydrolysis of singly esterified groups	Bone	Mg^{++}	—	I, II, 539
Phosphomonoesterase	R-O-P + H_2O → P_i + ROH	Calf intestine	Mg^{++}	—	I, II, 530
Phosphomonoesterase	Glycerol-P + H_2O → P_i + glycerol	Buttermilk	Mg^{++}	9.5–10.0	I, II, 533
Phosphomonoesterase	R-O-P ⇌ R-O-H + P_i	Yeast	Mg^{++}	6.5	II, 224, 621 (1957)
Phosphoprotein phosphatase	Protein phosphate hydrolysis	Spleen	—	6.0	IV, 65, 261 (1957)
Phosphoribomutase	R-1-P ⇌ R-5-P	Muscle	Mg^{++}	7.4	I, I, 361
Phosphoribomutase	R-1-P ⇌ R-5-P	Yeast	—	6.7–7.2	II, 215, 515 (1955)
Phosphoribomutase	R-1-P ⇌ R-5-P	Bovine uterus	—	7	V, 20, 201 (1956)

Enzyme	Reaction / Specificity	Activator / Cofactor	Source	pH	Reference
Phosphoribulokinase	Ru-5-P + ATP → RuDP + ADP	Mg++	Spinach	7.9	II, *218*, 769 (1956)
Phosphorylase a*	Specific for α-D-Glucopyranosyl-1-P, α-1,4-Maltosidic bonds in polysaccharides	—	Rabbit muscle	6.8	I, *I*, 200
Phosphorylase b*	Specific for α-D-Glucopyranosyl-1-P, α-1,4-Maltosidic bonds in polysaccharides	AMP	Rabbit muscle	—	I, *I*, 205
Phosphorylase	Glycogen + P → Glucose-1-P	AMP, IMP	Liver	6.4	II, *218*, 459 (1956)
Phosphorylase*	α-DG-1-P + Primer → K₂HPO₄ + Amylose	—	Potatoes	5.9–6.1	I, *I*, 192
Phosphorylase kinase	4ATP + 2Phb → Pha·4P + 4ADP	Mn++, ATP	Rabbit muscle	9.0	V, *20*, 150 (1956)
5'-Phosphorylribo-pyrophosphorylase	R5P + ATP → 5'P-R-PP + AMP	Mg	Pigeon liver	7.5	II, *215*, 389 (1955)
Phosphotransacetylase	Ac~P + CoA ⇌ Ac~SCoA + Pi	K+ or NH₄+	C. kluyverii	7.4–8.4	I, *I*, 596
Plasma Ac-globulin	Prothrombin → Thrombin	Thrombin	Ox blood	—	I, *II*, 151
Polygalacturonase (PG)	Hydrolysis of pectic acid	Various electrolytes	Fungi, molds	4–4.2	I, *I*, 162
Polygalacturonase	Pectic acid → Galacturonic + Digalacturonic acids	—	Yeast	3.5–4.4	II, *218*, 875 (1956)
Polygalacturonase	Cleaves polygalacturonic acid	—	S. fragilis	4.4	VI, *48*, 23 (1954)
Polynucleotide phosphorylase	nX-R-P-P ⇌ (XRP)ₙ + nP	Mg++	A. vinelandii	8.1	V, *20*, 269 (1956)
Polyol dehydrogenase (ketose reductase)	L-Xylulose → Xylitol	Pyridine nucleotides	Liver	7.4	II, *225*, 87 (1957)
Polyol dehydrogenase	Polyols → Ketoses	DPN	Pseudomonas sp.	10	IV, *64*, 394 (1956)
Polysaccharide phosphorylase	Polysaccharide + Pi ⇌ G-1-P	—	Dog liver	6.4	I, *I*, 215
Porphobilinogenase	Porphobilinogen → uroporphyrin III	—	Erythrocytes	—	IV, *67*, 8p (1957)
PR enzyme of muscle	Phosphorylase a → Phosphorylase b	—	Rabbit muscle	6.6	II, *214*, 127 (1955)
Proconvertin	Precursor of convertin	—	Oxalated human plasma	—	I, *II*, 153
Profibrinolysin	Activated enzyme dissolves clots in *vitro* & in *vivo*	—	Blood	—	I, *II*, 163
Prolidase	Hydrolysis of peptide bond lacking H atom	Mn++	Swine kidney	7.8–8.0	II, *224*, 261 (1957)
Proline racemase	D-Proline → L-Proline	SH	Cl. sticklandii	6.7–8.1	II, *228*, 983 (1957)
Proline reductase	Proline → δ-aminovaleric	Mg++	Cl. sticklandii	8.7	II, *228*, 983 (1957)
Proteinase I	Protein hydrolysis	—	Lung	4.0	II, *215*, 45, 55 (1955)
Proteinase II	Protein hydrolysis	—	Lung	8.4	II, *215*, 45 (1955)
Proteinase	Peptidase activity	SH	Tetrahymen puriformis	5–6	VI, *61*, 410 (1956)

Enzyme	Reaction	Source	Cofactor	pH	Reference
Proteinase A	Denatured protein hydrolysis	Yeast	—	3.7	II, *221*, 919 (1956)
Proteinase B	Denatured protein hydrolysis	Yeast	—	6.2	II, *221*, 919 (1956)
Prothrombin	Prothrombin → Thrombin	Blood	Thromboplastin, Ca^{++}	—	I, *II*, 140 (1955)
Protocatechuic acid oxidase	Protocatechuic acid → cis,cis-Muconic	Aerobic bacteria	—	9±	I, *II*, 284
Protocatechuic acid oxidase	Protocatechuic cis,cis-β- → Carboxy-muconic	Neurospora	Fe^{++}	7	II, *223*, 307 (1956)
Protopectinase	Protopectin → Pectin + Cellulose	Plants	—	—	I, *I*, 158
Pseudocholinesterase	Butyrylcholine hydrolysis	Brain	—	—	IV, *62*, 62 (1956)
Purine nucleosidase	PuR + H_2O → Pu + R	Yeast	—	7-8	I, *II*, 462
Purine nucleoside phosphorylase	Pu-R + P_i → R-1-P + Pu	Erythrocytes	—	6.0	II, *224*, 879 (1957)
Purine nucleoside phosphorylase	Pu-R + P_i → Pu + R-1-P	Erythrocytes	—	7.5	II, *221*, 971 (1956)
Pyridine nucleotide pyrophosphatase (reduced)	DPNH → NMNH + AMP	Liver	—	8.0-8.5	II, *226*, 427 (1957)
Pyridine nucleotide quinone reductase	DPNH + H^+ + p-Benzoquinone → DPN^+ + Hydroquinone	Pea seeds	—	6.5	I, *II*, 725
Pyridine nucleotide transhydrogenase	TPNH + DPN → TPN + DPNH (1)	P. fluorescens, beef heart	—	6-7	I, *II*, 681
	DPNH + Deamino-DPN → DPN + Deamino-DPNH (2)	Brewer's yeast	—	6.9	I, *II*, 646
Pyridoxal kinase	Pyridoxal + ATP → Pyridoxal-5-P + ADP				
Pyrocatechase	Catechol $\xrightarrow{O_2}$ cis,cis-Muconic acid	Aerobic bacteria	Fe^{++}	—	I, *II*, 281
Pyrophosphatase	PP → $2P_i$	Potato	Mg^{++}	9	IV, *60*, 215 (1955)
Pyrophosphatase	PP → $2P_i$	Potato	—	5-6	IV, *60*, 215 (1955)
Pyrophosphatase*	$HP_2O_7^{\equiv}$ + H_2O → $2HPO_4^-$ + H^+	Yeast	Mg^{++}, Co^{++}, Mn^{++}	7.0	I, *II*, 570
Pyruvate kinase	Phosphoenolpyruvate + ADP ⇌ Pyruvate + ATP	Muscle	Mg^{++}	—	I, *I*, 435
Pyruvic acid oxidase	Pyruvate + P + O_2 → Ac∼P + CO_2 + H_2O_2	L. delbruckii	—	—	I, *I*, 482
Pyruvic oxidase	Pyruvate → Acetate + CO_2 + 2H	P. vulgaris	TPP, FAD, Mg^{++}, P_i	6.0	II, *218*, 831 (1956)
Pyruvic oxidase	Pyruvate + DPN^+ + CoA ⇌ Ac∼SCoA + DPNH + H^+ + CO_2	Pig heart	—	—	I, *I*, 486
Pyruvic oxidase	Pyruvate + DPN^+ + CoA ⇌ Ac∼SCoA + CO_2 + DPNH + H^+	E. coli	—	—	I, *I*, 490
Q (branching) enzyme	Amylose → Glycogen (transglucosylation)	P. coeca	Maltosaccharides	7	X, 4051 (1953)
Q (branching) enzyme	Amylose → Glycogen (transglucosylation)	Yeast	—	7.0	IV, *63*, 16p (1956)

Enzyme	Reaction	Source	Cofactor	pH	Reference
Quinic dehydrogenase	Quinic acid + DPN⁺ → 5-Dehydroquinic acid + DPNH + H⁺	A. aerogenes	DPN	9.8	I, II, 307
Renin	Hypertensinogen → Hypertensin	Kidney	—	—	I, II, 124
Renin*	Coagulation of milk	Stomach	—	—	I, II, 69
L-Rhamnose isomerase	L-Rhamnose → L-Rhamnulose	E. coli B	—	7	VII, 73, 410 (1957)
L-Rhamnulose kinase	L-Rhamnulose + ATP → L-Rhamnulose-1-P + ADP	E. coli B	—	—	VII, 73, 415 (1957)
Rhodanese*	$CN^- + S_2O_3^= \to CNS^- + SO_3^-$	Beef liver	—	8.6	I, II, 334
Ribokinase	R + ATP → R-5-P + ADP	Liver	Mg^{++}	7.1-7.8	II, 219, 221 (1956)
Ribonuclease*	Hydrolysis of RNA	Bovine pancreas	—	7.7	I, II, 427
Ribosidase	Adenosine → Adenine + Ribose	B. cereus	—	6-7.5	IV, 62, 381 (1956)
Riboside hydrolase	Nucleoside → Ribose + N Base	Fish muscle	—	5.6	IV, 59, 386 (1955)
Riboside hydrolase	Nucleoside → Ribose + N Base	L. delbruckii	—	6.5	II, 225, 77 (1957)
Ribulokinase	Ru + ATP → Ru-5-P + ADP	A. aerogenes	—	7.4	III, 78, 5452 (1956)
L-Ribulokinase	Ru + ATP → Ru-5-P + ADP	L. pentosus	Mg^{++}	7.0	V, 24, 660 (1957)
Sarcosine oxidase	Sarcosine → Active formaldehyde + Glycine	Liver	—	7.8	II, 217, 275 (1955)
Sedoheptulose kinase (specific)	Sedoheptulose + ATP → Sedoheptulose-7-P + ADP	Bacillus sp. strain W-2	Mg^{++}	6.4-9.0	VIII, 42, 705 (1955)
Serine aldolase	Glycine + Formaldehyde → Serine	Liver	Pyridoxal phosphate, tetrahydrofolic	—	II, 226, 329 (1956)
L-Serine dehydrase	L-Serine → Pyruvic + NH₃	Liver	Pyridoxal phosphate	7.2	II, 220, 787 (1956)
D-Serine dehydrase	D-Serine → Pyruvic + NH₃	E. coli	Pyridoxal phosphate	—	I, II, 322
Serum Ac-globulin	Plasma Ac-globulin → Serum Ac-globulin	Blood	—	—	I, II, 153
Sorbitol dehydrogenase	Sorbitol → Fructose	A. suboxydans	DPN, Mg^{++}, Mn^{++}	8.0-8.5	II, 226, 301 (1955)
Sorbitol dehydrogenase	Sorbitol + DPN⁺ → D-Fructose + DPNH + H⁺	Liver	—	7.9-8.1	I, I, 348
Succinic dehydrogenase	Succinate → Fumarate + 2H	Heart muscle	Fe^{++}, flavin	7-8	II, 223, 599 (1956)
Succinyl CoA deacylase	Succinyl~SCoA + H₂O → Succinate + HSCoA	Pig heart	—	—	I, I, 602
Sucrose phosphorylase	Sucrose + Pᵢ → α-D-Glucose-1-P + D-Fructose	P. saccharophila	—	6.6	I, I, 225
Sulfatase	Phenyl sulfates → Phenols + Sulfate	Liver	—	8	IV, 66, 357 (1957)
Taurocyamine-P-kinase	Taurocyamine → P-Taurocyamine	A. marina	—	7.1-8.9	Chem. Abst. 51, 12169 (1957)
Thiaminase	PyCH₂Th⁺ + BH → PyCH₂B + Th + H⁺	B. thiamolyticus culture media	Aromatic amines, SH	—	I, II, 626
Thiaminase	PyCH₂Th⁺ + BH → PyCH₂B + Th + H⁺	Clam viscera	Aromatic amines	—	I, II, 622
Thiaminokinase	Thiamin + ATP → Thiamin PP + AMP	Baker's yeast	Mg^{++}, P_i	6-8	V, 8, 310 (1955)

Enzyme	Reaction	Source	Cofactor	pH	Reference
Thiaminokinase	Thiamine + ATP → TPP + AMP	Brewer's yeast	Mg^{++}, Mn^{++}, orthophosphate	6–7.5	I, II, 636
Thiolesterase	Hydrolysis of acyl & amino acyl GSH and N-acetylcysteine	Brain	Fe^{++}, Mn^{++}	8.2	II, *212*, 223 (1955)
L-Threonine deaminase I	Deamination of threonine	E. coli	Pyridoxal phosphate	8	VII, *73*, 105 (1957)
L-Threonine deaminase II	Deamination of threonine	E. coli	Pyridoxal phosphate, AMP, GSH	8	VII, *73*, 105 (1957)
L-Threonine dehydrase	L-Threonine → α-Ketobutyric + NH_3	Liver	Pyridoxal phosphate	7.2–7.6	II, *220*, 787 (1956)
D-Threonine dehydrase	D-Threonine → α-Ketobutyric + NH_3	N. crassa	Pyridoxal phosphate	—	I, II, 322
Thrombin	Fibrinogen → Fibrin	Plasma		7.3–7.4	I, II, 156
Thromboplastin	Prothrombin → Thrombin	Fresh beef lung	Ca^{++}	—	I, II, 146
Transaldolase	Sedoheptulose-7-P + Glyceraldehyde-3-P → Fructose-6-P + Tetrose-P	Yeast		7.3–8.1	II, *212*, 811 (1955)
Transamidinase	Arginine + Glycine → Ornithine + Guanidinoacetic	Hog kidney		7.5	VI, *63*, 277 (1956)
Transaminases	$R-\overset{H}{\underset{COOH}{C}}-NH_2 + R'COCOOH \rightarrow RCOCOOH + R'CHNH_2COOH$	Various bacteria	Pyridoxal phosphate	8	I, II, 170
Transformylase	IMP + Glycine → Serine + 4-NH_2-5-Imidazole-carboxamide ribotide	Liver	Glutamine, ATP, leucovorin	7.5	III, *78*, 4497 (1956)
Transfructosidase	Sucrose → Glucofructosans + Glucose	A. vera cruz		5.6–5.8	IV, *61*, 171 (1955)
Transglucosidase	Maltose → Di, tri, tetra saccharides	A. oryzae		7	II, *196*, 265 (1952)
Transhydrogenase	TPNH + DPN ⇌ DPNH + TPN	Animal tissues		6.3	IV, *65*, 546 (1957)
Transketolase*	Xylulose-5-P + Ribose-5-P → Sedoheptulose-7-P + Triose P	Baker's yeast	TPP, Mg^{++}	7.6	II, *214*, 409 (1955)
Transketolase	Xylulose-5-P + Ribose-5-P → Sedoheptulose-7-P + Triose P	Liver, spinach	TPP	7.5	II, *223*, 1009 (1956)
Transoximinase	Oxime¹ + Keto acid² → Keto acid¹ + Oxime²	Liver	Pyridoxal phosphate	6.9	*Enzymologia, 17*, 359 (1956)
Tributyrinase	Tributyrin hydrolysis	Plasma		7.4	IV, *60*, 481 (1955)
Triose-P dehydrogenase*	Triose-P + DPN^+ + P_i → DPNH + 1,3 diP Glyceric	Yeast	SH	8.3–8.5	I, I, 407
Triose-P isomerase*	D-3-Glyceraldehyde-P → Dihydroxyacetone-P	Calf muscle		7–8	I, I, 387
Tripeptidase	Tripeptide hydrolysis	Horse erythrocytes		7.8	II, *214*, 209 (1955)
Tripeptidase	Tripeptide hydrolysis	Human erythrocytes		7.0	VI, *68*, 54 (1957)
Triphosphatase	$Na_2P_2O_{10}$ → $2Na_2HPO_4$ + NaH_2PO_4	Animal organs	Mg^{++}	6–8	I, II, 580
TPN diaphorase	TPNH + Dye → TPN + Leuco dye	Chloroplasts, spinach	FAD	9.0	VI, *65*, 475 (1956)

Enzyme	Reaction	Source	Cofactor	pH	Reference
TPN-ethylene reductase	$TPNH + RCH=CHCOOCoA \rightarrow TPN + RCH_2—CH_2COOCoA$			7.5	III, *77*, 5190 (1955)
TPN-triosephosphate dehydrogenase	$D\text{-}G\text{-}3\text{-}P + PO_4 + TPN^+ \rightarrow 1,3\text{-}DiPGA + TPNH$	Pea leaves	—	8.5–8.8	I, I, 411
Trypsin*	Hydrolysis of peptide bonds	Beef pancreas	—	7.0–8.0	I, II, 26
Tryptophan activating enzyme	$Tryptophan + ATP \rightarrow Adenyltryptophan + PP$	Beef pancreas	Mg^{++}	7.0	VI, *65*, 21 (1956)
L-Tryptophan peroxidase	$L\text{-}Tryptophan + H_2O_2 \xrightarrow{O_2} Formylkynurenine + H_2O_2$	Liver	Peroxide	7.0	I, II, 242
Tryptophan synthetase	$Indole + L\text{-}Serine \rightarrow L\text{-}Tryptophan$	Neurospora	Pyridoxal phosphate	7.8	I, II, 233
Tryptophanase	$Tryptophan \rightarrow Indole + NH_3 + Pyruvic$	E. coli	Pyridoxal phosphate	7.5	I, II, 238
Tyrosinase	$Tyrosine \rightarrow DOPA \rightarrow Melanin$	Cytoplasma of melanocytes	Cu^{++}	—	I, II, 827
Tyrosinase	Tyrosine oxidation	Mammalian	Cu^{++}	—	III, *79*, 2647 (1957)
Tyrosinase	Oxidation of monohydric to polyhydric phenols	Mushrooms	Cu^{++}	5–7	I, II, 817
Tyrosine-glutamic acid transaminase	$L\text{-}Tyrosine + \alpha\text{-}Ketoglutarate \rightarrow p\text{-}Hydroxyphenylpyruvate + L\text{-}Glutamate$	Liver	—	—	I, II, 289
L-Tyrosine oxidizing system	$L\text{-}Tyrosine + 2O_2 + \alpha\text{-}Ketoglutarate \rightarrow Acetoacetate + Fumarate + CO_2 + L\text{-}Gluconate$	Rat liver	Ascorbate	—	I, II, 287
Uracil-thymine oxidase	$Uracil + \tfrac{1}{2}O_2 \rightarrow Barbituric$	Mycobacterium	—	8.5–9	I, II, 490
Urease*	$Urea \rightarrow NH_3 + CO_2$	Jackbean meal	—	7	I, II, 378
Ureidosuccinase	$Ureidosuccinic \rightarrow Aspartic + CO_2 + NH_3$	Z. oroticum	Mn^{++}, SH	7.8–8.5	II, *212*, 909 (1955)
Uricase	$Uric + O_2 \rightarrow Allantoin + CO_2 + H_2O_2$	Pork liver	Cu^{++}	8	II, *216*, 625 (1955)
		Beef liver		9.4	V, *21*, 290 (1956)
		Ox kidney		9.3	I, II, 485
Uridine diphosphoglucose dehydrogenase	$UDPG + 2DPN^+ \rightarrow UDP\ glucuronic + 2DPNH + 2H^+$	Calf liver	DPN^+	8.7	II, *224*, 79 (1957)
		Pea seedlings	DPN^+	8.5	IV, *66*, 567 (1957)
Uridine diphospho-glucose-4-hydroxyl epimerase	$UDPG \rightarrow UDP\ gal$	Calf liver	DPN^+	8.7	III, *78*, 1074 (1956)
Uridine diphosphoglucose pyrophosphorylase	$UDPG + PP \rightarrow UTP + G\text{-}1\text{-}P$	Brewer's yeast	—	7.5	I, II, 675
Uridine nucleosidase	$UR \rightarrow U + R$	Yeast	—	7.0	I, II, 461
Urocanase	Urocanic acid degradation	Pseudomonas	—	7.0	I, II, 231
Verdoperoxidase	$H_2O_2 + HA \rightarrow HOA + H_2O$	Chloroma	—	7.4	III, *79*, 1643 (1957)

Enzyme	Reaction	Source	Cofactor	pH	Reference
Xanthine oxidase*	Hypox + O₂ → Uric + H₂O₂	Milk	FAD, Mo	8.2	IX, *173*, 1230 (1954)
		Chicken liver	Fe, Mo, FAD	8.2	II, *217*, 293 (1955)
Xanthosine-5'-P-aminase	Xanthosine-5-P + NH₃ + ATP → Guanosine-5'-P + PP + AMP	A. aerogenes	—	8.6	II, *226*, 351 (1957)
Xylanase	Xylan → Xylose	Rumen	—	6.2	Chem. Abst. *61*, 10610 (1957)
Xylose isomerase	Xylose ⇌ Xylulose	Pseudomonas hydrophilia	**Mn**	7.5	VI, *48*, 120 (1954)
		Pasturella pestis	Mn	8	III, *77*, 1663 (1955)
Xylulose kinase	Xylulose + ATP → Xylulose-5-P + ADP	Lactobacillus pentosus	Mg	7.0-7.9	II, *218*, 753 (1956)
Xylulose-reductase	Xylulose + TPNH + H⁺ → TPN⁺ + Xylitol	Liver	—	8.1	II, *225*, 87 (1957)

[1] For purposes of improvement of later editions, readers are invited to submit more complete references.

[2] The authors are indebted to Juanita L'Esperance for assistance in preparing this table.

[3] Literature key: I, Methods in Enzymology, Vol. I and II, Academic Press, 1955; II, J. Biol. Chem.; III, J. Am. Chem. Soc.; IV, Biochem. J.; V, Biochem. Biophys. Acta; VI, Arch. Biochem. Biophys.; VII, J. Bact.; VIII, J. Biochem. (Japan); IX, Nature; X, J. Chem. Soc.; XI, Science.

* Crystalline enzyme.

Index[1]

Absolute group specificity, 185
Absolute specificity, 185
Absorption spectra, proteins, 72
Acetic acid, ionization, 11
Acetone, enzyme fractionation, 48
Acetone powder, 46
Acetyl CoA, hydrolysis free energy, 147
Acetyl esterase, 44
Acetyl glutathione, spectrum, 180
Acetyl imidazole, hydrolysis free energy, 149
Acetyl phosphate, 148
Acid phosphatase, 242
Acid strengthening effect, 19
Acids, ionization of weak, 9
Aconitase, 335
Activating enzyme, 349
Activation energy, 123
Activators, 203
Active center, 194
Active site, 194
Activity measurements, 43
Acyl CoA dehydrogenase, 352
Acyl mercaptides, hydrolysis free energy, 147
Addition reactions, 241
Adenosine phosphate coenzymes, 216
Adenyl acyl pyrophosphorylase, 365
ADH, 178
ADH-DPNH compound, 178
ADP, 217
Adsorption chromatography, 49
Affinity constant, 99

Alcohol, enzyme fractionation, 48
Alcohol dehydrogenase (ADH), 178
Alcoholic fermentation, 314
Aldolase, 311
Alkaline phosphatase, 242
Alpha aminobeta keto adipic acid, 258
Alpha amino group, ionization, 17
Alpha carboxyl group, ionization, 17
Amino acid decarboxylases, 245
Amino acid oxidases, D and L, 254
Amino acid sequence, 76
  determination, 76
  in insulin, 370
Amino acids as zwitterions, 14
Aminopeptidase, 282
Aminotripeptidase, 282
Ammonia, ionization, 13
Ammonium sulfate, fractionation, 48
AMP, 141
Amylase, 239
Amylomaltase, 242
Antimycin A, 274
Apoenzyme, 248
Apparent equilibrium constant, 9
Appendix, 385
Arginine phosphate, 141
Arrhenius equation, 123
Arsenate, 119
Arsenicals, 119
Arsenolysis, 119
Ascorbic acid, 231
Aspartic acid, titration curve, 18
Asymmetric degradation, 188
Atmungsferment, 268

[1] Individual enzymes are listed in the appendix (p. 385).